IN THE GARDENS OF *LA BECHELLERIE*

Anatole France in "the flower of his age"—nearly 80 years old—is here seen in the garden of his country place. Officer of the Legion of Honor, Academician, Nobel Prize winner, he remains "the laughing philosopher" gazing out on the world with compassionate irony.

THE WELL OF SAINT CLARE

BY ANATOLE FRANCE

A TRANSLATION BY
ALFRED ALLINSON

BOOKLOVERS' EDITION

NEW YORK: WM. H. WISE & CO.
MCMXXX

PRINTED IN U. S. A. BY
FERRIS PRINTING COMPANY
BINDING BY - VAN REES
BOOK BINDING CORPORATION

CONTENTS

	PAGE
PROLOGUE—THE REVEREND FATHER ADONE DONI	3
SAN SATIRO	17
MESSER GUIDO CAVALCANTI	53
LUCIFER	75
THE LOAVES OF BLACK BREAD	87
THE MERRY-HEARTED BUFFALMACCO	97
i. The Cockroaches	98
ii. The Ascending up of Andria Tafi	108
iii. The Master	121
iv. The Painter	127
THE LADY OF VERONA	137
THE HUMAN TRAGEDY	145
i. Fra Giovanni	145
ii. The Lamp	154
iii. The Seraphic Doctor	157
iv. The Loaf on the Flat Stone	160
v. The Table under the Fig-tree	163
vi. The Temptation	167

CONTENTS

THE HUMAN TRAGEDY—*continued*

 vii. The Subtle Doctor 172
 viii. The Burning Coal 180
 ix. The House of Innocence 182
 x. The Friends of Order 189
 xi. The Revolt of Gentleness 196
 xii. Words of Love 202
 xiii. The Truth 207
 xiv. Giovanni's Dream 218
 xv. The Judgment 226
 xvi. The Prince of this World 234

THE MYSTIC BLOOD 245
A SOUND SECURITY 259
HISTORY OF DOÑA MARIA D'AVALOS AND THE DUKE D'ANDRIA 273
BONAPARTE AT SAN MINIATO 291
MARGUERITE 311

THE WELL OF SAINT CLARE

THE WELL OF SAINT CLARE

PROLOGUE

THE REVEREND FATHER ADONE DONI

Τὰ γὰρ φυσικὰ, καὶ τὰ ἠθικὰ, ἀλλὰ καὶ τὰ μαθηματικὰ, καὶ τοὺς ἐγκυκλίους λόγους, καὶ περὶ τεχνῶν, πᾶσαν εἶχεν ἐμπειρίαν.—*Diogenes Laërtius, IX, 37.*[1]

I WAS spending the Spring at Sienna. Occupied all day long with meticulous researches among the city archives, I used after supper to take an evening walk along the wild road leading to Monte Oliveto, where I would encounter in the twilight huge white oxen under ponderous yokes dragging a rustic wain with wheels of solid timber—all unchanged since the times of old Evander. The church bells knelled the peaceful ending of the day, while the purple shades of night descended sadly and majestically on the low

---

[1] "For of physical and ethical science, no less than of mathematics and the common round of learning, as well as concerning arts, he possessed full knowledge and experience."

chain of neighbouring hills. The black squadrons of the rooks had already sought their nests about the city walls, but relieved against the opalescent sky a single sparrow-hawk still hung floating with motionless wings above a solitary ilex tree.

I moved forward to confront the silence and solitude and the mild terrors that lowered before me in the growing dusk. The tide of darkness rose·by imperceptible degrees and drowned the landscape. The infinite of starry eyes winked in the bushes with their trembling love-lights.

These living sparks cover all the Roman Campagna and the plains of Umbria and Tuscany, on May nights. I had watched them in former days on the Appian Way, round the tomb of Cæcilia Metella—their playground for two thousand years; now I found them dancing the selfsame dance in the land of St. Catherine and of Pia de' Tolomei, at the gates of Sienna, that most melancholy and most fascinating of cities. All along my path they quivered in the bents and brushwood, chasing one another, and ever and anon, at the call of desire, tracing above the roadway the fiery arch of their darting flight.

On the white ribbon of the road, in these clear Spring nights, the only person I used to encounter was the Reverend Father Adone Doni, who at the time was, like myself, working in the old Academy *degli Intronati*. I had taken an instant liking for the Cordelier in question, a man who, grown grey in study, still preserved the cheerful, facile humour of a simple, unlettered countryman. He was very willing to converse, and I greatly relished his bland speech, his cultivated yet artless way of thought, his look of old Silenus purged at the baptismal font, the play of his passions at once keen and refined, the strange, alluring personality that informed the whole man. Assiduous at the library, he was also a frequent visitor to the market-place, halting for choice in front of the peasant girls who sell oranges, and listening to their unconventional remarks. He was learning, he would say, from their lips the true *Lingua Toscana*.

All I knew of his past life, about which he never spoke, was that he was born at Viterbo, of a noble but miserably impoverished family, that he had studied the humanities and theology at Rome, as a young man had joined the Franciscans of Assisi, where he worked at the Archives, and had had difficulties on questions of faith with his ecclesiastical superiors. Indeed I thought I noticed myself a tendency in the Father towards peculiar views. He was a man of religion and a man of science, but not without certain eccentricities under either aspect. He believed in God on the evidence of Holy Scripture and in accordance with the teachings of the Church, and laughed at those simple philosophers who believed in Him on their own account, without being under any obligation to do so. So far he was well within the bounds of orthodoxy; it was in connection with the Devil that he professed peculiar opinions. He held the Devil to be wicked, but not absolutely wicked, and considered that the fiend's innate imperfection must always bar him from attaining to the perfection of evil. He believed he discerned some symptoms of goodness in the obscure manifestations of Satan's activity, and without venturing to put it in so many words, augured from these the final redemption of the pensive Archangel after the consummation of the ages.

These little eccentricities of thought and temperament, which had separated him from the rest of the world and thrown him back upon a solitary existence, afforded me amusement. He had wits enough; all he lacked was common sense and appreciation of ordinary everyday things. His life was divided between phantoms of the past and dreams of the future; the actual present was utterly foreign to his notions. For his political ideas, these came simultaneously from antique Santa Maria degli Angeli and the revolutionary secret societies of

London, and were a combination of Christian and socialist. But he was no fanatic; his contempt for human reason was too complete for him to attach great importance to his own share in it. The government of states appeared to him in the light of a huge practical joke, at which he would laugh quietly and composedly, as a man of taste should. Judges, civil and criminal, caused him surprise, while he looked on the military classes in a spirit of philosophical toleration.

I was not long in discovering some flagrant contradictions in his mental attitude. He longed with all the charity of his gentle heart for the reign of universal peace. Yet at the same time he had a *penchant* for civil war, and held in high esteem that Farinata degli Uberti, who loved his native Florence so boldly and so well that he constrained her by force and fraud, making the Arbia run red with Florentine blood the while, to will and think precisely what he willed and thought himself. For all that, the Reverend Father Adone Doni was a tender-hearted dreamer of dreams. It was on the spiritual authority of St. Peter's chair he counted to establish in this world the kingdom of God. He believed the Paraclete was leading the Popes along a road unknown to themselves. Therefore he had nothing but deferential words for the

Roaring Lamb of Sinigaglia and the *Opportunist Eagle of Carpineto,* as it was his custom to designate Pius IX and Leo XIII respectively.

Agreeable as was the Reverend Father's conversation to me, I used, out of respect for his freedom of action and my own, to avoid showing myself too assiduous in seeking his society inside the city walls, while on his side he observed an exquisite discretion towards myself. But in our walks abroad we frequently managed to meet as if by accident. Half a league outside the Porta Romana the high road traverses a hollow way between melancholy uplands on either hand, relieved only by a few gloomy larches. Under the clayey slope of the northern escarpment and close by the roadside, a dry well rears its light canopy of open ironwork.

At this spot I would encounter the Reverend Father Adone Doni almost every evening, seated on the coping of the well, his hands buried in the sleeves of his gown, gazing out with mild surprise into the night. The gathering dusk still left it possible to make out on his bright-eyed, flat-nosed face the habitual expression of timid daring and graceful irony which was impressed upon it so profoundly. At first we merely exchanged formal good wishes for each other's health, peace and happiness. Then I would take my place by his side on the old stone well-head, that bore some traces of carving. It was still possible, in full daylight, to distinguish a figure with a head bigger than its body and representing an Angel, as seemed indicated by the wings.

The Reverend Father never failed to say courteously:

"Welcome, Signore! Welcome to the Well of St. Clare."

One evening I asked him the reason why the well bore the name of this favourite disciple of St. Francis. He informed me it was because of a very edifying little miracle, which for all its charm had unfortunately never found a place in the collection of the *Fioretti*. I begged him to oblige me by telling it, which he proceeded to do in the following terms:

"In the days when the poor man of Jesus Christ, Francis, son of Bernardone, used to journey from town to town teaching holy simplicity and love, he visited Sienna, in company with Brother Leo, the man of his own heart. But the Siennese, a covetous and cruel generation, true sons of the She-Wolf on whose milk they boasted themselves to have been suckled, gave a sorry welcome to the holy man, who bade them take into their house two ladies of a perfect beauty, to wit Poverty and

Obedience. They overwhelmed him with obloquy and mocking laughter, and drove him forth from the city. He left the place in the night by the Porta Romana. Brother Leo, who tramped alongside, spoke up and said to him:—

" 'The Siennese have written on the gates of their city,—"Sienna opens her heart to you wider than her doors." And nevertheless, brother Francis, these same men have shut their hearts against us.'

"And Francis, son of Bernardone, replied:

" 'The fault is with me, be sure of that, brother Leo, little lamb of God. I have not known how to knock at the doors of their hearts forcefully and skilfully enough. I am far below the fellows who set a bear dancing in the Great Piazza. For they draw together a great crowd by exhibiting the rude coarse beast, whilst I that had ladies of celestial fairness to show them, I have attracted no one. Brother Leo, I charge you, on your holy obedience, to say thus to me: "Brother Francis, you are a poor man, without any merit whatsoever, a stumbling block and a very rock of offence!"' And all the while Brother Leo was hesitating to obey, the holy man suffered grievously within himself. As he went on his murky way, his thoughts turned to pleasant Assisi, where he had left behind him his sons in the spirit, and Clare, daughter of his soul. He knew how Clare was exposed to great tribulations for the love of holy Poverty. And he doubted whether his well-beloved daughter were not sick of body and soul, and weary of well-doing, in the house of St. Damian.

"So sore did these doubts weigh on him, that arrived at this spot where the road enters the hollow way between the hills, he seemed to feel his feet sink into the ground at each step he took. He dragged himself as far as the Well here, which was then in its pristine beauty and full of limpid water, and fell exhausted on the well-head where we are seated at this moment. A long while the man of God remained bent over the mouth of the well. After which, lifting up his head, he said joyfully to Brother Leo: 'What think you, brother Leo, lamb of God, I have seen in the Well?'

"And Brother Leo answered:

"'Brother Francis, you saw the moon reflected in the well.'

"'My brother,' replied the Saint of God, 'it is not our sister the Moon I saw in the well, but by the Lord, the true countenance of sister Clare, and so pure and shining so bright with a holy joy that all my doubts were instantly dispelled, and it was made plain to me that our sister enjoys at this present hour the full content God accords his chosen vessels, loading them with the treasures of Poverty.'

"So saying, the good St. Francis drank a few drops of water in the hollow of his hand, and arose refreshed.

"And that is why the name of St. Clare was given to this Well."

Such was the tale told by the Reverend Father Adone Doni.

Night after night I returned to find the amiable Cordelier sitting on the edge of the mystic well. I would seat myself by his side, and he would tell over for my benefit some fragment of history known only to himself. He had many delightful stories of the sort to relate, being better read than any one else in the antiquities of his country. These lived again and grew bright and young in his head, as if it contained an intellectual Fountain of Eternal Youth. Ever fresh pictures flowed from his white-fringed lips. As he spoke, the moonlight bathed his beard in a silver flood. The crickets accompanied the narrator's voice with the shrilling of their wing-cases, and ever and anon his words, uttered in the softest of all dialects of human speech, would be answered by the fluted plaintive croaking of the frogs, which hearkened from across the road—a friendly, if apprehensive audience.

I left Sienna towards the middle of June; and I have never seen the Reverend Father Adone Doni since. He clings to my memory like a figure in a dream; and I have now put into writing the tales he told me on the road of Monte Oliveto. They will be found in the present volume; I only hope they may have retained, in their new dress, some vestiges of the grace they had in the telling at the Well of St. Clare.

SAN SATIRO

TO ALPHONSE DAUDET

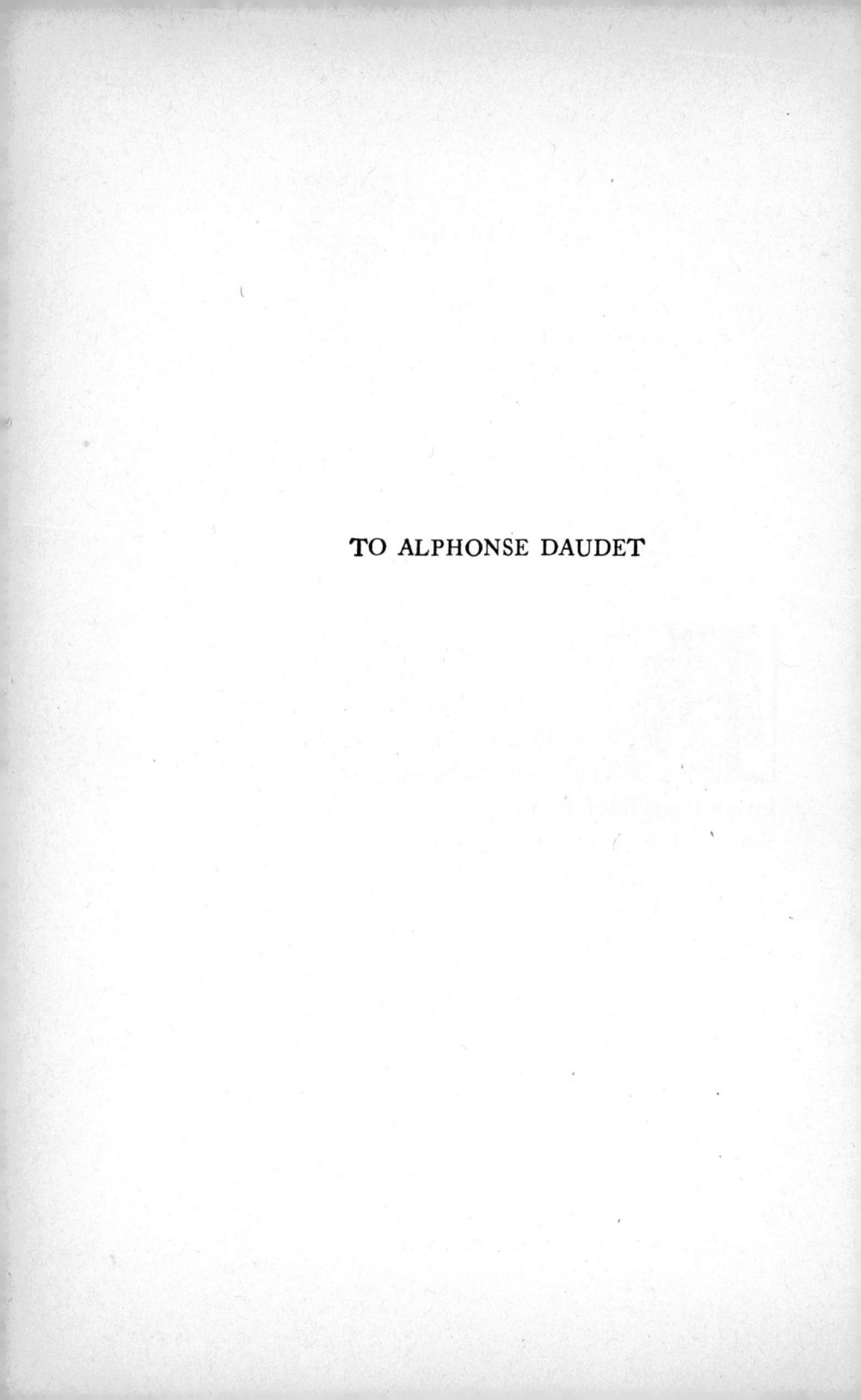

SAN SATIRO

Consors paterni luminis,
Lux ipse lucis et dies,
Noctem canendo rumpimus;
Assiste postulantibus.

Aufer tenebras mentium;
Fuga catervas dæmonum;
Expelle somnolentiam,
Ne pigritantes obruat.[1]

(*Breviarium Romanum*
Third day of the week: at matins.)

FRA MINO had raised himself by his humility above his brethren, and still a young man, he governed the Monastery of Santa Fiora wisely and well. He was devout, and loved long meditations and long prayers; sometimes he had ecstasies. After the example of his spiritual father, St. Francis, he composed songs in the vernacular tongue in celebration of perfect love, which is the love of God. And these

---

[1] "Partner of the Father's light, light of light and day of day, we break the dusk of night with psalms; help us now, Thy suppliants. Remove the darkness of our minds; scatter the demon hosts away; expel the sin of drowsiness, lest we be slack in serving Thee."

exercises were without fault whether of metre or of meaning, for had he not studied the seven liberal arts at the University of Bologna?

Now one evening, as he was walking under the cloister arches, he felt his heart filled with trouble and sadness at the remembrance of a lady of Florence he had loved in the first flower of his youth, ere the habit of St. Francis was a safeguard to his flesh. He prayed God to drive away the image; nevertheless his heart continued sad within him.

"The bells," he pondered, "say like the Angels, AVE MARIA; but their voice is lost in the mists of heaven. On the cloister wall yonder, the Master Perugia delights to honour has painted marvellous well the three Marys contemplating with a love ineffable the body of the Saviour. But the night has veiled the tears in their eyes and the dumb sobs of their mouths, and I cannot weep with them. Yonder Well in the middle of the cloister garth was covered but now with doves that had come to drink, but these are flown away, for they found no water in the hollows of the carven well-head. And behold, Lord! my soul falls silent like the bells, is darkened like the holy Marys, and runs dry like the well. Why, Jesus my God! why is my heart arid, and dark, and dumb, when Thou art its dayspring, and the song of birds, and the water-brook flowing from the hills?"

Fra Mino dreaded to return to his cell, and thinking prayer would dispel his melancholy and calm his disquiet, he passed into the Monastery Church by the low door leading from the cloister. Silence and gloom filled the building, raised more than a hundred and fifty years before on the foundations of a ruined Roman Temple by the great Margaritone. He traversed the Nave, and went and knelt in the Chapel behind the High Altar, dedicated to San Michele, whose legend was painted in fresco on the wall. But the dim light of the lamp hanging from the vault was insufficient to show the Archangel fighting with Satan and weighing souls in the balance. Only the moon, shining through the great window, threw a pale ray over the Tomb of San Satiro, where it lay under an arcade to the right of the Altar. This tomb, in shape resembling the great vats used at vintage time, was more ancient than the Church and in all respects similar to a Pagan sarcophagus, except that the sign of the Cross was to be seen traced in three different places on its marble sides.

Fra Mino remained for hours prostrate before the Altar; but he found it impossible to pray, and at midnight felt himself weighed down under the same heaviness that overcame Jesus Christ's disciples in the Garden of Gethsemane. And lo! as he lay there without courage or counsel, he saw as it were a white cloud rise above the tomb of San Satiro, and presently observed that this cloud was made up of a multitude of cloudlets, of which each one was a woman. They floated in the dim air; and through their light raiment shone the whiteness of their light limbs. Then Fra Mino saw how among them were goat-footed young men who were chasing them. These were naked, and nothing hid the terrifying ardour of their desires. And the nymphs fled away from them, while beneath their racing steps there sprang up flowery meadows and brooks of water. Each time a goat-foot put out his hand to seize one of them, a sallow would shoot up suddenly to hide the nymph in its hollow trunk as in a cave, and the grey leaves shivered with light murmurings and spurts of mocking laughter.

When all the women were hidden in the sallows, their goat-footed lovers, sitting on the grass of the new-come meadows, breathed in their flutes of reeds and drew from them sounds to destroy the peace of any creature of the earth. The nymphs were fascinated, and soon began to peep out between the branches, and one by one deserting the shady covert, drew near under the irresistible attraction of the music. Then the goat-men rushed upon them with a demoniac fury. Folded in the arms of their ruthless assailants, the nymphs strove to keep up a while longer their raillery and loud laughter, but the mirth died on their lips. With heads thrown back and eyes swooning with joy and terror, they could only call upon their mother, or scream a shrill "You are killing me," or keep a sullen silence.

Fra Mino longed to turn his head, but he could not, and his eyes remained wide open in spite of himself.

Meanwhile the nymphs, winding their arms about the goat-men's loins, fell to biting and caressing and provoking their hairy lovers, and body intertwined with body, they enfolded and bathed them in their tender flesh that was sweeter and softer and more living than the water of the brook which ran by them under the sallows.

At the sight, Fra Mino fell, in mind and intention, into deadly sin. He desired to be one of these demons, half men and half beasts, and hold to his bosom, after their carnal fashion, the fair lady of Florence he had loved in the flower of his years, and who was now dead.

But already the goat-men were scattering through the country-side. Some were busied gathering honey in the hollow trunks of oaks, others carving reeds into the shape of flutes, or butting one against the other, crashing their horned brows together. Meantime the bodies of the nymphs, sweet wrecks of love, lay motionless, strewing the meadows. Fra Mino lay groaning on the Chapel flags; for so fierce had been the desire of sin within him that now he was filled full of bitter shame at his own weakness.

Suddenly one of the nymphs, chancing as she lay to turn her eyes upon him, cried out:

"A man! a man!"

And pointing him out to her companions:

"Look, sisters; yonder is no goat-herd, he has no flute of reed beside him. Nor yet do I recognize him for the master of one of those rustic farmsteads whose garden-close, sloping to the hill-side beneath the vines, is guarded by a Priapus hewn out of a stump of beech. What would he among us, if he is neither goat-herd, nor neat-herd, nor gardener? His looks are harsh and gloomy, and I cannot read in his eyes the love of the gods and goddesses that people the wide sky, the woods and mountains. He wears a barbarous habit; perhaps he is a Scythian. Let us approach the stranger, my sisters, and make sure he is not come as a foe to sully our fountains, hew down our trees, tear open our hill-sides and betray to cruel men the mystery of our happy lurking places. Come with me, Mnaïs; come, Ægle, Neæra and Melibœa.

"On! on!" returned Mnaïs, "on, with our arms in hand!"

"On! on!" all cried in chorus.

Then Fra Mino saw them spring up, and gather great handfuls of roses, and advance upon him in a long line, each armed with roses and thorns. But the distance that separated them from him, which at first had seemed very short, for indeed he thought almost to touch them and felt their breath on his face, appeared suddenly to increase, and he watched them coming as though from out a far-off forest. Impatient to be at him, they began to run, threatening him with their cruel flowers, while menaces flew from their flower-like lips. And lo! as they came nearer, a change was wrought in them; at each step they lost something of their grace and beauty, and the bloom of their youth faded as fast as the roses in their hands. First their eyes grew hollow and the mouth fell in. The neck, but now so pure and white, hung in great hideous folds, and grey elf-locks draggled over their wrinkled brows. On they came; and their eyes were circled with red, their lips drawn in upon the toothless gums. On they came, carrying dead roses on their arms, which were black and writhen as the old vine stocks the peasants of Chianti burn for firewood in the winter nights. On they came, with shaking heads and palsied thighs, tottering and trembling.

Arrived at the spot where Fra Mino stood rooted to the ground with affright, they were no better than a crowd of horrid witches, bald and bearded, nose and chin touching, and bosoms hanging loose and flabby. They came crowding round him:

"Ah, ha! the pretty darling!" cried one. "He is as white as a sheet, and his heart beats like a hare the dogs are snapping at. Ægle, sister mine, say, what must be done with him?"

"Neæra mine!" Ægle replied, "why! we must open his breast, tear out his heart and put a sponge in its place instead."

"Not so!" said Melibœa. "That were making him pay too dear for his curiosity and the pleasure he has had in surprising our frolic. Enough for this time to inflict a light chastisement. Say, shall we give him a good whipping?"

Straightway surrounding the Monk, the sisters dragged his gown above his head and belaboured him with the handfuls of thorns they still held.

The blood was beginning to come, when Neæra signed to them to stop:

"Enough!" she cried! "he is my gallant, I tell

you! I saw him just now casting tender eyes at me; I would content his wishes, and grant him my favours without more delay."

She smiled alluringly; and a long, black tooth projecting from her mouth tickled his nostril. She murmured softly:

"Come, come, my Adonis!"

Then suddenly, wild with rage:

"Fie, fie! his senses are benumbed. His coldness offends my charms. He scorns me; avenge me, comrades! Mnaïs, Ægle, Melibœa, avenge your sister!"

At this appeal, one and all, lifting their thorny whips, fell to scourging him so savagely that Fra Mino's body was soon one wound from head to toe. Now and again they would stop to cough and spit, only to begin afresh, plying their whips more vigorously than ever. Only sheer weariness induced them to leave off.

"I hope," Neæra then said, "next time he will not do me the undeserved insult I still blush to remember. We will spare his life; but if he betrays the secret of our sports and pleasures, we will surely kill him. Good-bye to you, my pretty boy!"

So saying, the old woman suddenly squatted down over the Monk and drowned him in a torrent of very filthy liquid. Each sister followed suit and did the like; then one after the other they re-entered the tomb of San Satiro, slipping in through a tiny crack in the lid, leaving their victim lying full length in a stream of a most intolerable stench.

When the last had disappeared, the cock crew. Then Fra Mino at last found himself able to rise from the earth. Broken with fatigue and pain, benumbed with cold, shuddering with fever, half stifled with the foul exhalations of the poisonous liquor, he set his clothing straight and dragged himself to his cell, just as day broke.

From that night on, Fra Mino never had a moment's peace. The recollection of what he had seen in the Chapel of San Michele, above San Satiro's tomb, disturbed him in the Church services and in all his pious exercises. He trembled when he visited the Church along with his fellows; and as his turn came, according to the rule, to kiss the pavement of the Choir, his lips shuddered to encounter the traces of the nymphs' presence, and he would murmur: "O! my Saviour, dost not Thou hear me say what Thou didst Thyself say to Thy Father, Lead us not, we beseech Thee, into temptation?" At first he had thought of sending to the Lord Bishop an account of what he had witnessed. But on riper reflexion, he had become convinced it were better to meditate at leisure on these extraordinary events and only divulge them after a more exhaustive study of all the circumstances. Besides it so happened that the Lord Bishop, allied with the Guelphs of Pisa against the Ghibellines of Florence, was at that moment waging war with such right good will that for a whole month he had not so much as unbuckled his cuirass. And that is why, without saying a word to any one, Fra Mino made profound researches on the tomb of San Satiro and the Chapel containing it. Deeply versed in the knowledge of books, he investigated many texts, both ancient and modern; yet found no glimmer of enlightenment in any of them. Indeed the only effect of the works on Magic which he studied was to double his uncertainty.

One morning, after labouring all the night as was his wont, he was fain to refresh his heart with a walk in the fields. He took the hilly path which, winding between the vines and the elms they are wedded to, leads to a wood of myrtles and olives, sacred in old days to the Roman gods. His feet bathed in the wet grass, his brow refreshed by the dew that distilled from the pointed leaves of the Guelder roses, Fra Mino wandered long in the forest, till he came upon a spring over which the wild tamarisks gently swayed their light foliage and the downy clusters of their pink berries. Lower down amid the willows, where the water formed a wider pool, herons stood motionless, while the smaller birds sang sweetly in the branching myrtles. The scent of mint rose moist and fragrant from the ground, and the grass was spangled with the flowers of which our Lord said that "Solomon in all his glory was not arrayed like one of these." Fra Mino sat down on a mossy stone and praising God, Who made the heavens and the dew, he fell to pondering the hidden mysteries of Nature.

Now the remembrance of all he had seen in the Chapel of San Michele never left his thoughts; so he sat meditating, his head between his hands, wondering for the thousandth time what the dream might signify: "For indeed," he said to himself, "such a vision must needs have a meaning; it should even have several, which it behoves to discover, whether by sudden illumination, or by dint of an exact applying of the scholastic rules. And I deem that, in this especial case, the poets I studied at Bologna, such as Horace the Satirist and Statius, should likewise be of great help to me, seeing many verities are intermingled with their fables."

After long pondering these thoughts within his breast, and others more subtle still, he lifted his eyes and perceived he was not alone. Leaning against the cavernous trunk of an ancient holm-oak, an old man stood gazing at the sky through the leaves, and smiling to himself. Above his hoary brow peeped out two short, blunt horns. His nose was flat with wide nostrils, and from his chin depended a white beard, through which were visible the rugged muscles of the neck. A shaggy growth of hair covered his breast, while from the thighs downwards his limbs showed a thick fleece that trailed down to his cloven feet. He held to his lips a flute of reed, from which he drew a feeble sound of music. Then he began to sing in a voice that left the words barely distinguishable:

>Laughing she fled,
>Her teeth in the golden grape;
>After I sped,
>And clasping her flying shape,
>I quenched my drouth
>On the fruit of her mouth.

Astounded at these strange sights and sounds, Fra Mino crossed himself. Still the old man showed no mark of confusion, but cast a long and artless look at the Monk. Amid the deep wrinkles that scored his face, the clear blue eyes sparkled like the waters of a spring through the rugged bark of a grove of oaks.

"Man or beast," shrilled Mino, "I command

you in the name of the Saviour to say who you are."

"My son," replied the old man, "I am San Satiro! Speak not so loud, for fear of frightening the birds."

Then Fra Mino resumed, in a quieter tone:

"Forasmuch, old man, as you shrank not before the dread sign of the Cross, I cannot hold you to be a demon or some foul spirit escaped out of Hell. But if verily and indeed you are a man, as you say you are, or rather the soul of a man sanctified by the deeds of a good life and by the merits of our Lord Jesus Christ, expound, I pray you, the mystery of your goat's horns and your shaggy limbs ending in those black, cloven hoofs."

At the question, the old man lifted up his arms towards heaven, and said:

"My son, the nature of men and animals, of plants and stones, is the secret of the immortal gods, and I know as little as yourself what is the reason of these horns wherewith my brow is decked, and which the Nymphs used in olden days to wind about with garlands of flowers. I cannot tell you the meaning of the two wrinkled folds that droop from my neck, nor why I have the feet of a wanton goat. But I would have you know, my son, there was once in these woods a race of women having horned brows like mine and shaggy thighs. Yet were their bosoms round and white, and their belly and polished loins shone in the light. The sun was young then, and loved to fleck them with his golden arrows, as they lay beneath the shady foliage. They were very fair, my son; but alas! they have vanished from the woods, every one. My mates have perished likewise, and I am left lonely, the last of my tribe."

"I would fain know your age, old man, and your lineage and country."

"My son, I was born of the Earth long ere Jupiter had dethroned Saturn, and my eyes have looked upon the flowery freshness of the new-created World. Not yet had the human race emerged from the clay. Alone with me, the dancing Satyr girls set the ground ringing with the rhythmic beat of their double hoofs. They were taller and stronger and fairer than either Nymphs or Women; and their ample loins received abundantly the seed of the first-born of Earth.

"Under the reign of Jupiter the Nymphs began to inhabit fountains and forests and mountains; while the fauns, accoupling with the Nymphs formed light-footed bands that roamed the woods together. Meantime I spent a happy life, tasting at will the clusters of the wild grapes and the lips of the laughing Faun-girls. I enjoyed deep and restful slumbers amid the lush grass; and I would celebrate on my rustic flute Jupiter, Saturn's successor, for it is of my nature to praise the gods, masters of the world.

"Alas! and I am grown old, for I am but a god, and the centuries have blanched the hairs of my head and of my bosom, and have extinguished the fire of my reins. I was already heavily weighted with years when the Great Pan died, and Jupiter, meeting the same lot he had laid upon Saturn, was dethroned by the Galilean. Since then I have dragged out an ever-flagging life, so feeble and languid that at last it fell out I died, and was entombed. And verily I am now but the shadow of myself. If I still exist a little, it is because nothing ever really perishes, and none is suffered altogether to die out. Death must never be more perfect and complete than life. Beings lost in the Ocean of Things are like the waves you may watch, my child, rising and falling in the Adriatic Sea. They have neither beginning nor end, they are born and die insensibly. Insensibly as the waves, my soul passes. A faint far-off memory of the satyr girls of the Golden Age yet brightens my eyes, and on my lips float soundlessly the ancient hymns of praise."

This said, he fell silent. Fra Mino gazed at the old man, and knew him, that he was a phantom and nothing more.

"Yet! you may indeed be a goat-foot," he told him gravely, "without being a demon; 'tis not a thing wholly incredible. Such creatures as God framed to have no part in Adam's heritage, these can no more be damned than they can be saved. I can never believe that the Centaur Cheiron, who was wiser than men are, is suffering eternal torments in the belly of Leviathan. A traveller who penetrated once into Limbo, relates how he saw him seated in a grassy spot and conversing with Rhipheus, the most righteous man of all the Trojans. Others indeed affirm that Holy Paradise itself has been opened to admit Rhipheus of Troy. Any way the case is one where doubt is not unlawful. But you lied, old man, when you told me you were a Saint, who are not so much even as a man."

The goat-foot made answer:

"My son, when I was young, I was no more used to lie than the sheep whose milk I sucked or the he-goats with which I would butt in the joy of my strength and beauty. Lies were unknown in those times, nor had the sheep's fleece yet learned to assume factitious hues; and my soul has remained unchanged from that day to this. See, I go naked as in the golden age of Saturn; and my spirit is veiled as little as my body. I am no liar. And why indeed should you deem it a thing so extraordinary, my son, that I have become a Saint in the train of the Galilean, albeit no offspring of the first mother some name Eve and others Pyrrha, and whom it is very meet to reverence under either title? Nay! for that matter, neither is St. Michael woman-born. I know him, and at times we have talks together, he and I. He tells me of the days when he was an ox-herd on Mount Garganus . . ."

But here Fra Mino interrupted the Satyr:

"I cannot suffer you to say St. Michael was an ox-herd, because he guarded the cattle of a man whose name was Garganus, the same as the Mountain. But there, I would fain learn, old man, how you were made a Saint."

"Listen," replied the goat-foot, "and your curiosity shall be satisfied.

"When men coming from the East proclaimed in the fair vale of Arno how that the Galilean had dethroned Jupiter, they hewed down the oaks whereon the country folk were used to hang up little goddeses of clay and votive tablets; they planted crosses over against the holy fountains, and forbade the shepherds any more to carry to the grottos of the Nymphs offerings of wine and milk and cakes. Naturally enough this angered all the tribe of Fauns and Pans and Sylvan Genii, and in their wrath these attached the apostles of the new God. When the holy men were asleep of nights, on their bed of dry leaves, the Nymphs would steal up and pull their beards, while the young Fauns, slipping into their stable, would pluck out hairs from their she-ass's tail. In vain I sought to disarm their simple malice and exhort them to submission. 'My children,' I would warn them, 'the days of easy gaiety and light laughter are gone by.' But they were reckless, and would not harken; and a sore price they paid for their heedlessness.

"But for myself, had I not seen the reign of Saturn come to an end? and I deemed it natural and just that Jupiter should perish in his turn. I was prepared to acquiesce in the downfall of the great old gods, and offered no resistance to the emissaries of the Galilean. Nay! I did them sundry little services. Better acquainted than they with the forest paths, I would gather mulberries and sloes, and lay them on leaves at the threshold of their grotto, and make them little presents of plovers' eggs. Then, if they were building a cabin, I would carry the timber and stones for them on my back. In gratitude, they poured water on my brow, invoking on my head the peace of Jesus Christ.

"So I lived with them and in their way; and those who loved them, loved me. As they were honoured, so was I, and my sanctity seemed as great as theirs.

"I have told you, my son, I was already very old in those days. The sun had scarce heat enough to warm my benumbed limbs. I was no better than an old rotten tree, that has lost its crown of fresh leaves and singing birds. Each returning Autumn brought my end nearer; and one Winter's morning they found me stretched motionless by the roadside.

"The Bishop, followed by his Priests and all the people, celebrated my obsequies. Then I was laid in a great tomb of white marble, marked in three places with the sign of the Cross, and bearing carved on the slab in front the words *Sanctus Satyrus,* within a garland of roses.

"In those times, my son, tombs were erected along the roadsides. Mine was placed two miles out from the city, on the Florence road. A young plane-tree grew up over it, and threw its shadow across it, dappled with sunlight and full of bird songs and twitterings, freshness and joy. Near by, a fountain flowed over a bed of water-weed, where the boys and girls came laughing merrily to bathe together. It was a charming spot—and soon a holy one as well. Thither young mothers would bring their babies and let them touch the marble of the tomb, that they might grow up sturdy and straight in all their limbs. The country folk one and all believed that new-born infants presented at my grave must one day surpass their fellows in strength and courage. This is why they brought me all the flower of the gallant Tuscan race. Moreover the peasants often led their asses thither in hopes of making them prolific. My memory was revered; each year at the return of Spring, the Bishop used to come with his Clergy to pray over my bones, and I could watch far away through the meadow grass the slow approach of Cross and Candle in procession, the scarlet canopy, and the chanting acolytes. Thus it was, my son, in the days of good King Berengar.

"Meantime, the Satyrs and the Satyr girls, the Fauns and Nymphs, dragged out a wretched, wandering life. No more altars of meadow turf for them, no more wreaths of flowers, no more offerings of milk and wheat and honey. Only now and then at long intervals some goat-herd would furtively lay a tiny cheese on the threshold of the sacred grot, whose entrance was almost blocked now with thorns and brambles. But it was merely the rabbits and squirrels came to eat these poor dainties. The Nymphs were dwellers in distant forests and gloomy caves, driven forth of their old homes by the apostles from the East. And to hinder their ever returning more, the priests of the Galilean God poured over trees and stones a charmed water, and pronounced magic words, and set up crosses where roads met in the forest; for the Galilean, my son, is learned in the art of incantations. Better than Saturn, better than Jupiter, he knows the virtue of formularies and mystic signs. Thus the poor rustic Divinities could no more find refuge in their sacred woods. The company of long-haired, goat-footed Satyrs, that beat of yore their mother earth with sounding hoof, was but a cloud of pale, dumb shadows trailing along the mountain-side like the morning mist the Sun melts and dispels.

"Buffeted, as by a fierce wind, by the wrath of Heaven, their spectral forms would be whirled eddying all day long in the dust of the roads. The night on the contrary was somewhat less hostile to them. Night is not wholly the Galilean God's; He shares its dominion with the devils. As the shades of night descended from the hills, Fauns and Faun-women, Nymphs and Pans, came huddling beneath the shelter of the tombs along the roadside, and there under the kindly empire of the infernal powers would enjoy a brief repose. Of all the tombs they liked mine the best, as that of a reverend ancestor of their own. Soon all assembled under that part of the cornice which, giving South, was quite free of moss and always dry. Thither the airy folk came flying every evening as surely as doves to the dovecote. They easily found room, grown tiny now and light as the chaff that scuds before the winnowing-fan. For my own part, sallying out from my quiet death-chamber, I would sit down sometimes in the midst of them under shelter of the marble edge-tiles, and in a feeble, whistling voice sing them songs of the days of Saturn and Jupiter; then they would remember the happy times gone by for ever. Under the eyes of Diana, they would join to make a show of their ancient pastimes, and the belated traveller would seem to see the night mists of the meadows in the moonlight mimic the intertwining limbs of lovers. And in very deed they were little more than a fleeting fog themselves. The cold tried them sorely. One night, when the snow shrouded the fields, the Nymphs Ægle, Neæra, Mnaïs and Melibœa glided through the cracks in the marble into the narrow, gloomy chamber where I dwell. Their comrades crowded after in their train, and the Fauns, dashing in pursuit of them, quickly joined them too. My house became their house. We scarcely ever left it, except to visit the woods, when the night was fine and clear. Even then they would make haste to return at the first cock-crow. For you must know, my son, that alone of the horned race I have leave to appear on this earth by the light of day. It is a privilege attached to my Saintship.

"My tomb now inspired more veneration than ever among the country people, and every day young mothers came to present their nurslings to me, lifting the naked babies in their arms. When the sons of St. Francis settled in the land and built a monastery on the hill-side, they craved the Bishop's leave to transfer my monument to their Church and there keep it as a sacred thing. The favour was granted, and I was borne in great pomp to the Chapel of San Michele, where I repose to this day. My rustic family was carried thither along with me. It was a signal honour; but I confess I regretted the broad highway, where I could watch at dawn the peasant women carrying on their heads their basketfuls of grapes and figs and red aubergines. Time has hardly softened my regret, and I would I were still beneath the plane-tree on the Sacred Way.

"Such is my life," ended the old Satyr. "It flows on pleasantly, gentle and unobtrusive, down all the ages of the world. If a touch of sadness mingles with the joy of it, 'tis because the gods have willed it so. Oh! my son, let us praise the gods, masters of the universe!"

Fra Mino stood thinking a while. Then he said:

"I understand now the meaning of what I saw, during that evil night, in the Chapel of San Michele. Still one point remains dark to my mind. Tell me why, old man, the Nymphs who dwell with you, and couple with the fauns, changed into old women of squalid ugliness when they came nigh me."

"Alas! my son," answered the Saint, "time spares neither men nor gods. These last are immortal only in the imagination of the short-lived race of men. In reality they suffer the penalties of age, and verge, as the centuries go by, towards irreparable decay. Nymphs grow old as well as women. No rose but turns into an arid hip at last; no Nymph but ends as an ugly Witchwife. Watching as you did the frolic of my little household, you saw how the memory of their bygone youth yet beautifies the Nymphs and Fauns in the moment of their loves, and how their ardour, reanimated an instant, can reanimate their charms. But the ruin of centuries shows again directly after. Alas! alas! the race of the Nymphs is old, very old and decrepit."

Fra Mino asked yet another question:

"Old man! if what you say is true, and you have won to blessedness by mysterious ways, if it is true—however absurd—that you are a Saint, how comes it you house in your tomb with these phantoms which know not to praise God, and which pollute with their indecencies the temple of the Lord? Answer me, old man!"

But the goat-footed Saint, without a word of answer, vanished softly away into thin air.

Seated on a mossy stone beside the spring, Fra Mino pondered the discourse he had just listened to, and found it contained, along with some passages impenetrably obscure, others that were full of clearness and enlightenment.

"This Satyr Saint," he reflected, "may be likened to the Sibyl, who in the pantheon of the false gods, proclaimed the coming Redeemer to the Nations. The mire of old-world falsehoods yet clings about the hoofs of his feet, but his forehead is uplifted to the light, and his lips confess the truth."

As the shadow of the beeches was lengthening along the grassy hill-side, the Monk rose up from his stone and began to descend the narrow path that led to the House of the Sons of St. Francis. But he dared not let his eyes rest on the flowers sleeping on the surface of the pools, for he saw in them the likeness of the wanton nymphs. He got back to his cell at the moment when the bells were sounding the *Ave Maria*. It was a small, white chamber, furnished simply with a bed, a stool, and one of the high desks writers use. On the wall a mendicant friar had painted years ago, in the manner of Giotto, a representation of the holy Marys at the foot of the Cross. Below this painting, a shelf of wood, as black and polished as the beams of an ancient oil-press, was covered with books. Of these, some were sacred, others profane, for Fra Mino was a student of the classic poets, to the end he might praise God in all the works of men, and blessed the good Virgil for having prophesied the birth of the Saviour, when the bard of Mantua declares to the Nations: *Jam redit et Virgo.*[1]

On the window-sill a tall lily stood in a vase of coarse earthenware, for Fra Mino loved to trace the name of the Blessed Virgin inscribed in the

[1] Now the Virgin too returns.

gold dust of the flower's calyx. The window itself, which opened very high up in the wall, was small, but the sky could be seen from it, blue above the purple hills.

Ensconced in this pleasant tomb of his life and longings, Mino sat down before the narrow desk, with its two shelves at top, where he was accustomed to devote himself to his studies. Then, dipping his reed in the inkhorn fastened to the side of the little coffer that held his sheets of parchment, his brushes, and his colours and gold dust, he besought the flies, in the name of the Lord, not to annoy him, and began to write the account of all he had seen and heard in the Chapel of San Michele, during his night of torment, as well as on the day just done, in the woods by the stream side. And first of all, he traced these lines on the parchment:

"*A true record of those things which Fra Mino, of the Order of Friars Minors, saw and heard, and which he doth here relate for the instruction of the Faithful. To the praise of Jesus Christ and the glory of the blessed and humble poor man of Christ, St. Francis. Amen.*"

Then he set down in order in writing, without omitting aught, all he had noted of the nymphs that turned into witches and the old man with horns on his brow, whose voice quavered in the woods like a last sigh of the Classic flute and a first prelude of the Christian harp. While he wrote, the birds sang; and night closed in slowly, blotting out the bright colours of the day. The Monk lighted his lamp, and went on with his writing. As he recounted each several marvel he had made acquaintance with, he carefully expounded its literal, and its spiritual, signification, all according to the rules of rhetoric and theology. And just as men fence about cities with walls and towers to make them strong, so he supported all his arguments with texts of Scripture. He concluded from the singular revelations he had received: firstly, that Jesus Christ is Lord of all creatures, and is God of the Satyrs and the Pans, as well as of men. This is why St. Jerome saw in the Desert Centaurs that confessed Jesus Christ; secondly, that God had communicated to the Pagans certain glimmerings of light, to the end they might be saved. Likewise the Sibyls, for instance the Cumæan, the Egyptian and the Delphic, did these not foreshadow, amid the darkness of the Gentiles, the Holy Cradle, the Rods, the Reed, the Crown of Thorns and the Cross itself? For which reason St. Augustine admitted the Erythræan Sibyl into the City of God. Fra Mino gave thanks to God for having taught him so much learning; and a great joy flooded his heart to think Virgil was among the elect. And he wrote gleefully at the bottom of the last leaf:

"*Here endeth the Apocalypse of Brother Mino, the poor man of Jesus Christ. I have seen the aureole of the blessed Saints crowning the horned forehead of the Satyr, in token that Jesus Christ hath redeemed from the shades of limbo the sages and poets of Antiquity.*"

The night was already far spent when, having finished his task, Fra Mino stretched himself upon his bed to snatch a little repose. Just as he was dropping asleep, an old woman came in at the window, riding on a moonbeam. He recognized her instantly for the ugliest of the witches he had seen in the Chapel of San Michele.

"My sweet," she said, addressing him, "what have you been doing this day? Yet we warned you, I and my pretty sisters, you must not reveal our secrets. For if you betrayed us, we told you we should kill you. And sorry I should be, for indeed I love you tenderly."

She clipped him in her arms, called him her heavenly Adonis, her darling, her little white ass, and lavished a thousand ardent caresses on him.

Anon, when he repulsed her with a spasm of disgust,

"Child, child!" she said to him, "you scorn me,

because my eyes are rimmed with red, my nostrils rotted with the acrid, fetid humour they distil, and my gums adorned with a single tooth, and that black and extravagantly long. Such is your Neæra to-day, it is too true. But if you love me, I shall once more become, by you and for you, what I was in the golden days of Saturn, when my youth was in blossom amid the blossoms of the young, flower-decked world. 'Tis love, oh! my young god, that makes the beauty of things. To restore my beauty, all that is needed is a little courage. Up, Mino, be bold and show your mettle!"

At these words, which were accompanied by appropriate gestures, Fra Mino, shuddering with fear and horror, felt himself swoon away, and slipped from his bed on to the pavement of his cell. As he fell, he seemed to catch a glimpse, between his half-closed lids, of a nymph of perfect shape and peerless beauty, whose naked body rolled over his like waves of milk.

He woke in broad daylight, bruised and broken by his fall. The leaves of the manuscript he had written the night before still littered the desk. He read them through again, folded and sealed them with his seal, put the roll inside his gown, and unheeding the menaces the witches had twice over given him, started to carry his revelations to the Lord

Bishop, whose Palace lifted its battlements above the roofs in the middle of the city. He found him donning his spurs in the Great Hall, surrounded by his men-at-arms. For the Bishop was just then at war with the Ghibellines of Florence. He asked the Monk to what he owed his visit, and on being informed of the matter, invited him there and then to read out his report. Fra Mino obeyed, and the Bishop heard out his tale to the end. He had no special lights on the subject of apparitions; but he was animated with an ardent zeal for the interests of the Faith. Without a day's delay, and not suffering the cares of the War to distract him from his purpose, he appointed twelve famous Doctors in Theology and Canon Law to examine into the affair, urging them to give a definite and speedy decision. After mature inquiry and not without again and again cross-questioning Fra Mino, the Doctors determined the best thing to do was to open the tomb of San Satiro in the Chapel of San Michele, and go through a course of special exorcisms on the spot. As to the points of doctrine raised by Fra Mino, they declined to pronounce a formal opinion, inclining however to regard as rash, frivolous and newfangled the arguments advanced by the Franciscan.

Agreeably to the advice of the learned Doctors and by order of the Bishop, the tomb of San Satiro was opened. It was found to contain nothing but a handful of ashes, which the priests sprinkled with holy water. At this there rose a white vapour, from which issued a sound of faint and feeble groans.

The night following this pious ceremony Fra Mino dreamed that the witches, bending over his bed, were tearing his heart out of his bosom. He rose at dawn, tortured with sharp pains and devoured by a raging thirst. He dragged himself as far as the cloister well, where the doves used to drink. But no sooner had he drained down a few drops of water that filled a hollow in the well-head than he felt his heart swell within him like a sponge, and with a stifled cry to God, he choked and died.

MESSER GUIDO CAVALCANTI

TO JULES LEMAÎTRE

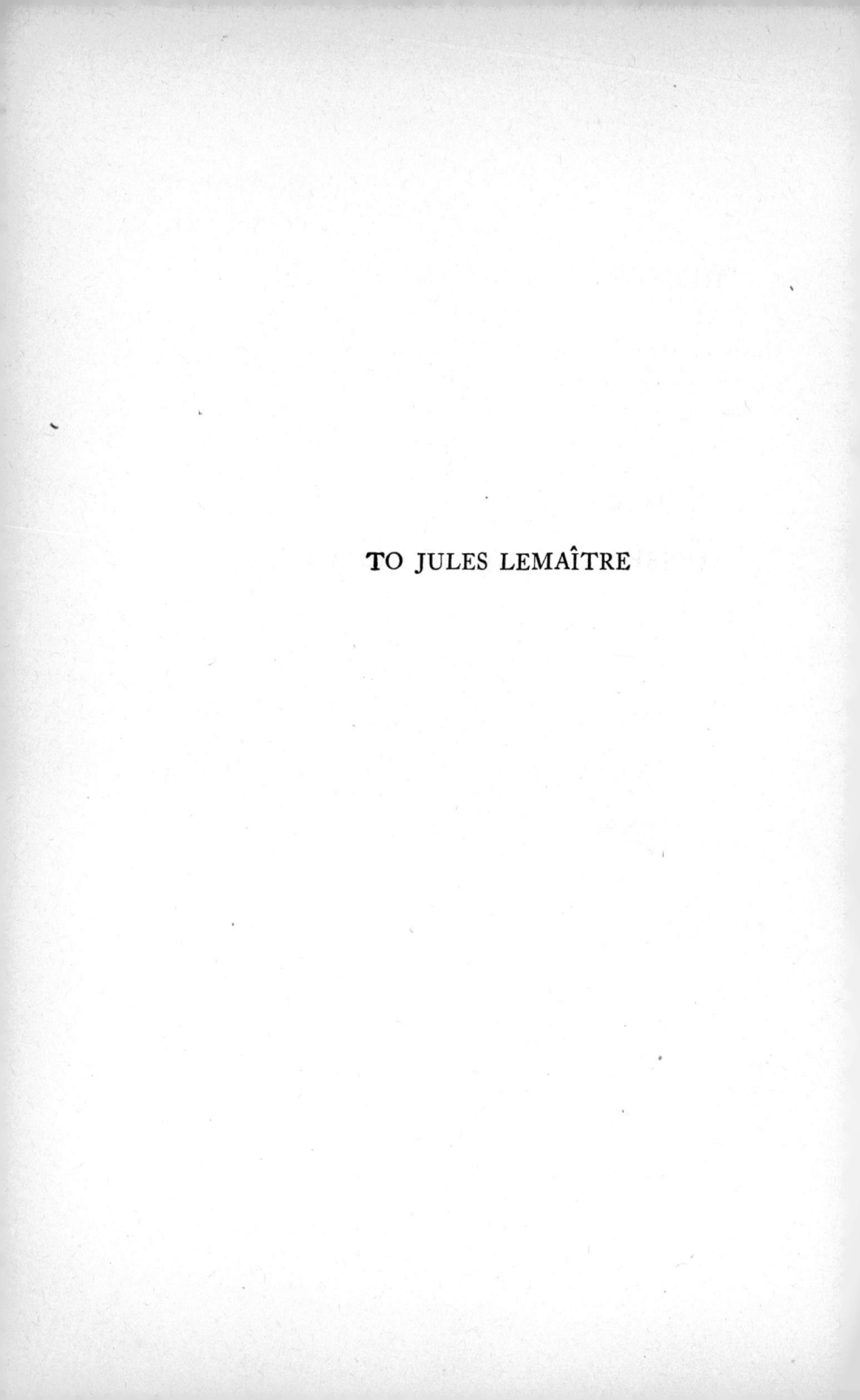

MESSER GUIDO CAVALCANTI

Guido, di Messer Cavalcante de' Calvalcanti, fu un de' migliori loici che avesse il mondo, et ottimo filosofo naturale. . . . E perciò che egli alquanto tenea della opinione degli Epicuri, si diceva tra la gente volgare che queste sue speculazioni eran solo in cercare se trovar si potesse che Iddio non fosse.[1]

(The Decameron of Messer Giovanni
Boccaccio, Sixth Day, Novella IX.)

DIM
NON. FVI. ME.
MINI. NON. SVM.
NON. CVRO. DO
NNIA. ITALIA. AN.
NORVM. XX. HIC.
QVIESCO.[2]

(Inscription from the Cippus of Donnia
Italia, as read by M. Jean-François
Bladé.)

[1] "Guido, son of Messer Cavalcante de' Cavalcanti, was one of the best Logicians the world held, and a most finished Natural Philosopher. . . . And forasmuch as in some degree he held by the opinion of the Epicureans, it was therefore said among the vulgar folk how that these his speculations were only pursued for to discover if it might be there was no God."

[2] "To the Gods of the Lower World.—I was not. I remember. I am not and I heed not. I, Donnia Italia, a maid of twenty, rest here."

MESSER Guido Cavalcanti was, in the twentieth year of his age, the most agreeable and the best-built man of all the Florentine nobles. Beneath his long, dark locks, which escaping from under his cap, fell in jetty curls over his white brow, his eyes, that had a golden gleam in them, shone out with a dazzling brilliance. He possessed the arms of Hercules and the hands of a Nymph. His shoulders were broad, and his figure slim and supple. He was well skilled in breaking difficult horses and wielding heavy weapons, and a peerless rider at the ring. Whenever he passed along the city streets to hear Mass at San Giovanni or San Michele, or walked by the Arno side in the water-meadows, that were pranked with flowers like a beautiful picture, if any fair ladies, going in a troop together, met him in the way, they never failed to say the one to the other with a blush: "See, yonder is Messer Guido, son of the Lord Cavalcante de' Cavalcanti. 'Tis a very St. George for comeliness, pardi!" And men report that Madonna Gemma, wife of Sandro Bujamonte, one day sent her Nurse to let him know how she loved him with all her soul, and was like to die of longing. Nor less ardently was he invited to join the Companies the young Florentine lords were used in those days to form among themselves, feasting, supping, gaming and hunting together, and sometimes so dearly loving each other that one and all would wear garments of a like cut and colour. But with equal disdain he shunned the society of Florentine ladies and the assemblages of her young Nobles; for so proud and fierce was his humour, he took no pleasure but in solitude.

He would often stay all the day shut up in his chamber, then forth to wander solitary beneath the holm-oaks that bordered the Ema road at the hour when the first stars are a-tremble in the pale evening sky. If by chance he encountered riders of his own age, he never laughed, and said little—and that little was not always comprehensible. His strange bearing and ambiguous words were a grief and a grievance to his comrades—and above all to Messer Betto Brunelleschi, for he dearly loved Messer Guido, and had no fonder wish than to make him one of the Brotherhood which embraced the richest and the handsomest young noblemen of Florence, and of which he was himself the glory and the delight. For indeed Messer Betto Brunelleschi was reputed the fine flower of chivalry and the most perfect knight of all Tuscany—after Messer Guido.

One day as the latter was just entering the Porch of Santa Maria Novella, where the Monks of the Order of Saint Dominic kept at that time a number of books that had been brought to Italy by the Greeks, Messer Betto, who was crossing the Piazza at the moment, loudly hailed his friend:

"Hola! Guido mine," he shouted, "whither away now, this bright day, that invites you, methinks, to go fowling in the hills rather than hide in the gloom of the Cloister yonder? Do me a favour, and come to my house at Arezzo, where I will play the flute to you, for the pleasure of seeing you smile."

"Grammercy!" replied Messer Guido, without so much as deigning to turn his head. "I am away to see my Lady."

And so saying, he entered the Church, which he crossed with a rapid step, recking as little of the Blessed Sacrament exposed on the Altar as of Messer Betto, sitting stiff on his horse outside the door, astounded at the words he had just heard. Guido pushed open a low portal leading to the Cloisters, followed the Cloister wall, and arrived in the Library, where Fra Sisto was painting the figures of angels. There, after saluting the good Brother, he drew out from a great painted chest

MESSER GUIDO CAVALCANTI 57

one of the books newly come from Constantinople, laid it on a desk and began to turn over the leaves. It was a Treatise on Love, writ in Greek by the divine Plato. Messer Guido sighed; his hands began to tremble and his eyes filled with tears.

"Alas!" he muttered; "hid beneath these signs is the Light, and I cannot see it."

He said thus to himself, because the knowledge of the Greek tongue was then altogether lost in the West. After many a long-drawn groan, he took the book, and kissing it, laid it in the iron chest like a beautiful dead woman in her coffin. Then he asked the good Fra Sisto to give him the Manuscript of the Speeches of Cicero, which he read, till the shades of evening, glooming down on the cypresses in the Cloister garden, spread their batlike wings over the pages of his book. For you must know Messer Guido Cavalcanti was a searcher after truth in the writings of the Ancients, and was for treading the arduous ways that lead mankind to immortality. Devoured by the noble longing of discovery, he would set out in canzones the doctrines of the old-world Sages concerning Love which is the path to Virtue.

A few days later, Messer Betto Brunelleschi came to visit him at his own house on the promenade of the Adimari, at the peep of day, the hour when the lark sings in the corn. He found him still abed, and after kissing him, said tenderly:

"My Guido, my Guido lad! put me out of my pain. Last week you told me you were on your way to visit your Lady in the Church and Cloister of Santa Maria Novella. Ever since I have been turning, turning your words in my head, without fathoming their meaning. I shall have no peace till you have given me an explanation of them. I beseech you, tell me what you meant—so far, that is, as your discretion shall suffer you, seeing the matter doth concern a lady."

Messer Guido burst out a-laughing. Raising himself on his elbow in bed, he looked Messer Betto in the eyes.

"Friend!" said he, "the Lady I spoke to you of hath more than one habitation. The day you saw me going to visit her, I found her in the Library of Santa Maria Novella. But alack! I heard but the one half of her discourse, for she spoke to me in both of the two languages that flow like honey from her adorable lips. First she delivered me a discourse in the tongue of the Greeks, which I could not comprehend, then she addressed me in the dialect of the Latins with a wondrous wisdom. And so well pleased was I with her conversation that I am right fain to marry her."

" 'Tis at the least," said Messer Betto, "a niece of the Emperor of Constantinople, or his natural daughter. . . . How name you her?"

"If needs be," answered Messer Guido, "we must give her a love name, such as every poet gives to his mistress. I will call her Diotima, in memory of Diotima of Megara, who showed the way to the lovers of Virtue. But her public and avowed name is Philosophy, and 'tis the most excellent bride a man can find. I want no other, and I swear by the gods to be faithful unto death, which doth put an end to life and thought."

When he heard these sentiments, Messer Betto struck his forehead with his hand and cried:

"Per Bacco! but I never guessed the riddle! Friend Guido, you have the subtlest wit under the red lily of Florence. I heartily commend your taking to wife so high a dame. Of a surety, will spring of this union a numerous progeny of canzones, sonnets and ballades. I promise to baptize you these pretty babes to the sound of my flute, with dainty mottoes galore and gallant devices. I am the more rejoiced at this spiritual wedlock, seeing it will never hinder you, when the time comes, to marry according to the flesh some fair and goodly lady of the city."

"Nay! you are out," returned Messer Guido.

"They that celebrate the espousals of the mind should leave carnal marriage to the profane vulgar, which includes the great Lords, the Merchants and the Handicraftsmen. If like me you had known my Diotima, you would have learned, friend Betto, that she doth distinguish two sorts of men, on the one hand such as, being fruitful only by the body, strive but for that coarse and commonplace immortality that is won by the generation of children, on the other they whose soul conceives and engenders what is meet for the soul to produce, to wit the Good and Beautiful. My Diotima hath willed I should be of the second sort, and I will not go against her good pleasure, and copy the mere brutes that breed and procreate."

Messer Betto Brunelleschi by no means approved of this resolution. He pointed out to his friend that in life we must adapt ourselves to the different conditions and modes of existence suitable to the different ages, that after the epoch of pleasures comes that of ambition, and that it was good and prudent, as youth waned, to contract alliance with some rich and noble family, affording access to the great offices of the Republic, such as Prior of the Arts and Liberty, Captain of the People, or Gonfalonier of Justice.

Seeing however that his friend only received his

advice with a lip of disgust, as if it were some bitter drug, he said no more on the point, for fear of angering him, deeming it wise to trust to time, which will change men's hearts and reverse the strongest resolutions.

"Sweet Guido," he interposed gaily, "tell me this much at any rate. Doth your lady suffer you to have delight with pretty maids and to take part in our diversions?"

"For that matter," replied Messer Guido, "she hath no more care of such things than of the encounters that small dog you see asleep yonder at the foot of my bed may make in the street. And in very deed they are of no account, provided a man doth himself attach no value to them."

Messer Betto left the room a trifle piqued at his friend's scornful bearing. He continued to feel the liveliest affection for his friend, but thought it unbecoming to press him overmuch to attend the fêtes and entertainments he gave all the Winter long with an admirable liberality. At the same time the gentlemen of his Company resented hotly the slight the son of the Signor Cavalcante de' Cavalcanti did them by refusing to share their society. They began to rally him on his studies and poring over books, declaring that by dint of so feeding on parchment, like the Monks and the rats, he would end up by growing to resemble these, and would anon have nothing to show but a pointed snout and three long hairs for beard, peeping out from under a black hood, and that Madonna Gemma herself would cry out at sight of him:

"Venus, my Patroness! what a pass have his books brought my handsome St. George to! He is good for naught now but to throw away his lance and hold a writing-reed in hand instead." So they miscalled him sore, saying he toyed only with the bookworms and spiders, and was tied to the apron-strings of Mistress Philosophia. Nor did they stop short at such-like light raillery, but let it be understood he was too learned by far to be a good Christian, that he was given over to Magic Arts, and held converse with the Devils of Hell.

"Folk do not lurk in hiding like that," they said to each other, "for any reason but to foregather with the Devils, male and female, and get gold of them as the price of revolting and shameful acts."

To crown all, they charged him with sharing those false and pernicious doctrines of Epicurus which had already seduced an Emperor at Naples and a Pope in Rome, and threatened to turn the peoples of Europe into a herd of swine, without a thought of God and their own immortal souls. "A mighty fine gain," they ended up, "when his studies have brought him to forswear the Holy Trinity!" This last charge they bruited abroad was the most formidable of all, and might easily work ruin on Messer Guido.

Now Messer Guido Cavalcanti was well aware of the mockery they made of him in the Companies by reason of the careful heed he had of eternal things; and this was why he shunned the society of living men and sought rather to the dead.

In those days the Church of San Giovanni was surrounded with Roman tombs. Thither would Messer Guido often come at *Ave Maria,* and meditate far into the silent night. He believed, as the Chronicles reported, that this fair Church of San Giovanni had been a Pagan Temple before it was a Christian Church, and the thought pleased his soul, which was enamoured of the old-world mysteries. Especially he loved to look on these tombs, where the sign of the Cross found no place, but which bore Latin inscriptions and were adorned with carven figures of men and gods. They were long cubes of white marble, on the sides of which could be made out representations of banquets and hunting parties, the death of Adonis, the fight of Lapithæ and Centaurs, the refusal of the chaste Hippolytus, the Amazons. Messer Guido would read the lettering with anxious care, and try hard to penetrate the meaning of these fables. One tomb in particular occupied him more than all the rest, for it showed him two Loves, each holding a torch, and he was curious to discover the nature of these two Loves Well! one night that he was pondering on these things more deeply than ever, a shadow rose up above the lid of the tomb—a luminous shadow, as when you see, or fancy you see, the moon shining faintly through a cloud. Gradually it took the shape of a beautiful virgin, and said thus in a voice softer than the reeds waving in the wind:

"I am she that sleeps within this tomb, and I am called Julia Læta. I lost the light on my marriage-day, at the age of sixteen years, three months and nine days. Since then, whether I am, or am not, I cannot tell. Never question the dead, stranger, for they see naught, and a thick night environs them. 'Tis said that such as in life knew the cruel joys of Venus roam the glades of a dense forest of myrtles. For me who died a virgin, I sleep a dreamless sleep. They have graven two Loves on the stone of my sepulchre. One gives mortals the light of day; the other quenches it in their tender eyes for ever. The countenance of both is the same, a smiling countenance, for birth and death are two twin brothers, and all is joy to the Immortal Gods. I have spoken."

The voice fell silent, like the rustling of leaves when the wind drops. The transparent shadow vanished away in the light of dawn, which descended clear and white on the hills; and the tombs of San Giovanni grew wan and silent once again in the morning air. And Messer Guido pondered:

"The truth I foresaw, hath been made manifest to me. Is it not writ in the Book the Priests use, 'Shall the dead praise Thee, O Lord?' The dead are without thought or knowledge, and the divine Epicurus was well advised when he enfranchised the living from the vain terrors of the life to come."

A troop of horsemen pricking across the Piazza abruptly broke up his meditations. It was Messer Betto and his Company away to hunt the cranes along the brookside of Peretola.

"So ho!" cried one of them, whose name was Bocca, "see yonder, Messer Guido the Philosopher, who scorns us for our good life and gentle ways and merry doings. He seems half frozen."

"And well he may be," put in Messer Doria, who was reputed a wag. "His lady, the Moon, whom he kisses tenderly all night, hath hied her behind the hills to sleep with some shepherd swain. He is eat up with jealousy; look you, how green he is!"

They spurred their horses among the tombs, and drew up in a ring about Messer Guido.

"Nay! nay! Messer Doria," returned Bocca, "the lady Moon is too round and bright for so black a gallant. If you would know his mistresses, they be here. Here he comes to find them in their bed, where he is less like to be stung of fleas than of scorpions."

"Fie! Out upon the vile necromancer!" exclaimed Messer Giordano, crossing himself; "see what learning leads to! Folk disown God, and go fornicating in Pagan graveyards."

Leaning against the Church wall, Messer Guido let the riders have their say. When he judged they had voided all the froth of their shallow brains over him:

"Gentle cavaliers," he answered, smiling, "you are at home. I am your host, and courtesy constrains me to receive your insults without reply."

So saying, he bounded over the tombs and walked quietly away. The horsemen looked at one another in amazement; then bursting out laughing, they gave spur to their steeds. As they were galloping along the Peretola Road, Messer Bocca said to Messer Betto:

"Who can doubt now but this Guido is gone mad? He told us we were at home in the graveyard. And to say such a thing, he must needs have lost his wits."

"True it is," replied Messer Betto, "I cannot imagine what he meant to have us understand by talking in such a sort. But he is used to expressing himself in dark sayings and subtle parables. He hath tossed us a bone this time must be opened to find the marrow."

"Pardi!" ejaculated Messer Giordano; "my dog may have this bone to gnaw, and the Pagan that threw it to boot."

They soon reached the banks of the Peretola brook, whence the cranes may be seen rising in flocks at daybreak. During the chase, which was abundantly successful, Messer Betto Brunelleschi never ceased pondering the words Guido had used. And by dint of much thinking, he discovered their signification. Hailing Messer Bocca with loud cries, he said to him:

"Come hither, Messer Bocca! I have just guessed what it was Messer Guido meant us to understand. He told us we were at home in a graveyard, because the ignorant be for all the world like dead men, who, according to the Epicurean doctrine, have no faculty of thought or knowledge."

Messer Bocca replied, shrugging his shoulders, he understood better than most how to fly a Flanders hawk, to make knife-play with his enemies, and to upset a girl, and this was knowledge sufficient for his state in life.

Messer Guido continued for several years more to study the science of Love. He embodied his reflexions in canzones, which it is not given to all men to interpret, composing a book of these verses that was borne in triumph through the streets, garlanded with laurel. Then, seeing the purest souls are not without alloy of terrestrial passions, and life bears us one and all along in its sinuous and stormy course, it fell out that at the turning-point of youth and age, Messer Guido was seduced by the ambitions of the flesh and the powers of this world. He wedded, to further his projects of aggrandizement, the daughter of the Lord Farinata degli Uberti, the same who one time reddened the Arbia with the blood of the Florentines. He threw himself into the quarrels of the citizens with all the pride and impetuosity of his nature. And he took for mistresses the Lady Mandetta and the Lady Giovanna, who represented the one the Albigensians, the other the Ghibellines. It was the time when Messer Dante Alighieri was Prior of the Arts and Liberty. The city was divided into two hostile camps, those of the Bianchi and the Neri. One day when the principal citizens were assembled in the Piazza of the Frescobaldi, the Bianchi on one side the square and the Neri on the other, to assist at the obsequies of a noble lady of Florence, the Doctors and the Knights were seated as the custom was, on raised benches, while in front of them the younger men sat on the ground on rush mats. One of the latter standing up to settle his cloak, those who were opposite thought he was for defying them. They started to their feet in turn, and bared their swords. Instantly every one unsheathed, and the kinsmen of the dead lady had all the difficulty in the world to separate the combatants.

From that day, Florence ceased to be a town gladdened by the work of its handicraftsmen, and became a forest full of wolves ravening for each other's blood. Messer Guido shared these savage passions, and grew gloomy, restless and sullen. Never a day passed but he exchanged sword-thrusts with the Neri in the streets of Florence, where in old days he had meditated on the nature and constitution of the soul. More than once he had felt the assassin's dagger on his flesh, before he was banished with the rest of his faction and confined in the plague-stricken town of Sarzana. For six months he languished there, sick with fever and hate. And when eventually the Bianchi were recalled, he came back to his native city a dying man.

In the year 1300, on the third day after the Assumption of the Blessed Virgin Mary, he found strength enough to drag himself as far as his own fair Church of San Giovanni. Worn out with fatigue and grief, he lay down on the tomb of Julia Læta, who in the old days had revealed to him the mysteries the profane know nothing of. It was the hour when the Church bells ring out through the quivering air of evening a long-drawn farewell to the setting sun. Messer Betto Brunelleschi, who was crossing the Piazza on his way home from his country house, saw amid the tombs two haggard falcon's eyes burning in a fleshless face, and recognizing the friend of his youth, was seized with wonder and pity.

He approached him, and kissing him as he used in former days, said with a sigh:

"Ah! Guido mine! what fire is it hath consumed you away thus? You burned up your life in science first, and then in public affairs. I beseech you, quench somewhat the ardour of your spirit; comrade, let us husband our strength, and, as Riccardo the blacksmith says, make up a fire to last.

But Guido Cavalcanti put his hand on his lips.

"Hush!" he whispered, "hush! not a word more, friend Betto. I wait my lady, her who shall console me for so many vain loves that in this world have betrayed me and that I have betrayed. It is equally cruel and useless to think and to act. This I know. The curse is not so much to live, for I see you are well and hearty, friend Betto, and many another man is the same. The curse is not to live, but to know we live. The curse is to be conscious and to will. Happily there is a remedy for these evils. Let us say no more; I await the lady whom I have never wronged, for never have I doubted but she was gentle and true-hearted, and I have learned by much pondering how peaceful and secure it is to slumber on her bosom. Many fables have been told of her bed and dwelling-places. But I have not believed the lies of the ignorant crowd. So it is, she cometh to me as a mistress to her lover, her brow garlanded with flowers and her lips smiling."

He broke off with these words, and fell dead over the ancient tomb. His body was buried without any great pomp in the Cloister of Santa Maria Novella.

LUCIFER

TO LOUIS GANDERAX

LUCIFER

E si compiacque tanto Spinello di farlo orribile e contrafatto, che si dice (tanto può alcuna fiata l' immaginazione) che la detta figura da lui dipinta gli apparve in sogno, domandandolo dove egli l' avesse veduta si brutta.[1]

(*Vite de' piu eccellenti pittori*, da Messer Giorgio Vasari.—"Vita di Spinello.")

ANDREA TAFI, painter and worker-in-mosaic of Florence, had a wholesome terror of the Devils of Hell, particularly in the watches of the night, when it is given to the powers of Darkness to prevail. And the worthy man's fears were not unreasonable, for in those days the Demons had good cause to hate the Painters, who robbed them of more souls with a single picture than a good little Preaching Friar could do in thirty sermons. No doubt the Monk, to instil a

---

[1] "And so successful was Spinello with his horrible and portentous Production that it was commonly reported—so great is always the force of fancy—that the said figure (of Lucifer trodden underfoot by St. Michael in the Altar-piece of the Church of St. Agnolo at Arezzo) painted by him had appeared to the artist in a dream, and asked him in what place he had beheld him under so brutish a form."
Lives of the most Excellent Painters, by Giorgio Vasari.—"Life of Spinello."

soul-saving horror in the hearts of the faithful, would describe to the utmost of his powers "that day of wrath, that day of mourning," which is to reduce the universe to ashes, *teste David et Sibylla,* borrowing his deepest voice and bellowing through his hands to imitate the Archangel's last trump. But there! it was "all sound and fury, signifying nothing," whereas a painting displayed on a Chapel wall or in the Cloister, showing Jesus Christ sitting on the Great White Throne to judge the living and the dead, spoke unceasingly to the eyes of sinners, and through the eyes chastened such as had sinned by the eyes or otherwise.

It was in the days when cunning masters were depicting at Santa-Croce in Florence and the Campo Santo of Pisa the mysteries of Divine Justice. These works were drawn according to the account in verse which Dante Alighieri, a man very learned in Theology and in Canon Law, wrote in days gone by of his journey to Hell and Purgatory and Paradise, whither by the singular great merits of his lady, he was able to make his way alive. So everything in these paintings was instructive and true, and we may say surely less profit is to be had of reading the most full and ample Chronicle than from contemplating such representative works of art. Moreover, the Florentine masters took heed to paint, under the shade of orange groves, on the flower-starred turf, fair ladies and gallant knights, with Death lying in wait for them with his scythe, while they were discoursing of love to the sound of lutes and viols. Nothing was better fitted to convert carnal-minded sinners who quaff forgetfulness of God on the lips of women. To rebuke the covetous, the painter would show to the life the Devils pouring molten gold down the throat of Bishop or Abbess, who had commissioned some work from him and then scamped his pay.

This is why the Demons in those days were bitter enemies of the painters, and above all of the Florentine painters, who surpassed all the rest in subtlety of wit. Chiefly they reproached them with representing them under a hideous guise, with the heads of birds and fish, serpents' bodies and bats' wings. This sore resentment which they felt will come out plainly in the history of Spinello of Arezzo.

Spinello Spinelli was sprung of a noble family of Florentine exiles, and his graciousness of mind matched his gentle birth; for he was the most skilful painter of his time. He wrought many and great works at Florence; and the Pisans begged him to complete Giotto's wall-paintings in their Campo Santo, where the dead rest beneath roses in holy earth shipped from Jerusalem. At last, after working long years in divers cities and getting much gold, he longed to see once more the good city of Arezzo, his mother. The men of Arezzo had not forgotten how Spinello, in his younger days, being enrolled in the Confraternity of Santa Maria della Misericordia, had visited the sick and buried the dead in the plague of 1383. They were grateful to him beside for having by his works spread the fame of their city over Tuscany. For all these reasons they welcomed him with high honours on his return.

Still full of vigour in his old age, he undertook important tasks in his native town. His wife would tell him:

"You are rich, Spinello. Do you rest, and leave younger men to paint instead of you. It is meet a man should end his days in a gentle, religious quiet. It is tempting God to be for ever raising new and worldly monuments, mere heathen towers of Babel. Quit your colours and your varnishes, Spinello, or they will destroy your peace of mind."

So the good dame would preach, but he refused to listen, for his one thought was to increase his fortune and renown. Far from resting on his laurels, he arranged a price with the Wardens of Sant' Agnolo for a history of St. Michael, that was to cover all the Choir of the Church and contain an infinity of figures. Into this enterprise he threw himself with extraordinary ardour. Rereading the parts of Scripture that were to be his inspiration, he set himself to study deeply every line and every word of these passages. Not content with drawing all day long in his workshop, he persisted in working both at bed and board; while at dusk, walking below the hill on whose brow Arezzo proudly lifts her walls and towers, he was still lost in thought. And we may say the story of the Archangel was already limned in his brain when he started to sketch out the incidents in red chalk on the plaster of the wall. He was soon done tracing these outlines; then he fell to painting above the high altar the scene that was to outshine all the others in brilliancy. For it was his intent therein to glorify the leader of the hosts of Heaven for the victory he won before the beginning of time. Accordingly Spinello represented St. Michael fighting in the air against the serpent with seven heads and ten horns, and he figured with delight, in the bottom part of the picture, the Prince of the Devils, Lucifer, under the semblance of an appalling monster. The figures seemed to grow to life of themselves under his hand. His success was beyond his fondest hopes; so hideous was the countenance of Lucifer, none could escape the nightmare of its foulness. The face haunted the painter in the streets and even went home with him to his lodging.

Presently when night was come, Spinello lay down in his bed beside his wife and fell asleep. In his slumbers he saw an Angel as comely as St. Michael, but black; and the Angel said to him:

"Spinello, I am Lucifer. Tell me, where had you seen me, that you should paint me as you have, under so ignominious a likeness?"

The old painter answered trembling, that he had never seen him with his eyes, never having gone down alive into Hell, like Messer Dante Alighieri; but that, in depicting him as he had done, he was for expressing in visible lines and colours the hideousness of sin.

Lucifer shrugged his shoulders, and the hill of San Gemignano seemed of a sudden to heave and stagger.

"Spinello," he went on, "will you do me the pleasure to reason awhile with me? I am no mean Logician; He you pray to knows that."

Receiving no reply, Lucifer proceeded in these terms:

"Spinello, you have read the books that tell of me. You know of my enterprise, and how I forsook Heaven to become the Prince of this World. A tremendous adventure,—and a unique one, had not the Giants in like fashion assailed the god Jupiter, as yourself have seen, Spinello, recorded on an ancient tomb where this Titanic war is carved in marble."

"It is true," said Spinello, "I have seen the tomb, shaped like a great tun, in the Church of Santa Reparata at Florence. 'Tis a fine work of the Romans."

"Still," returned Lucifer, smiling, "the Giants are not pictured on it in the shape of frogs or chameleons or the like hideous and horrid creatures."

"True," replied the painter, "but then they had not attacked the true God, but only a false idol of the Pagans. 'Tis a mighty difference. The fact is clear, Lucifer, you raised the standard of revolt against the true and veritable King of Earth and Heaven."

"I will not deny it," said Lucifer. "And how many sorts of sins do you charge me with for that?"

"Seven, it is like enough," the painter answered, "and deadly sins one and all."

"Seven!" exclaimed the Angel of Darkness; "well! the number is canonical. Everything goes by sevens in my history, which is close bound up with God's. Spinello, you deem me proud, angry and envious. I enter no protest, provided you allow that glory was my only aim. Do you deem me covetous? Granted again; Covetousness is a virtue for Princes. For Gluttony and Lust, if you hold me guilty, I will not complain. Remains *Indolence*."

As he pronounced the word, Lucifer crossed his arms across his breast, and shaking his gloomy head, tossed his flaming locks:

"Tell me, Spinello, do you really think I am indolent? Do you take me for a coward? Do you hold that in my revolt I showed a lack of courage? Nay! you cannot. Then it was but just to paint me in the guise of a hero, with a proud countenance. You should wrong no one, not even the Devil. Cannot you see that you insult Him you make prayer to, when you give Him for adversary a vile, monstrous toad? Spinello, you are very ignorant for a man of your age. I have a great mind to pull your ears, as they do to an ill-conditioned schoolboy."

At this threat, and seeing the arm of Lucifer already stretched out towards him, Spinello clapped his hand to his head and began to howl with terror.

His good wife, waking up with a start, asked him what ailed him. He told her with chattering teeth, how he had just seen Lucifer and had been in terror for his ears.

"I told you so," retorted the worthy dame; "I knew all those figures you will go on painting on the walls would end by driving you mad."

"I am not mad," protested the painter. "I saw him with my own eyes; and he is beautiful to look on, albeit proud and sad. First thing to-morrow I will blot out the horrid figure I have drawn and set in its place the shape I beheld in my dream. For we must not wrong even the Devil himself."

"You had best go to sleep again," scolded his wife. "You are talking stark nonsense, and unchristian to boot."

Spinello tried to rise, but his strength failed him and he fell back unconscious on his pillow. He lingered on a few days in a high fever, and then died.

THE LOAVES OF BLACK BREAD

TO MADEMOISELLE MARY FINALY

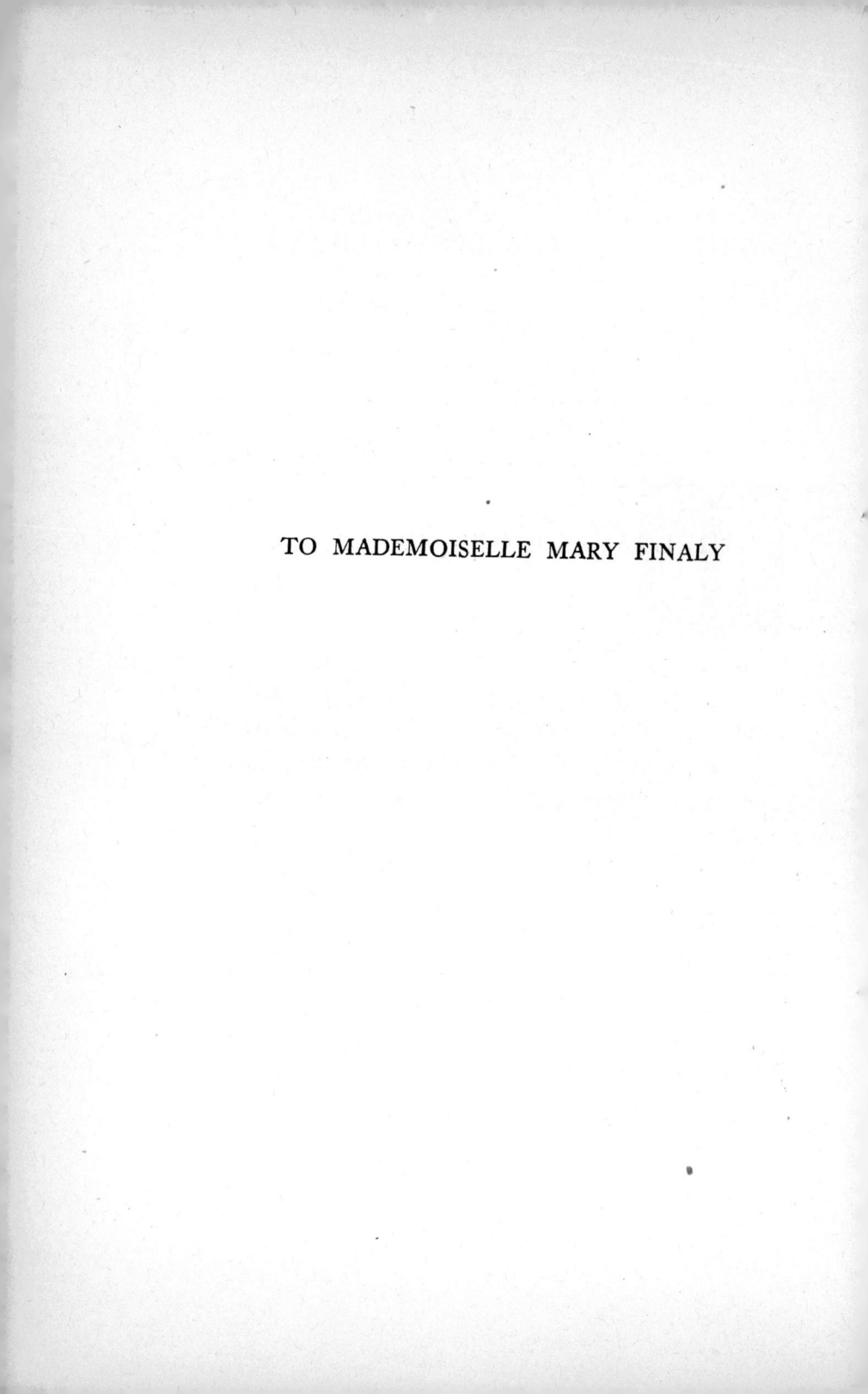

THE LOAVES OF BLACK BREAD

Tu tibi divitias stolidissime congeris amplas,
Negasque micam pauperi;
Advenit ecce dies qua saevis ignibus ardens
Rogabis aquae guttulam.[1]

(*Navis stultifera*, Sebastian Brandt, 1507, fol. xix.)

IN those days Nicolas Nerli was a banker in the noble city of Florence. Tierce was no sooner sounded than he was at his desk, and at nones he was seated there still, poring all day long over the figures he wrote in his table-books. He lent money to the Emperor and to the Pope. And if he did not lend to the Devil, it was only because he was afraid of bad debts with him they call the Wily One, and who is full of cunning and trickery. Nicolas Nerli was bold and unscrupulous; he had won great riches and robbed many folks of their own. Wherefore he was highly honoured in the city of Florence. He dwelt in a Palace where the light of God's day entered only by narrow win-

[1] "You heap up in your folly ample riches for yourself, and refuse a crumb of bread to the poor man; lo! the day is at hand when burning in cruel flames, you shall beg for a drop of water."
—*Ship of Fools.*

dows; and this was a wise precaution, for the rich man's house must be a castle, and they who possess much wealth do well to defend by force what they have gotten by cunning.

Accordingly the windows were guarded with bars and the doors with chains. Outside, the walls were painted in fresco by clever craftsmen, who had depicted thereon the Virtues under the likeness of women, the Patriarchs, the Prophets and the Kings of Israel. Tapestries hung in the rooms within, displaying the histories of Alexander and Tristram, as they are told us in legends. Nicolas Nerli set all the city talking of his wealth by the pious foundations he established. He had raised an Hospital beyond the walls, the frieze of which, carved and painted, represented the most honourable actions of his own life; in gratitude for the sums of money he had given towards the completion of Santa Marja Novella, his portrait was suspended in the choir of that Church. In it he was shown kneeling, with praying hands, at the feet of the Blessed Virgin, easily recognizable by his cap of red worsted, his furred hood, his yellow face swimming in fatness and his little keen eyes. His good wife, Monna Bismantova, a worthy-looking woman with a mournful air, and seeming as though no man could ever have taken aught of pleasure with her, was on the other side of the Virgin in the humble attitude of supplication. Nicolas Nerli was one of the chiefest citizens of the Republic; seeing he had never spoken against the laws, and because he had never regarded the poor nor such folk as the great and powerful condemn to fine and exile, nothing had lowered in the estimation of the Magistrates the high repute he had won in their eyes by reason of his great riches.

Returning one winter evening later than usual to his Palace, he was surrounded on the threshold by a band of half-naked mendicants who held out their hands and asked alms.

He repulsed them with hard words. But hunger making them as fierce and bold as wolves, they formed a circle round him, and begged him for bread in hoarse lamentable voices. He was just stooping to pick up stones to throw at them when he saw one of his serving-men coming, carrying on his head a basketful of loaves of black bread, intended for the stablemen, kitchen helpers and gardeners.

He signed to the pantler to approach, and diving both hands into the basket, tossed the loaves to the starving wretches. Then entering the house, he went to bed and fell asleep. In the night, he was smitten with apoplexy and died so suddenly he believed himself still in his bed when he saw, in a place "as dark as Erebus," St. Michael the Archangel shining in the brightness that issued from his own presence.

Balance in hand, the Archangel was engaged in filling the scales. Recognizing in the scale that hung lowest certain jewels belonging to widow women that he had in pledge, a great heap of clippings from pieces he had filched dishonestly, and sundry very fine gold coins which were unique and which he had acquired by usury or fraud, Nicolas Nerli comprehended it was his own life, now come to an end, that St. Michael was at that instant weighing before his eyes.

"Good Sir!" he said, "good St. Michael! if you put in the one scale all the lucre I have gotten in my life, set in the other, if it please you, the noble foundations whereby I have so splendidly shown my piety. Forget not the Duomo of Santa Maria Novella, to which I contributed a good third; nor my Hospital beyond the walls, that I built entirely out of my own pocket."

"Never fear, Nicolas Nerli," answered the Archangel; "I will forget nothing."

THE LOAVES OF BLACK BREAD

And with his own heavenly hands he set in the lighter scale the Duomo of Santa Maria Novella and the Hospital with its frieze all carved and painted. But the scale did not drop an inch.

At this the Banker was sorely disquieted.

"Good St. Michael! think again. You have not put this side of the balance my fine holy-water stoup I gave to San Giovanni, nor the pulpit in Sant' Andrea, where the baptism of Our Lord Jesus Christ is depicted life-size. The artist charged me a pretty penny for it."

The Archangel put both pulpit and stoup atop of the Hospital in the scale, but still it never stirred. Nicolas Nerli began to feel a cold sweat bathing his brow.

"Good Sir! dear Archangel!" he asked, "are you quite certain your balances are true?"

St. Michael replied, smiling, that they were of a different pattern from the balances the brokers of Paris use and the money-changers of Venice, and were precisely accurate.

"What!" sighed Nicolas Nerli, his face as white as chalk. "Duomo, pulpit, basin, Hospital with all its beds, do they weigh no more than a bit of straw, a pinch of down from a bird's breast?"

"See for yourself, Nicolas!" said the Archangel; "so far the weight of your iniquities much outweighs the light load of your good works."

"Then I must go to Hell," cried the Florentine; and his teeth chattered with horror.

"Patience, Nicolas Nerli," returned the Weigher of Souls, "patience! we are not done yet. There is something left."

So saying, the Blessed St. Michael took the loaves of black bread the rich man had tossed the night before to the poor beggars. He laid them in the scale containing the good works, which instantly fell, while the other rose, and the two scales remained level. The beam dropped neither to right nor left, and the needle marked the exact equality of the two loads.

The Banker could not believe his eyes; but the glorious Archangel said solemnly:

"See, Nicolas Nerli; you are good neither for Heaven nor Hell. Begone! Go back to Florence! multiply through the city the loaves you gave last night with your own hand, in the dusk, when no man saw you—and you shall be saved. It is not enough that Heaven open its doors to the thief that repented and the harlot that wept. The mercy of God is infinite, and able to save even a rich man. Do this; multiply the loaves whose weight

THE LOAVES OF BLACK BREAD

you see weighing down my balances. Begone!"

Then Nicolas Nerli awoke in his bed. He resolved to follow faithfully the counsel of the Archangel, and multiply the bread of the poor, and so enter into the kingdom of Heaven.

For the three years he spent on earth after his first death, he was very pitiful to the unfortunate and a great giver of alms.

THE MERRY-HEARTED
BUFFALMACCO

TO EUGENE MUNTZ

THE MERRY-HEARTED BUFFALMACCO

Buonamico di Cristofano detto Buffalmacco pittore Fiorentino, il qual fu discepolo d' Andrea Tafi, e come uomo burlevole celebrato da Messer Giovanni Boccaccio nel suo Decamerone, fu come si sa carissimo compagno di Bruno e di Calendrino pittori ancor essi faceti e piacevole, e, come si può vedere nell' opere sue sparse per tutta Toscana, di assai buon giudizio nell' arte sua del dipignere.

(*Vite de' più eccellenti pittori,* da Messer Giorgio Vasari.—"Vita di Buonamico Buffalmacco.")1

[1] "Buonamico di Cristofano, known as Buffalmacco, a Florentine painter, the same that was pupil of Andrea Tafi, and celebrated as a burlesque character by Messer Giovanni Boccaccio in his *Decameron,* was as we know bosom friend of Bruno and Calendrino, also painters and of an even more witty and merry humour than himself, and as may be seen in his works scattered throughout Tuscany, of no mean judgement in his art of painting." (*Lives of the most Excellent Painters,* by Messer Giorgio Vasari.— "Life of Buonamico Buffalmacco.")

I

THE COCKROACHES

IN his callow youth, Buonamico Cristofani, Florentine, surnamed Buffalmacco by reason of his merry humour, served his apprenticeship in the workshop of Andrea Tafi, painter and worker-in-mosaic. Now the said Tafi was a very knowledgeable master. Sojourning at Venice in the days when Apollonius was covering the walls of San Marco with mosaics, he had discovered by means of a trick certain secrets the Greek craftsmen were for keeping sedulously to themselves. Returning to his native city, he won so high a repute in the art of composing pictures by arranging together a countless number of little differently coloured cubes of glass, he could not supply all the demands addressed to him for works of the sort, and all day and every day, from matins to vespers, he was busy, mounted on a scaffold in some Church or other, depicting the dead Christ, or Christ in His glory, the Patriarchs and Prophets, or the history of Job or of Noah. And as he was likewise keen to paint in fresco, with pounded colours, in the manner of the Greeks, which was then the only one known, he refused himself all rest, and gave his apprentices none either. He used to tell them:

"They who like myself are in possession of noble secrets and excel in their art should keep both mind and hand ceaselessly active to carry out their enterprises, so as to win much wealth and leave a long memory behind them. And if I, old and broken down as I am, spare myself no trouble, you are bound to do your utmost to help me with all your strength, which is fresh, hearty and undiminished."

And in order that his colours, his tesseræ of molten glass and his impastos might be all ready prepared by dawn of day, he forced the lads to rise in the middle of the night. Nothing could well be more hateful to Buffalmacco, who was in the habit of supping plentifully, and loved to run the streets at an hour when, as they say, all cats are grey. He went to bed late and slept sound, his conscience being clear enough after all. Accordingly, when Tafi's shrill voice woke him up out of his beauty sleep, he would only turn round on his pillow and pretend to be deaf. But his master invariably persisted, and at a pinch would go into the apprentice's room and very soon have the sheets dragged off the bed and a jug of cold water emptied over the sluggard's head.

Poor Buffalmacco, shivering and half dressed, would away grumbling, to grind the colours in the dark, cold workroom, cudgelling his wits the while, grinding and cursing all the time, to think of some way of escaping such harsh and humiliating treatment in future. Long he sought in vain; but his mind was an active one, and one morning early a happy thought struck him.

To put this in execution, Buffalmacco waited till his master was out of the way. Directly day broke, Andrea Tafi, as his habit was, pocketed the flask of Chianti and the three eggs that formed his regular breakfast, and bidding his pupils melt the glass tesseræ according to the directions, and take every possible pains, went off to work in the famous church of San Giovanni, a marvellously beautiful building, constructed with admirable art in the Classical manner. At the time he was executing on its walls a series of mosaics representing the Angels, Archangels, Cherubim and Seraphim, Powers, Thrones and Dominions; the chief acts of the Almighty, from the Creation of Light to the Deluge; the history of Joseph and his brethren, the history of Jesus Christ from the moment He was conceived in His Mother's womb till His Ascension into Heaven, and the life of

St. John Baptist. Seeing the infinite pains he took to fix the pieces truly in the cement and arrange them artistically, he expected both profit and fame as the result of this great work and the host of figures it contained. Then, directly the master was gone, Buffalmacco hastened to make his preparations for the enterprise he was bent upon. He went down into the cellar, which, communicating as it did with a baker's next door, was full of cockroaches drawn thither by the smell of the sacks of flour. Everybody knows how cockroaches, or kitchen-beetles, swarm in bakeries, inns and corn-mills. These are a sort of crawling, stinking insects, with long, ungainly, shaggy legs and an ugly shell of a dirty yellow.[1]

During the Civil Wars that stained the Arbia red and fertilized the olive-yards with the blood of nobles, these loathsome insects had two names in Tuscany: the Florentines called them Siennese, and the Siennese Florentines.[2]

The good Buffalmacco laughed to see the creatures all moving up and down and in and out, look-

---

[1] It would be better to speak of the wing-cases. "Shell" is an utterly unsuitable word—not in the least fitting. The Oriental cockroach is in question, an insect familiar in almost every part of Europe.

[2] In Russia they are termed Prussians, and in Prussia Russians. The French call them *cafards* (canting creatures, hypocrites).

ing for all the world like tiny shields of a host of pigmy knights jousting in a fairy tourney.

"Ah, ah!" he cried to himself, "they are maybugs bedevilled, that's what they are! They would not enjoy the springtime, and Jupiter punished them for their sluggishness. He has condemned them to crawl about in the dark, weighed down by their useless wings—an object-lesson to men to make the most of life in the heyday of youth and love."

This was what Buffalmacco said to himself; for he was ready enough, like other folk, to see in nature a symbol of his own passions and inclinations, which were to drink, to divert himself with pretty women and sleep his fill in a warm bed in winter and a nice cool one in summer.

However, he had not visited the cellar to ponder on symbols and emblems, and he was not long in carrying out his plan. He caught two dozen of the cockroaches, without regard to sex or age, and popped them in a bag he had brought with him for the purpose. This done, he proceeded to hide the bag under his bed, and returned to the workroom, where his comrades Bruno and Calendrino were painting, from the master's sketches, the good St. Francis receiving the stigmata, and meantime devising some way of hoodwinking Memmi the cobbler, whose wife was comely and obliging.

Buffalmacco, who was not less expert, far from it, than his two comrades, mounted the ladder and started painting the wings of the seraphic crucifix that came down from heaven to mark the Blessed Saint with the five wounds of love, taking the utmost pains to blend in the celestial pinions all the tenderest hues of the rainbow. The task occupied him all day, and when old Tafi came back from San Giovanni, he could not refrain from bestowing a few words of commendation on his pupil. This cost him no small effort, for age and riches had made him both cross and critical.

"My lads," he said, addressing the apprentices, "those wings are painted with a good deal of spirit. Buffalmacco might go far in the art of painting, if he would only apply himself more vigorously. But there, his mind is far too much set on self-indulgence and great achievements can only be accomplished by steady labour. Now Calendrino here would beat you all, with his industry—if he were not a born fool."

In such fashion Andrea Tafi improved the occasion with a proper severity. Then, having said his say, he went to the kitchen to take his supper, which consisted of a bit of salt fish; after that he betook himself to his chamber, lay down in his bed, and was soon snoring. Meantime Buffalmacco made his usual round through every quarter of the city where wine was to be had cheap and girls cheaper still. This done, he got home again half an hour or so before the time Tafi generally woke. He drew out the bag from under his bed, took the cockroaches one by one, and by means of a short, sharp needle fastened a little wax taper on the back of each. Lighting the tapers, he let the insects loose, one after the other, in the room. The creatures are too stupid to feel pain, or if they do, to manifest any great panic. They set off crawling over the floor, at a pace which surprise and perhaps some vague terror made a trifle quicker than usual. Before long they started describing circles, not because it is, as Plato says, a perfect figure, but as a result of the instinct that always makes insects turn round and round, in their efforts to escape any unknown danger. Buffalmacco looked on from the vantage-ground of his bed, on which he had thrown himself, and congratulated himself on the success of his device. And indeed nothing could be more marvellous than these lights showing a miniature presentment of the harmony of the spheres, such as it is set out by Aristotle and his commentators. The cockroaches themselves were invisible; only the little flames they carried could be seen, which seemed to be all alive. Just as these same lights were weaving in the darkness of the room more cycles and epicycles than ever Ptolemy and the Arabs observed as they watched the motions of the planets, Tafi's voice made itself heard, shriller than ever, what with a cold in the head and what with annoyance.

"Buffalmacco! Buffalmacco, I say!" screamed the old fellow, coughing and spitting, "get up, I say! Get up, you scoundrel! In less than an hour's time, it will be broad daylight. The bugs in your bed must be built like very Venuses, you are so loath to leave 'em. Up, you sluggard! If you don't rise this instant, I'll drag you from between the sheets by the hair of your head and your long ears!"

These were the sort of terms in which the master would call his pupil out of bed in the dusk of every morning, such was his zeal for painting and mosaic-work. On this occasion receiving no reply, he drew on his hose, but without taking time to pull them any higher than his knees, and started for his apprentice's bedroom, stumbling at every step. This was exactly what Buffalmacco expected, and directly he heard the clatter of his master's footsteps on the stairs, he turned his nose to the wall and pretended to be fast asleep. And there was old Tafi shouting up the stairs:

"Hilloa! but you're a grand sleeper. I'll have

you out of your slumbers, I will, though you should be dreaming this very moment that the eleven thousand virgins are slipping into your bed, begging you to teach 'em what's what."

With these words on his lips, Andrea Tafi shoved the door of the room violently open.

Then, catching sight of the points of fire running all over the floor, he stopped dead on the landing and fell a-trembling in every limb.

"They're devils," he thought, "never a doubt of it,—devils and evil spirits. Why! they move with a sort of mathematical precision, which is their strong point, I've always been told. Naturally the Demons hate us painters, who depict them under hideous shapes, in contrast with the Angels we represent in glory, an aureole about their brows and waving wings of dazzling splendour. The unhappy boy is beset with devils; I can count at least a thousand around his pallet. No doubt he has angered Lucifer himself, by drawing some horrible picture of him. 'Tis only too likely these ten thousand imps here will leap upon him and carry him off alive to Hell. His doom is fixed. And alack! I have myself figured, in mosaic and other ways, very odious caricatures of devils, and they have good reason to bear me a grudge too."

The thought redoubled his fears, and hauling up

his hose, he took to his heels, too much terrified to think of facing the hundred thousand hobgoblins he had seen wheeling round and round with bodies of fire, and dashed down the stairs as fast as ever his old legs would carry him. Buffalmacco had a fine laugh under the sheets, and for once in a way slept on till broad daylight. Nor did his master ever again dare to go and wake him.

II

THE ASCENDING UP OF ANDREA TAFI

ANDREA TAFI, of Florence, being chosen to decorate the cupola of San Giovanni with mosaics, carried out the said work in the most perfect fashion. Every figure was treated in the Greek manner, which Tafi had learned during his sojourn at Venice, where he had seen workmen busy adorning the walls of San Marco. He had even brought back with him from that city a Greek by name Apollonius, who knew excellent secrets for designing in mosaic. This Apollonius was a skilful workman and a very clever man. He knew the proportions to be given to the different parts of the human body and the material for mixing the best cement.

Fearing the Greek might carry his knowledge and address to some other painter of the city, Andrea Tafi never left his side day or night. Every morning he took him with him to San Giovanni, and brought him home every evening to his own house, facing San Michele, and made him sleep there with his two apprentices, Bruno and Buffalmacco, in a room separated merely by a partition from his own bed-chamber. And as this partition left half a foot between the top and the beams of the ceiling, whatever was said in one room could easily be overheard in the other.

Now Tafi was a man of decent manners and pious. He was not like some painters who, on leaving the Churches where they have been depicting God creating the world and the infant Jesus in his holy mother's arms, go straight to houses of ill fame to play dice and drink, play the pipes and cuddle the girls. He had never wished for better than his good wife, albeit she was by no means made and moulded by the Creator to afford any great delight to men; for she was a very dry and a very chilling personage. Then, after God had removed her from this world to a better, in his loving mercy, Andrea took no other woman to his bosom either by marriage or otherwise. On the contrary he was strictly continent, as became his years, sparing himself both expense and vexation, and pleasing God to boot, who recompenses in the next world the privations men endure in this. Andrea Tafi was chaste, sober and well-advised.

He said his prayers with unfailing regularity,

and being got to bed, he never fell asleep without first invoking the Blessed Virgin in these words:

"Holy Virgin, Mother of God, which for Thy merits wast exalted alive to Heaven, stretch forth Thy hand full of grace and mercy to me, lift me up to that blessed Paradise where Thou sittest on a chair of gold."

And this petition old Tafi did not mumble between the two or three teeth he had left, but spoke it out in a loud, strong voice, persuaded it is the singing, as they say, makes the song, and that if you want to be heard, it is best to shout. Thus it came about that Master Tafi's supplication was overheard every night by Apollonius the Greek and the two young Florentines who lay in the next chamber. Now it so happened Apollonius was likewise of a merry humour, every whit as ready for a jest as Bruno or Buffalmacco. All three itched sore to play off some trick on the old painter, who was a just man and a godfearing, but hard-fisted withal and a cruel taskmaster. Accordingly one night, after listening to the old fellow's customary address to the Virgin, the three comrades fell a-laughing under the bedclothes and cutting a hundred jokes. Presently, when they heard him snoring, they began asking each other in whispers what jape they could play off on him. Well knowing the holy terror the old man had of the Devil, Apollonius proposed to go, dressed in red, with horns and a mask, to drag him out of bed by the feet. But the ingenious Buffalmacco had a better suggestion to offer:

"To-morrow we will provide ourselves with a good stout rope and a pulley, and I undertake to give you the same evening a highly diverting exhibition."

Apollonius and Bruno were curious to know what the pulley and rope were to be used for, but Buffalmacco refused to say. Nevertheless they promised faithfully to get him what he wanted; for they knew him to possess the merriest wit in the world and the most fertile in amusing contrivances, having earned his nickname of Buffalmacco for these very qualities. And truly he knew some excellent turns, that have since become legendary.

The three friends, having nothing now to keep them awake, fell asleep under the moon, which looking in at the garret window, pointed the tip of one of her horns, as if in mockery, at old Tafi. They slept sound till daybreak, when the master began hammering on the partition, and called out, coughing and spitting as usual.

"Get up, master Apollonius! Up with you, apprentices! Day's come; Phœbus has blown out the sky candles! Quick's the word! 'Life is short, and art long.'"

Then he began threatening Bruno and Buffalmacco he would come and start them out with a bucket of cold water, jeering and asking them:

"Is your bed so delicious, eh? Have you got Helen of Troy there, you're so loath to quit the sheets?"

Meanwhile he was slipping on his hose and his old, worn hood. This done, he sallied out, to find the lads waiting on the landing, fully dressed and with their tools all ready.

That morning, in the fair Church of San Giovanni, on the planking that mounted to the cornice, the work went on merrily for a while. For the last week the master had been trying his hardest to give a good representation according to the recognized rules of art of the baptism of Jesus Christ. He had just begun putting in the fishes swimming in the Jordan. Apollonius was mixing the cement with bitumen and chopped straw, pronouncing words of might known only to himself; while Bruno and Buffalmacco were picking the little cubes of stone to be used, and Tafi arranging them according to the sketch he had made on a slab of slate he held in

MERRY-HEARTED BUFFALMACCO 113

his hand. But just when the master was busiest over the job, the three friends sprang lightly down the ladder and slipped out of the Church. Bruno went off to the house of Calendrino, outside the walls, in search of a pulley that was used for hoisting corn into the granary. At the same time Apollonius hurried away to Ripoli to see an old lady, the wife of a Judge, whom he had promised to provide with a philtre to draw lovers to her side, and persuading her that hemp was indispensable for compounding the potion, got her to hand him over the well-rope, a good stout piece of cord.

The two friends next met at Tafi's house, where they found Buffalmacco awaiting them. The latter at once set to work to attach the pulley firmly to the king-post of the roof, above the partition separating the master's sleeping-room from his apprentices'. Then, after passing the old lady's well-rope through the pulley, he left one end hanging down in their own chamber, while he went into his master's apartment and fastened the bed to the other extremity, by each corner. He took good care the rope should be concealed behind the curtains, so that nothing out of the way might be visible. When all was done, the three companions went back to San Giovanni.

The old man, who had been so busily engaged as scarcely to have noticed their absence, addressed them with a beaming face:

"Look you," he said, "how those fish sparkle with divers colours, and particularly with gold, purple and blue, as creatures should which inhabit the ocean and the rivers, and which possess so marvellous a brilliancy of hues only because they were the first to submit to the empire of the goddess Venus, as is all explained in the legend."

Thus the master discoursed in a way full of grace and good sense. For you must know he was a man of wit and learning, albeit his humour was so saturnine and grasping, above all when his thoughts turned toward filthy lucre. He went on:

"Now is not a painter's trade a good one and deserving of all praise? it wins him riches in this world and happiness in the next. For be sure Our Lord Jesus Christ will welcome gratefully in His holy Paradise craftsmen like myself who have portrayed his veritable likeness."

And Andrea Tafi was glad at heart to be at work upon this great picture in mosaic, whereof several portions are yet visible at San Giovanni to this day. Presently when night came and effaced both form and colour in all the Church, he tore himself regretfully from the river Jordan and sought his house.

He supped in the kitchen off a couple of tomatoes and a scrap of cheese, went upstairs to his room, undressed in the dark and got into bed.

No sooner was he laid down than he made his customary prayer to the Blessed Virgin:

"Holy Virgin, Mother of God, which for Thy merits wast exalted alive to Heaven, stretch forth Thy hand full of grace and mercy to me, to lift me up to Paradise!"

The moment was come which the three companions had been eagerly awaiting in the neighbouring room.

They grasped the rope's end that hung down the partition from the pulley, and scarcely had the good old fellow finished his supplication when at a sign from Buffalmacco they hauled so vigorously on the cord, that the bed fastened at the other end began to rise from the floor. Master Andrea, feeling himself being hoisted aloft, yet without seeing how, got it into his head it was the Blessed Virgin answering his prayer and drawing him up to Heaven. He was panic-stricken and fell a-screaming in a quavering voice:

"Stop, stop, sweet Lady! I never asked it should be now!"

And as the bed rose higher and higher, the rope working smoothly and noiselessly over the pulley, the old man poured out the most pitiful supplications to the Virgin Mary:

"Good Lady! sweet Lady! don't pull so! Ho, there! Let go, I say!" But she seemed not to hear a word. At this he grew furiously angry and bellowed:

"You must be deaf, you wooden-head! Let go, *bitch of a Madonna!*"

Seeing he was leaving the floor for good and all, his terror increased yet further; and, calling upon Jesus, he besought Him to make His holy Mother listen to reason. It was high time, he asseverated, she should give up this mischancy Assumption. Sinner that he was, and son of a sinner, he could not, and he would not, go up to Heaven before he'd finished the river Jordan, the waves and the fishes, and the rest of Our Blessed Lord's history. Meanwhile the canopy of the bed was all but touching the beams of the roofing, and Tafi was crying in desperation:

"Jesus, unless you stop your Blessed Mother this instant, the roof of my house, which cost a fine penny, will most certainly be burst up. For I see for sure I'm going slap through it. Stop! stop! I can hear the tile cracking."

Buffalmacco perceived that by now his master's voice was actually strangling in his throat, and he ordered his companions to let go the rope. This they did, the result being that the bed, tumbling suddenly from roof to floor of the room, crashed down on the boards, breaking the legs and splitting the panels; simultaneously the bedposts toppled over and the canopy, curtains, hangings and all fell atop of Master Andrea, who, thinking he was going to be smothered, started howling like a devil incarnate. His very soul staggered under the shock, and he could not tell whether he was fallen back again into his chamber or pitched headlong into Hell.

At this point the three apprentices rushed in, as if just awakened by the noise. Seeing the ruins of the bed lying smothered in clouds of dust, they feigned intense surprise, and instead of going to the old man's help, asked him if it was the Devil had done the mischief. But he only sighed heavily, and said:

"It's all up with me; pull me out of this. I'm a dying man!"

At last they dragged him from among the débris, under which he was ready to suffocate, and placed him sitting up with his back to the wall. He breathed hard, coughed and spat, and:

"My lads," he said, "but for the timely succour of Our Lord Jesus Christ, who hurled me back to earth again with a violence you can plainly see the effects of, I should at this present moment be in the circle of Heaven named the crystalline or primum mobile. His holy Mother would not listen to a word. In my fall, I have lost three teeth, which, without being exactly sound, still did me good service. Moreover, I have an agonizing pain in my right side and in the arm that holds the brush."

"My master," said Apollonius pityingly, "you must have received some internal hurts, which is a very dangerous thing. At Constantinople, in the risings, I discovered how much more deadly such injuries are than mere external wounds. But never fear, I am going to charm away the mischief with spells."

"Not for worlds!" put in the old man; "that were a deadly sin. But come hither, all three and do me the service, an you will, of rubbing me well in the worst places."

They did as he asked, and never left him till they had pretty well scarified every bit of skin off the old fellow's back and loins.

The good lads made it their first business to sow the story broadcast through the city. This they did to such good effect that there was not man, woman nor child in Florence could look Master Andrea Tafi in the face without bursting out laughing. Now one morning Buffalmacco was passing down the Corso, Messer Guido, the son of the Signor Cavalcanti, who was on his way to the marshes to shoot crane, stopped his horse, called the apprentice to him, and tossed him his purse with the words:

"Ho! gentle Buffalmacco, here's somewhat to drink to the health of Epicurus and his disciples."

You must know Messer Guido was of the sect of the Epicureans and loved to marshal well-arranged arguments against the existence of God. He was used to declare the death of men is precisely the same as that of beast.

"Buffalmacco," added the young nobleman, "this purse I have given you is for payment of the very instructive, complete and profitable experiment you made, when you sent old Tafi to Heaven—who, seeing his carcass taking the road to the Empyrean, began to squeal like a pig being killed. This proves plainly he had no real assurance in the promised joys of Paradise—which are, it must be allowed, far from certain. In the same way as nurses tell children fairy-tales, vague things are talked concerning the immortality of mortal men. The vulgar herd thinks it believes these tales, but it does not really and truly. Hard fact comes and shivers the poets' fables. There is nothing assured but the sad life of this world. Horace, the Roman poet, is of my opinion when he says: *Serus in cælum redeas.*" [1]

[1] "*May it be long ere you return to heaven your home.*"—Ode 2 of Book I, addressed to Augustus.

III

THE MASTER

HAVING learned the art of preparing and using the proper coats and colours, as well as the secret of painting figures in the good manner of Cimabuë and Giotto, the young Buonamico Cristofani, the Florentine, surnamed Buffalmacco, abandoned the workshop of his master Andrea Tafi, and proceeded to establish himself in the quarter of the fullers, immediately opposite to the house known by the sign of the Goose's Head. Now in those days, like fair ladies outvying one another in wearing gowns broidered with flowers, the towns of Italy made it their pride to cover the walls of their Churches and Cloisters with paintings. Among all these, Florence was the most sumptuous and magnificent, and was the place of all others for a Painter to live in. Buffalmacco knew how to give his figures movement and expression; and, while far behind the divine Giotto for beauty of design, he pleased the eye by the gay exuberance of his inventions. So he was not long in getting commissions in considerable numbers. It only depended on himself to win riches and fame with all speed. But his chief idea was to amuse himself in company of Bruno di Giovanni and Nello, and squander along with them, in debauchery, all the money he made.

Now the Abbess of the Ladies of Faenza, established at Florence, determined about this time to have the Church of their Nunnery decorated with frescoes. Hearing that there lived in the quarter of the fullers and wool-carders a very clever painter named Buffalmacco, she despatched her Steward thither to come to an arrangement with him as to the execution of the proposed paintings. The master agreed to the terms offered and undertook the commission readily enough. He had a scaffolding erected in the Nunnery Church and on the still moist plaster began to paint, with wondrous vigour of execution, the history of Jesus Christ. First of all, to the right of the Altar, he illustrated the massacre of the Holy Innocents, and succeeded in expressing so vividly the grief and rage of the mothers trying vainly to save their little ones from the Roman soldiers' hands, that the very wall seemed to chant like the faithful in Church, *"Cur, Crudelis Herodes? . . ."* Drawn thither by curiosity, the Nuns used to come, two

MERRY-HEARTED BUFFALMACCO

or three of them together, to watch the master at work. At sight of all these despairing mothers and murdered babes, they could not help sobbing and shedding tears. In particular there was one little fellow Buffalmacco had drawn lying in his swaddling bands, smiling and sucking his thumb, between a soldier's legs. The Nuns begged and prayed this one might not be killed:

"Oh! spare him," they said to the Painter. "Do take care the soldiers don't see him and kill him!"

The good Buffalmacco answered:

"For love of you, dear sisters, I will protect him all I can. But these murderers are filled with so savage a rage, it will be a difficult matter to stop them."

When they declared "The baby *is* such a little darling! . . ." he offered to make each of them a little darling prettier still.

"Thank you kindly!" they answered back, laughing.

The Abbess came in her turn to assure herself with her own eyes that the work was being done satisfactorily. She was a lady of very high birth, named Usimbalda, a proud, severe and careful personage. Seeing a man working without cloak or hood, and like a common labourer wearing only shirt and hose, she mistook him for some apprentice lad and did not condescend so much as to speak to him. She came again and again, five or six times, to the Chapel, without ever seeing any one more important than this working fellow she deemed only fit to grind the colours. Out of all patience at last, she showed him she was far from satisfied.

"My lad," she bade him, "tell your master from me he must come and work himself at the pictures I commissioned him to paint. I meant them to be the work of his own hand, not a mere apprentice's."

Far from declaring himself, Buffalmacco put on the look and voice of a poor working-man, and humbly answered Usimbalda, that he saw plain enough he was not of the sort to inspire confidence in so noble a lady, and that his duty was to obey.

"I will inform my master," he went on; "and he will not fail to put himself at the orders of My Lady Abbess."

With this assurance, the Lady Usimbalda left the Church. No sooner was he alone than Buffalmacco arranged on the scaffolding, just at the spot where he was at work, two stools with a crock on the top. Then going to the corner where he had laid them, he pulled out his cloak and hat, which as it happened were in a very fair state of freshness, and put them on the lay figure he had improvised; next, he stuck a brush in the spout of the crock, which was turned towards the wall. This done, after assuring himself the thing had quite the look of a man busy painting, he decamped with all speed, determined to keep away till he had seen what happened.

Next day the Nuns paid their usual visit to the scene of action. But finding instead of the merry fellow they were accustomed to, a stately gentleman who held himself in the stiffest of attitudes and seemed entirely indisposed to laugh and talk, they were afraid and took to flight.

Madame Usimbalda on the contrary, when *she* returned to the Church, was delighted to see the master at work in lieu of the apprentice.

She proceeded to give him much valuable advice, exhorting him for a good ten minutes to paint figures that should be modest, noble and expressive—before she discovered she was addressing her remarks to a crock.

She would hardly have found out her mistake even then, had she not grown impatient at receiving no reply, and pulling the master by his cloak, brought crock, stool, hat, brush and all tumbling at her feet. Then, as she was by no means wanting in sense, she saw it was intended as a lesson not to judge the artist by his dress. She sent her steward to Buffalmacco, and begged him to finish what he had begun.

He completed the work greatly to his credit. Connoisseurs especially admired in these frescoes the figure of the Crucified Redeemer, the three Marys weeping at the foot of the Cross, Judas hanged on a tree, and a man blowing his nose. Unfortunately the paintings were all destroyed along with the Church of the Nunnery of the Ladies of Faenza.

IV

THE PAINTER

EQUALLY famous for his wit and humour and for his skill in devising figure subjects on the walls of Church and Cloister, Buonamico, surnamed Buffalmacco, had already left his youth behind when he was invited from Florence to Arezzo by the Lord Bishop of that city, who wished the halls of his Palace decorated with paintings. Buffalmacco undertook the commission, and directly the walls were duly laid with stucco, started on a picture of the Adoration of the Wise Men.

In the course of a few days he had painted in King Melchior complete, mounted on a white horse, looking for all the world as if he were alive. His horse's saddle-cloth was scarlet, dotted with precious stones.

Now all the time he was at work, the Bishop's pet monkey sat staring intently at his proceedings, never taking his eyes off him. Whether the painter was squeezing his tubes, mixing his colours, beating up his eggs or laying on the colour with his brush on the moist surface, the creature never lost one of his movements. It was a baboon brought from Barbary for the Doge of Venice in one of the State Galleys. The Doge made a present of it to the Bishop of Arezzo, who thanked his Magnificence, reminding him prettily how King Solomon's ships had in like fashion imported from the land of Ophir apes and peacocks, as is related in the First Book of Kings (x. 22). And there was nothing in all his Palace Bishop Guido held more precious than this baboon.

He left the animal to roam at liberty about the halls and gardens, where it was for ever at some mischievous trick or another. One Sunday, during the painter's absence, the creature climbed up on the scaffolding, laid hold of the tubes, mixed up the colours in a way of its own, broke all the eggs it could find, and began plying the brush on the wall, as it had seen the other do. It worked away at King Melchior and his horse, never leaving off till the whole composition was repainted according to its own ideas.

Next morning Buffalmacco, finding his colours all topsy-turvy and his work spoiled, was both grieved and angry. He was persuaded some painter of Arezzo, who was jealous of his superior skill, had played him this dirty trick, and went straight to the Bishop to complain. The latter urged him to set to work again and repair with all speed what had been ruined in a manner so mysterious. He undertook that for the future two soldiers should keep guard night and day before the frescoes, with orders to drive their lances through any one who should dare to come near. On this condition, Buffalmacco agreed to resume his task, and two soldiers were put on sentry close at hand. One evening, just as he was leaving the hall, his day's work finished, the soldiers saw the Lord Bishop's ape spring so nimbly into his place on the scaffold and seize the colour-tubes and brushes with such rapidity there was no possibility of stopping him. They shouted lustily to the painter, who came back just in time to see the baboon paint over for the second time King Melchior, the white horse and the scarlet saddle-cloth. The sight was like to move poor Buffalmacco at one and the same time to laughter and tears.

He went off to the Bishop and thus addressed him:

"My Lord Bishop, you are good enough to admire my style of painting; but your baboon prefers a different. What need to have me summoned here, when you have had a master painter in your own household? It may be he lacked experience. But now he has nothing left to learn, my presence here is quite unnecessary, and I will back to Florence."

Having so said, the good Buffalmacco returned to his inn, in great vexation. He ate his supper without appetite and went to bed in a very dismal frame of mind.

Then the Lord Bishop's ape appeared to him in a dream, not as a mere mannikin as he was in reality, but as tall as Monte San Gemignano, cocking up a prodigious tail and tickling the moon. He was squatted in an olive wood among the farms and oil-presses, while betwixt his legs a narrow road ran alongside a row of flourishing vineyards. Now the said road was thronged with a multitude of pilgrims, who defiled one by one before the painter's eyes. And lo! Buffalmacco recognized the countless victims of his practical jokes and merry humour generally.

He saw, to begin with, his old master Andrea Tafi, who had taught him how men win renown by practice of the arts, and whom in return he had befooled again and again, making him mistake for devils of hell a dozen wax tapers pinned on the backs of a lot of great cockroaches, and hoisting him in his bed to the joists of the ceiling, so that the poor old fellow thought he was being carried up to heaven and was in mortal terror.

He saw the wool-carder of the *Goose's Head,* and his wife, that notable woman, at the spinning-wheel. Into this good dame's cooking-pot Buffalmacco had been wont every evening to throw big handfuls of salt through a crack in the wall, so that day after day the wool-carder would spit out his porridge and beat his wife.

He saw Master Simon de Villa, the Bolognese physician, to be known by his Doctor's cap, the same he had pitched into the cesspool beside the Convent of the Nuns of Ripoli. The Doctor ruined his best velvet gown, but nobody pitied him, for regardless of his good wife's claims, a plain woman but a Christian, he had longed to bed with Prester John's Chinchimura, who wears horns betwixt her sinful buttocks. Good Buffalmacco had persuaded the Doctor he could take him o' nights to the Witches' Sabbath, where he went himself with a merry company to make love to the Queen of France, who gave him wine and spices for his doughty deeds. Simon accepted the invitation, hoping he should be treated right royally too. Then Buffalmacco having donned a beast's skin and a horned mask such as they wear at merry-makings, came to Master Simon, declaring he was a devil ordered to conduct him to the Sabbath. Taking him on his shoulders, he carried him to the edge of a pit full of filth, where he pitched him in head first.

Next Buffalmacco saw Calendrino, whom he had got to believe that the stone Heliotropia was to be found in the plain of the Mugnone, which stone possesses the virtue of rendering invisible whosoever bears it about his person. He took him to Mugnone along with Bruno da Giovanni, and when Calendrino had picked up a very large number of stones, Buffalmacco suddenly pretended he could not see him, crying out: "The scamp has given us the slip; an I catch him, I'll bang his behind with this paving-stone!" And he landed the stone exactly where he said he would, without Calendrino having any right to complain, because he was invisible. This same Calendrino was without any sense of humour, and Buffalmacco played on his simplicity so far as to make him actually believe he was a child, and got a brace of fat capons out of him as fee for his safe delivery.

Next Buffalmacco saw the countryman for whom he had painted the Blessed Virgin with the Infant Jesus in her arms, afterwards changing the babe into a bear's cub.

He saw moreover the Abbess of the Nuns of Faenza, who had commissioned him to paint the walls of the Convent Church in fresco, and he told her on his oath and honour you must mix good wine with the colours, if the flesh tints are to be really brilliant. So the Abbess gave him for every Saint, male or female, depicted in his pictures a flask of the wine reserved for Bishops' drinking, which he poured down his throat, trusting to vermilion to bring out the warm tints. The same Lady Abbess it was he deceived, making her take a pitcher with a cloak thrown over it for a master painter, as has been already recounted.

Buffalmacco saw, besides, a long line of other folks he had befooled, cajoled, cozened and bemocked. Closing the rear, marched with crozier, mitre and cope, the great Sant' Ercolano, whom in a merry mood he had represented in the Great Square of Perugia, girt about with a garland of gudgeons.

All as they passed paid their compliment to the ape which had avenged them; and the monster, opening a great mouth wider than the jaws of hell, broke into a mocking laugh.

For the first time in his life Buffalmacco had a downright bad night's rest.

THE LADY OF VERONA

TO HUGUES REBELL

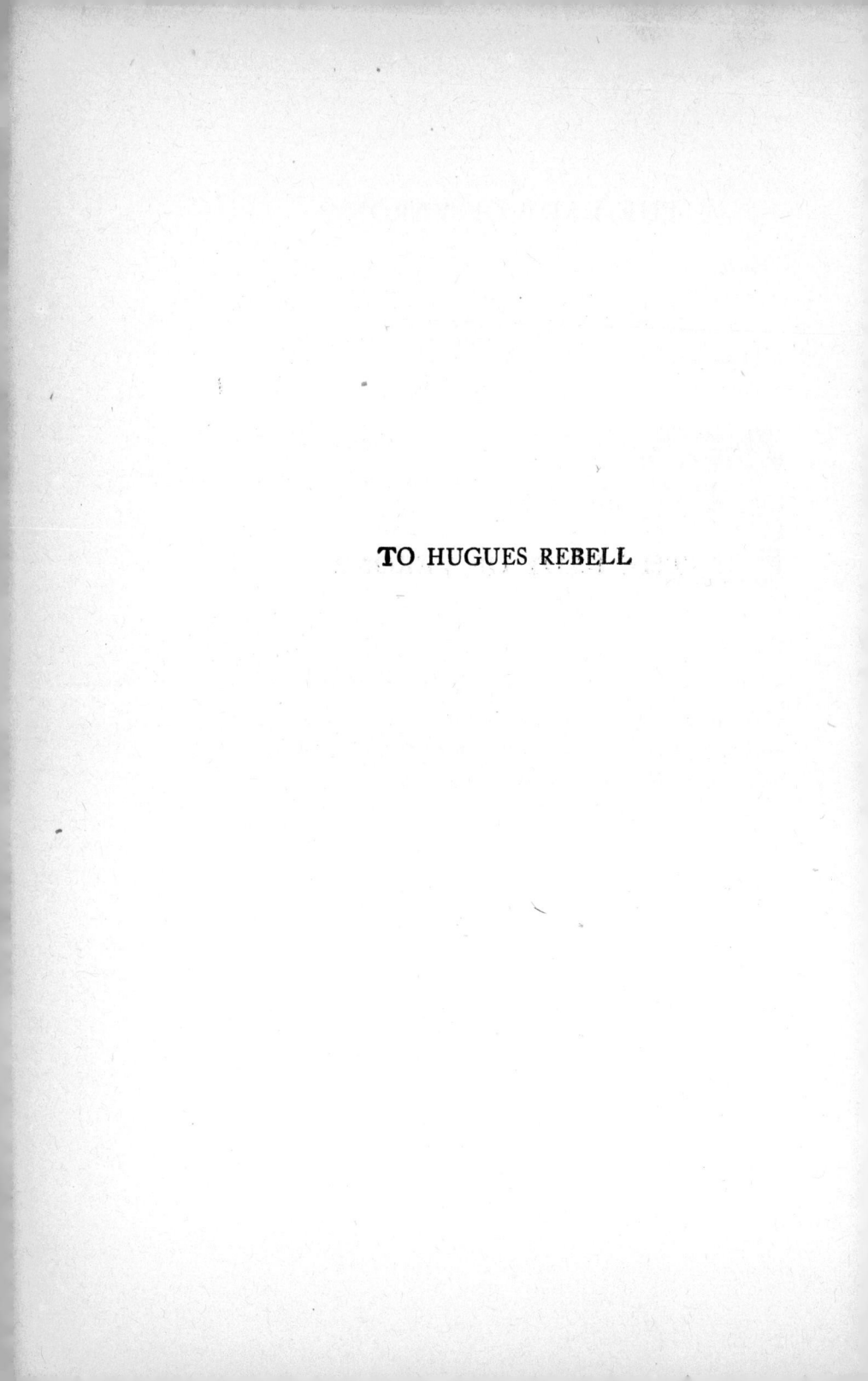

THE LADY OF VERONA

"Puella autem moriens dixit: 'Satanas, trado tibi corpus meum cum anima mea.'" (Quadragesimale opus declamatum Parisiis in ecclesia Sti. Johannis in Gravia per venerabilem patrem Sacrae scripturae interpretem eximium Ol. Maillardum, 1511.)[1]

THE following was found by the Reverend Father Adone Doni, in the Archives of the Monastery of Santa Croce, at Verona.

Signora Eletta of Verona was so wondrous fair and of so perfect a grace of body, that the learned of the city, they who had knowledge of history and legend, were used to call her lady mother by the names of Latona, Leda and Semele, making implication thereby of their belief that the fruit of her womb had been framed in her by a god, Jupiter, rather than by any mortal man, such as were her husband and lovers. But the wiser heads, notably the Fra Battista, whose successor I am as Superior of Santa Croce, held that

[1] "But the dying girl said, 'Satan, I give over my body to you along with my soul.'" (Lenten Sermon preached at Paris in the Church of St. Jean-en-Grève by that venerable father and excellent expounder of Holy Scripture, Oliver Maillard, 1511.)

such exceeding beauty of the flesh came of the operation of the Devil, who is an artist in the sense the dying Nero understood the word when he said, *"Qualis artifex pereo!"* [1] And we may be sure Satan, the enemy of God, who is cunning to work the metals, excels likewise in the moulding of human flesh.

I myself, who am writing these lines, possessing no small acquaintance with the world, have many a time seen church bells and figures of men wrought by the Enemy of Mankind—and the craftsmanship thereof admirable. Likewise have I had knowledge of children engendered in women by the Devil, but on this matter my tongue is tied by the obligation of secrecy binding on every Confessor. I will limit myself, therefore, to saying that many strange tales were bruited concerning the birth of the Signora Eletta. I saw this lady for the first time on the Piazza of Verona on Good Friday of the year 1320, when she had just completed her fourteenth year. And I have beheld her since in the public walks and the Churches ladies most favour. She was like a picture painted by a very excellent limner.

She had hair of wavy gold, a white brow, eyes of a colour never seen but in the precious stone

---

[1] "What an artist dies in me!" "Oh! the loss to Art! the loss to Art!"

called aquamarine, cheeks of rose, a nose straight and finely cut. Her mouth was a Cupid's bow, that wounded with its smiles; and the chin was as full of laughter as the mouth. Her whole body was framed to perfection for the delight of lovers. The breasts were not of exaggerated size; yet showed beneath the muslin two swelling globes of a full and most winsome roundness. As well by reason of my sacred character, as because I never saw her but clad in her walking dress and her limbs half hidden, I will not describe the other parts of her fair body, which one and all proclaimed their perfection through the stuffs that veiled them. I will only assure you, that when she was in her accustomed place in the Church of San Zenone, there was never a movement she could make, whether to rise to her feet or drop on her knees or prostrate herself with forehead touching the stones, as is meet to do at the instant of the elevation of the blessed body of Jesus Christ, without straightway inspiring the men that saw her with an ardent longing to hold her pressed to their bosom.

Now it came about that Signora Eletta married, when about the age of fifteen, Messer Antonio Torlota, an Advocate. He was a very learned man, of good repute, and wealthy, but already far advanced in years, and so heavy and misshapen, that seeing him carrying his papers in a great leathern bag, you could scarcely tell which bag it was dragging about the other.

It was pitiful to think how, as the result of the holy sacrament of wedlock, which is instituted among men for their glory and eternal salvation, the fairest lady of Verona was bedded with so old a man, all ruinate in health and vigour. And wise folk saw with more pain than wonder that, profiting by the freedom allowed her by her husband, busied all night long as he was solving the problems of justice and injustice, Messer Torlota's young wife welcomed to her bed the handsomest and most proper cavaliers of the city. But the pleasure she took therein came from herself, not from them at all. It was her own self she loved, and not her lovers. All her enjoyment was of the loveliness of her own proper flesh, and of nothing else. Herself was her own desire and delight; and her own fond concupiscence. Whereby, methinks, the sin of carnal indulgence was, in her case, enormously aggravated.

For, albeit, this sin must ever divide us from God —a sufficient sign of its gravity—yet is it true to say that carnal offenders are regarded by the Sovereign Judge, both in this world and the next, with less indignation than are covetous men, traitors, murderers, and wicked men who have made traffic of holy things. And the reason of this is that the naughty desires sensualists entertain, being directed towards others rather than to themselves, do still show some degraded traces of true love and gentle charity.

But nothing of the kind was to be seen in the adulterous amours of the Signora Eletta, who in every passion loved herself and herself only. And herein was she much wider separated from God than so many other women who gave way to their wanton desires. For in their case these desires were towards others, whereas the Lady Eletta's had none but herself for their object. What I say hereanent, I say to make more understandable the conclusion of the matter, which I must now relate.

At the age of twenty she fell sick and felt herself to be dying. Then she bewailed her fair body with the most piteous tears. She made her women dress her out in her richest attire, looked long and steadfastly at herself in the mirror, fondled with both hands her bosom and hips, to enjoy for the last time her own exceeding beauty. And, aghast at the thought of this body she so adored being eaten of the worms in the damp earth, she said, as she breathed her last, with a great sigh of faith and hope:

"Satan, best beloved Satan! take thou my soul and my body; Satan, gentle Satan! hear my prayer: take, take my body along with my soul."

She was borne to San Zenone, as custom ordains, with her face uncovered; and, within the memory of man, none had ever seen a dead woman look so lovely. While the priests were chanting the offices for the dead around her bier, she lay as if swooning with delight in the arms of an invisible lover. When the ceremony was over, the Signora Eletta's coffin, carefully closed and sealed, was deposited in holy ground, amid the tombs that surrounded San Zenone, and of which some are Ancient Roman monuments. But next morning the earth they had thrown over the dead woman was found removed, and there lay the coffin open and empty.

THE HUMAN TRAGEDY

TO J. H. ROSNY

THE HUMAN TRAGEDY

Πας δ' ὀδυνηρὸς βίος ἀνθρώπων,
κοὔκ ἔστι πόνων ἀνάπαυσις.
ἄλλο τι τοῦ ζῆν φίλτερον, ἀλλ' ὃ
σκότος ἀμπίσχων κρύπτει νεφέλαις.

(Euripides, *Hippolytus*, 190 sqq.)[1]

I

FRA GIOVANNI

IN those days the holy man, who, born though he was of human parents, was veritably a son of God, and who had chosen for his bride a maiden that folk open the door to as reluctantly as to Death itself, and never with a smile,—the poor man of Jesus Christ, St. Francis, was gone up to the skies. Earth, which he had perfumed with his virtues, kept only his body and the fruitful seed of his words. His sons in the spirit grew meantime, and multiplied among the Peoples, for the blessing of Abraham was upon them.

Kings and Queens girded on the cord of St.

---

[1] "All the life of man is full of pain, and there is no surcease of sorrow. If there be aught better elsewhere than this present life, it is hid shrouded in the clouds of darkness."

Francis, the poor man of Jesus Christ. Men in multitudes sought in forgetfulness of self and of the world the secret of true happiness; and flying the joy of life, found a greater joy.

The Order of St. Francis spread fast through all Christendom, and the Houses of the Poor Men of the Lord covered the face of Italy, Spain, the two Gauls and the Teutonic lands. In the good town of Viterbo arose a House of peculiar sanctity. In it Fra Giovanni took the vows of Poverty, and lived humble and despised, his soul a garden of flowers fenced about with walls.

He had knowledge by revelation of many truths that escape clever and world-wise men. And ignorant and simple-minded as he was, he knew things unknown to the most learned Doctors of the age.

He knew that the cares of riches make men ill-conditioned and wretched, and that coming into the world poor and naked, they would be happy, if only they would live as they were born.

He was poor and merry-hearted. His delight was in obedience; and renouncing the making of plans of any sort for the future, he relished the bread of the heart. For the weight of human actions is a heavy load, and we are trees bearing poisoned fruit. He was afraid to act, for is not all effort painful and useless? He was afraid to think, for thought is evil.

He was very humble, knowing how men have nothing of their own that they should boast of, and that pride hardens the heart. He knew, moreover, that they who possess for all wealth only the riches of the spirit, if they make boast of their treasure, so far lower themselves to the level of the great ones of the earth.

And Fra Giovanni outdid in humility all the Monks of the House of Viterbo. The Superior of the Monastery, the holy Brother Silvester, was less righteous than he, forasmuch as the master is less righteous than the servant, the mother less innocent than the babe.

Observing that Fra Giovanni had a way of stripping himself of his gown to clothe the suffering members of Jesus Christ, the Superior forbade him, in the name of holy obedience, to give away his garments to the poor. Now the same day this command was laid on him, Giovanni went, as his wont was, to pray in the woods that cover the slopes of Monte Cunino. It was Winter time; snow was falling, and the wolves coming down into the villages.

Fra Giovanni kneeling down at the foot of an

oak, spoke to God, as might one friend to another, and besought Him to take pity on all orphans, prisoners and captives, to take pity on the master of the fields sorely harried by the Lombard usurers, to take pity on the stags and hinds of the forest chased by the hunters, and on all trapped creatures, whether of fur or feathers. And lo! he was rapt away in an ecstasy, and saw a hand pointing in the sky.

When presently the sun had slipped behind the mountains, the man of God arose from his knees and took the path to the Monastery. On the white, silent road thither, he met a beggar, who asked him an alms for the love of God.

"Alas!" he told him, "I have nothing but my gown, and the Superior has forbidden me to cut it in two so as to give away the half. Therefore I cannot divide it with you. But if you love me, my son, you will take it off me whole and undivided."

On hearing these words, the beggar promptly stripped the Friar of his gown.

So Fra Giovanni went on his way naked under the falling snow, and entered the city. As he was crossing the Piazza with nothing on but a linen cloth about his loins, the children who were running at play in the Great Square made mock at him. In derision, they shook their fists in his face with the thumb stuck between the first and middle fingers, and threw snow at him mixed with mud and small stones.

Now there lay in the Great Square some logs of timber for the woodwork of a house, and one of the logs happened to be balanced across another. Two children ran and took their places, one at each end of the beam, and began playing see-saw—two of the same children who had made mock of the holy man and thrown stones at him.

He went up to them now smiling, and said:

"Dear little children, will you suffer me to share your game?"

And sitting down on one end of the beam, he see-sawed up and down against the two little ones.

And some of the citizens happening to pass that way, said, wondering:

"Truly and indeed the man is out of his wits."

But after the bells had rung the *Ave Maria,* Fra Giovanni was still at see-saw. And it chanced that certain Priests from Rome, who had come to Viterbo to visit the Mendicant Friars, whose fame was great through the world, just then crossed the Great Square. And hearing the children shouting, "Look! little Brother Giovanni's here," the Priests drew near the Monk, and saluted him very respectfully. But the holy man never returned their salute, but making as though he did not see them, went on see-sawing on the swaying beam. So the Priests said to each other:

"Come away; the fellow is a mere dunce and dullard!"

Then was Fra Giovanni glad, and his heart overflowed with joy. For these things he did out of humility and for the love of God. And he put his joy in the scorn of men, as the miser shuts his gold in a cedarn chest, locked with a triple lock.

At nightfall he knocked at the Monastery door, and being admitted, appeared among the Brethren naked, bleeding, and covered with mire. He smiled and said:

"A kind thief took my gown, and some children deemed me worthy to play with them."

But the Brothers were angry, because he had dared to pass through the city in so undignified a plight.

"He feels no compunction," they declared, "about exposing the Holy Order of St. Francis to derision and disgrace. He deserves the most exemplary punishment."

The General of the Order, being warned a great scandal was ruining the sacred Society, called together all the Brethren of the Chapter, and made Fra Giovanni kneel humbly on his knees in the midst of them all. Then, his face blazing with anger, he chid him harshly in a loud, rough voice. This done, he consulted the assembly as to the penance it was meet to impose on the guilty Brother.

Some were for having him put in prison or suspended in an iron cage from the Church steeple, while others advised he should be chained up for a madman.

And Fra Giovanni, beaming with satisfaction, told them:

"You are very right, my Brethren; I deserve these punishments, and worse ones still. I am good for nothing but foolishly to waste and squander the goods of God and of my Order."

And Brother Marcian, who was a man of great sternness both of life and doctrine, cried:

"Hear him! he talks like a hypocrite; that honeyed voice of his issues from a whited sepulchre."

And Fra Giovanni said again:

"Brother Marcian, I am indeed capable of every infamy—but for God's good help."

Meantime the General was pondering over the strange behaviour of Fra Giovanni, and he besought the Holy Spirit to inspire the judgment he was to give. And lo! as he prayed, his anger was changed into admiration. He had known St. Francis in the days when that Angel of Heaven, born of a woman, was a sojourner in this world, and the ensample of the favourite follower of Christ had taught him the love of spiritual perfection.

So his soul was enlightened, and he recognized in the works of Fra Giovanni a divine innocency and beauty.

"My brethren," he said at length, "far from blaming our Brother, let us admire the grace he receives so abundantly from God. In very truth he is a better man than we. What he has done, he has done in imitation of Jesus Christ, who 'suffered the little children to come unto Him,' and let the Roman soldiers strip Him of His garments."

Then he thus addressed the kneeling Fra Giovanni:

"This, Brother, is the penance I lay upon you. In the name of that holy obedience you owe St. Francis, I command you go forth into the country, and the first beggar you meet, beg him to strip you of your tunic. Then, when he has left you naked, you must come back into the city, and play in the Public Square with the little children."

Having so said, the General of the Order came down from his chair of state, and, raising Fra Giovanni from the ground, fell on his knees before him and kissed his feet. Then, turning to the assembled Monks, he said to them:

"In very truth, my Brethren, this man is the good God's plaything."

II

THE LAMP

IN those days the truth was revealed to Fra Giovanni that the riches of this world come from God and should be the heritage of the poor, who are the favourite children of Jesus Christ.

Christian folk were busy celebrating the Saviour's birth; and Fra Giovanni had come to the town of Assisi, which is set upon a mountain-top, and from this mountain first rose the Sun of Charity.

Now the day before Christmas eve, Fra Giovanni was kneeling in prayer before the Altar under which St. Francis sleeps in a stone coffin. And he was meditating, dreaming how St. Francis was born in a stable, like Jesus. And while he was pondering, the Sacristan came up to him and asked him of his goodness to look after the Church while he ate his supper. Church and Altar were both loaded with precious ornaments; gold and silver were there in abundance, for the sons of St. Francis had long fallen from their early poverty, and had received gifts from the Queens of the Earth.

Fra Giovanni assured the Sacristan:

"Go, Brother, and enjoy your meal. I will guard the Church, as Our Lord would have it guarded."

And so saying, he went on with his meditations. And as he knelt there alone in prayer, a poor woman entered the Church and asked an alms of him for the love of God.

"I have nothing," the holy man replied; "but the Altar is loaded with ornaments, and I will go see if I cannot find something to give you." A golden lamp hung above the Altar, decked about with silver bells. Examining the lamp, he said to himself:

"Those little bells are but idle vanities. The true ornament of yonder Altar is the body of St. Francis, which reposes naked under the flags with a black stone for a pillow."

And drawing his knife from his pocket, he detached the little silver bells, one after the other, and gave them to the poor woman.

Presently, when the Sacristan, his meal finished, returned to the Church, Fra Giovanni, the holy man of God, said to him:

"Never trouble, my brother, about the little bells that belonged to the lamp. I have given them away to a poor woman who had need of them."

Now Fra Giovanni did in this wise, because he

knew by revelation that all the things in this world, belonging to God, belong of rights to the poor.

And he was blamed on earth by men whose thoughts were given over to riches. But he was found praiseworthy in the sight of the Divine Goodness.

III

THE SERAPHIC DOCTOR

FRA GIOVANNI was not proficient in the knowledge of letters, and he rejoiced in his ignorance as being an abundant source of humiliations. But after watching one day in the Cloister of Santa Maria degli Angeli a number of Doctors of Theology in meditation on the perfections of the Most Holy Trinity and the Mysteries of the Passion, he began to doubt whether they did not possess the love of God more fully than he, by reason of their wider knowledge.

He was afflicted in his soul, and for the first time in his life fell into melancholy. But sadness was unnatural to one in his estate; for joy is the inheritance of the poor.

He resolved to carry his difficulty to the General of the Order, to be rid of it as of a galling burden. Now Giovanni di Fidanza was General of the Order in those days.

In the cradle he had received from St. Francis himself the name of Bonaventure. He had studied Theology at the University of Paris; and he excelled in the science of Love, which is the science of God. He knew the four degrees which lift the creature to his Creator, and he pondered on the mystery of the six wings of the Cherubim. This was the reason why he was called the Seraphic Doctor.

And he was well aware that Science is vain without Love. Fra Giovanni found him walking in his garden, on the terrace overlooking the city.

It was a Sunday; and the handicraftsmen of the town and the peasants who work in the vineyards were climbing, at the foot of the terrace, the steep street that leads to the Church.

And Fra Giovanni, seeing Brother Bonaventure in the garden, in the midst of the lilies, drew near and said:

"Brother Bonaventure, free my mind of the doubt that is tormenting me, and tell me: Can an ignorant man love God with as great love as a learned Doctor of the Church?"

And Brother Bonaventure answered:

"I will tell you the truth, Fra Giovanni; a poor old woman may not only equal but surpass all the Doctors of Theology in the world. And seeing the sole excellence of man lies in loving, I tell you again —the most ignorant of women shall be exalted in Heaven above the Doctors."

Fra Giovanni, on hearing these words, was filled

with great joy; and, leaning out over the low wall of the garden, looked lovingly at the passers-by. Then he cried out at the top of his voice:

"Ho! you poor women, ignorant and simple-minded, you shall be set in Heaven above Brother Bonaventure."

And the Seraphic Doctor, hearing the good Brother's proclamation, smiled sweetly where he stood among the lilies of his garden.

IV

THE LOAF ON THE FLAT STONE

FORASMUCH as the good St. Francis had bidden his sons to "Go, beg your bread from door to door," Fra Giovanni was one day sent to a certain city. Having passed the Gate, he went up and down the streets to beg his bread from door to door, according to the rule of the Order, for the love of God.

But the folk of that city were more covetous than the men of Lucca, and harder than they of Perugia. The bakers and tanners who were dicing before their shop-doors, repulsed the poor man of Jesus Christ with harsh words. Even the young women, holding their new-born babes in their arms, turned their faces from him. And when the good Brother, whose joy was in dishonour, smiled at the refusals and insults he received,

"He is laughing at us," said the townsmen to each other. "He is a born fool—or say rather a vagabond impostor and a drunkard. He has over-drunk himself with wine. It were a sin and a shame to give him so much as a crumb of bread from our hutch."

And the good Brother answered:

"You say true, my friends; I am not worthy to stir your pity, nor fit to share the food of your dogs and your pigs."

The children, who were just then coming out of school, overheard what was said, and ran after the holy man shouting:

"Madman! Madman!"—and pelted him with mud and stones.

Then Fra Giovanni went forth into the country. The city was built on the slope of a hill, and was surrounded by vineyards and oliveyards. He descended the hill by a hollow way, and seeing on either side the grapes of the vines that hung down from the branches of the elms, he stretched out his arm and blessed the clusters. Likewise he blessed the olive and the mulberry trees and all the wheat of the lowlands.

Meantime he was both hungry and thirsty; and he took delight in thirst and hunger.

At the end of a cross-road, he saw a wood of laurels; and it was the habit of the Begging Friars to go and pray in the woods, amongst the poor animals cruel men hunt and harry. Accordingly Fra Giovanni entered the wood, and fared on by the side of a brook that ran clear and singing on its way.

Presently he saw a flat stone beside the brook, and at the same moment a young man of a wondrous beauty, clad in a white robe, laid a loaf of bread on the stone, and disappeared.

And Fra Giovanni knelt down and prayed, saying:

"O God, how good art Thou, to send Thy poor man bread by the hand of one of Thy Angels; O blessed poverty! O very glorious and most sumptuous poverty!"

And he ate the loaf the Angel had brought, and drank the water of the brook, and was strengthened in body and in soul. And an invisible hand wrote on the walls of the city: "Woe, woe to the rich!"

V

THE TABLE UNDER THE FIG-TREE

FOLLOWING the example of St. Francis, his well-beloved Father, Fra Giovanni used to visit the Hospital of Viterbo to help the lepers, giving them to drink and washing their sores.

And if they blasphemed, he used to tell them, "You are the chosen sons of Jesus Christ." And there were some lepers of a very humble spirit whom he would gather together in a chamber, and with whom he took delight as a mother does surrounded by her children.

But the Hospital walls were very thick, and daylight entered only by narrow windows high up above the floor. The air was so fetid the lepers could scarce live in the place at all. And Fra Giovanni noted how one of them, by name Lucido, who showed an exemplary patience, was slowly dying of the evil atmosphere.

Fra Giovanni loved Lucido, and would tell him:

"My brother, you are Lucido, and no precious stone is purer than your heart, in the eyes of God."

And observing how Lucido suffered more sorely than the others from the poisonous air they breathed in the Lepers' Ward, he said to him one day:

"Friend Lucido, dear Lamb of the Lord, while the very air they breathe in this place is pestilence, in the gardens of Santa Maria degli Angeli we inhale the sweet scent of the laburnums. Come you with me to the House of the Poor Brethren, and you will find relief."

So speaking, he took the Leper by the arm, wrapped him in his own cloak and led him away to Santa Maria degli Angeli.

Arrived at the gate of the Monastery, he summoned the Doorkeeper with happy shouts of exultation:

"Open!" he cried, "open to the friend I am bringing you. His name is Lucido, and a good name it is, for he is a very pearl of patience."

The Brother opened the Gate; but the instant he saw in Fra Giovanni's arms a man whose face, livid and all but expressionless, was covered over with scales, he knew him for a leper, and rushed off in terror to warn the Brother Superior. The latter's name was Andrea of Padua, and he was a man of very holy life. Nevertheless when he learned that Fra Giovanni was bringing a leper into the House of Santa Maria degli Angeli, he was very wroth, and coming to him with a face burning with anger, bade him:

"Stay there outside, with the man. You are a senseless fool to expose your brethren thus to contagion."

Fra Giovanni only looked on the ground without venturing any reply. All the joy was gone from his face; and Lucido, seeing him troubled:

"Brother!" said he, "I am grieved you are made sad because of me."

And Fra Giovanni kissed the leper on the cheek. Then he said, turning to the Superior:

"Will you suffer me, my Father, to stay outside the Gate with this man, and share my meal with him?"—to which the Father Superior answered:

"Even do as you please, seeing you set up yourself above the holy rule of obedience."

And with these harsh words he went back again into the Monastery.

Now in front of the Gate was a stone bench under a fig-tree, and on this bench Fra Giovanni set down his bowl. But while he was supping with the Leper, the Father Superior had the Gate thrown open, and came and sat under the fig-tree and said:

"Forgive me, Fra Giovanni, for having given you offence. I am come hither now to share your meal."

VI

THE TEMPTATION

THEN Satan sat him down on the brow of a hill, and gazed down at the House of the Poor Brethren. He was black and beautiful, like a young Egyptian. And he thought in his heart:

"Forasmuch as I am the Enemy of Mankind and the Adversary of God, therefore will I tempt these Monks, and I will tell them what is kept hid by Him who is their Friend. Lo! I will afflict these men of Religion by telling them the truth, and I will darken their spirit, uttering to them words of verity and reasonableness. I will plunge reflexion like a sword in their reins; and so soon as they shall know the reality of things, they will be unhappy. For joy there is none but in illusion, and peace is only to be found in ignorance. And because I am the Master of such as study the nature of plants and animals, the virtue of stones, the secrets of fire, the courses of the stars and the influence of the planets, for this reason men have named me the Prince of Darkness. Likewise they call me the Wily One, because by me was constructed the plummet-line whereby Ulpian straightened out the Law. And my kingdom is of this world. Well then, I will try these Monks, and I will make them to know their works are evil, and that the tree of their Charity bears bitter fruit. Yea! I will tempt them without hate and without love."

Thus said Satan in his heart. Meantime, as the shades of evening were lengthening along the base of the hills and the cottage chimneys were smoking for the evening meal, the holy man Giovanni issued from out the wood where he was wont to pray, and turned into the road leading to Santa Maria degli Angeli, saying:

"My house is the house of joy and delight, because it is the house of poverty."

And seeing Fra Giovanni wending his way homewards, Satan thought:

"Lo! here is one of those men I am come to tempt";—and drawing his black cloak over his head, he advanced along the high road, which was bordered with terebinths, to meet the holy man.

Now Satan had made himself like a widow-woman with a veil, and when he had joined Fra Giovanni, he put on a honeyed voice and asked an alms of him, saying:

"Give me an alms for the love of Him who is

them, and so doing, fulfil the order given to your first father, Adam, when he was commanded, 'In the sweat of thy face, thou shalt eat bread.' Seeing work is good, the fruit of this work is good too. Yet you work not, neither have any care for the work of others. But you receive and give alms, in contempt of the law laid on Adam and on his seed through the ages."

"Alas!" sighed Brother Giovanni, "I am laden with crimes, and at once the most wicked and the most foolish man in all the world. Wherefore never heed me, but read in the Book. Our Lord said, 'Consider the lilies of the field; they toil not, neither do they spin.' Again he said, 'Mary hath chosen the good part, which shall not be taken away from her.'"

Then Satan lifted up his hand, with the gesture of one who disputes and prepares to count off his arguments on the fingers. And he said:

"Giovanni, Giovanni! what was written in one sense, you read in another; you are less like a Doctor at his desk than an ass at the manger. So must I correct you, as a master corrects his scholar. It is written the lilies of the field have no need to spin—because they are beautiful, and beauty is a virtue. Again it is written how Mary is not to do the household tasks, because she is doing lovingly to Him who has come to see her. But you, who are not beautiful nor yet instructed, like Mary, in the things of love, you drag out a contemptible existence wandering the highways."

Giovanni made reply:

"Sir! just as a Painter will depict on a narrow panel of wood an entire city with its houses and towers and walls, so you have painted in a few words my soul and my similitude with a wondrous exactness. And I am altogether what you describe. But if I followed perfectly the rule established by St. Francis, that Angel of God, and if I practised spiritual poverty to the full, I should be the lily of the fields and I should have the good part of Mary."

But Satan interrupted him, and cried:

"You profess to love the poor, yet you prefer the rich man and his riches, and adore Him who possesses treasures to give away."

And Fra Giovanni answered:

"He I love possesses not the good things of the body, but those of the spirit."

And Satan retorted:

"All good things are of the flesh, and are tasted of through the flesh. This Epicurus taught, and Horace the Satirist said the same in his Verses."

At these words the holy man only sighed and said:

"Sir! I cannot tell what you mean."

Satan shrugged his shoulders and said:

"My words are exact and literal, yet the man cannot tell what I mean. I have disputed with Augustine and Jerome, with Gregory and him of the Golden Mouth, St. Chrysostom. And they comprehended me still less. Miserable men walk groping in the dark, and Error lifts over their head her monstrous canopy. Simple and sage alike are the plaything of eternal falsehood."

And Satan said again to the holy man Giovanni:

"Have you won happiness? If you have happiness, I shall not prevail against you. A man's thoughts are only stirred by sorrow, and their meditations by grief. Then, tortured by fears and desires, he turns anxiously in his bed and rends his pillow with lies. What use to tempt this man? He is happy."

But Fra Giovanni sighed:

"Sir! I am less happy since listening to you. Your words trouble my mind."

On hearing this, Satan cast away his pastoral staff, his mitre and his cope; and stood there naked and unashamed. He was black and more beautiful than the loveliest of the Angels.

He smiled gently, and said to the holy man:

"Friend, be comforted. I am the Evil Spirit."

VIII

THE BURNING COAL

NOW Brother Giovanni was simple of heart and spirit, and his tongue was tied; he knew not the secret of speaking to his fellow-men.

But one day when he was praying, as his habit was, at the foot of an ancient holm-oak, an Angel of the Lord appeared to him, and saluting him, said:

"I salute you, because it is I who visit the simple-minded, and announce the mysteries to virgins."

And the Angel held in his hand a burning coal. This he laid on the holy man's lips, and spoke again, and said:

"By virtue of this fire shall your lips remain pure, and they shall glow with eloquence. I have burned them, and they shall be burned. Your tongue shall be loosed, and you shall speak to your fellows. For men must hear the word of life, and learn how they shall not be saved but by innocency of heart. For this cause the Lord has unloosed the tongue of the simple and innocent."

Then the Angel went back again to Heaven.

your friend, and whom I am not worthy so much as to name."

And Fra Giovanni answered:

"It happens so, I have with me a little silver cup a nobleman of the countryside gave me, to have it melted down and used for the Altar of Santa Maria degli Angeli. You may take that, lady; and I will go to-morrow and ask the nobleman to let me have another of the same weight for the Blessed Virgin. Thus will his wishes be accomplished, and over and above, you will have gotten an alms for the love of God."

Satan took the cup and said:

"Good brother, suffer a poor widow-woman to kiss your hand. For verily the hand that gives gifts is soft and fragrant."

Fra Giovanni replied:

"Lady, be heedful not to kiss my hand. On the contrary, begone with all speed. For, methinks, you are winsome of face, albeit black as the Magian King that bore the frankincense and myrrh; and it is not becoming I should look on you longer, seeing how danger is forever dogging the lonely man's steps. Wherefore suffer me now to leave you, commending you to God's care. And forgive me, if I have failed aught in politeness towards you, lady. For the good St. Francis was used to say: 'Courtesy shall be the ornament of my sons, as the flowers bedeck the hillsides.' "

But Satan said again:

"Good Father, inform me at the least of a guest-house, where I may pass the night honestly."

Fra Giovanni replied:

"Go, mistress, to the House of St. Damian, where dwell the poor ladies of Our Lord. She who will welcome you is Clare, and indeed she is a clear mirror of purity; the same is the Duchess of Poverty."

And Satan said again:

"My Father, I am an adulterous woman, and I have lain with many men."

And Fra Giovanni said:

"Lady, if I really deemed you laden with the sins you tell of, I would crave of you as a high honour to kiss your feet, for I am less worth than you, and your crimes are little compared with mine. Yet have I received greater favours of Heaven than have been accorded to you. For in the days when St. Francis and his twelve disciples were still upon earth, I lived with Angels of Heaven."

And Satan returned:

"My Father, when I asked you an alms for the love of Him who loves you, I was cherishing in my heart a wicked intent, and I am fain to tell you what this was. I wander the roads a-begging, in order to collect a sum of money I destine for a man of Perosa who is my paramour, and who has promised me, on handling this money, to kill traitorously a certain knight I hate, because when I offered my body to him, he scorned me. Well! the total was yet incomplete; but now the weight of your silver cup has made it up. So the alms you have given me will be the price of blood. You have sold a just man to death. For the Knight I told you of is chaste, temperate and pious, and I hate him for this cause. 'Tis you will have brought about his murder. You have laid a weight of silver in the scale of crime, to bear it down."

Hearing these words, the good Fra Giovanni wept, and drawing aside, he fell on his knees in a thorn-brake, and prayed the Lord, saying:

"O Lord, make this crime to fall neither on this woman's head nor on mine nor on that of any of Thy creatures, but let it be put beneath Thy feet, which were pierced with the nails, and be washed in Thy most precious blood. Distil on me and on this my sister of the highway a drop of hyssop, and we shall be purified, and shall overpass the snow in whiteness."

But the Enemy fled away, thinking:

"This man I have not been able to tempt by reason of his utter simplicity."

VII

THE SUBTLE DOCTOR

SATAN returned and sat on the Mountain that looks towards Viterbo, laughing under its crown of olives. And he said in his heart: "I will tempt that man yonder."

He conceived this purpose in his spirit, because he had seen Fra Giovanni, girt about with a cord, and a sack over his shoulder, crossing the meadows below on his way to the city to beg his bread there according to the rules.

So Satan took on the appearance of a holy Bishop, and came down into the plain. A mitre was on his head sparkling with precious stones, that flashed like actual fire in the sunlight. His cope was covered with figures embroidered and painted so beautifully no craftsman in all the world could have wrought their like.

Amongst the rest he was depicted himself, in silk and gold, under the guise of a St. George and a St. Sebastian, as also under that of a Virgin St. Catherine and the Empress Helena. The loveliness of the faces troubled the mind and saddened the heart. The garment was truly of a wondrous workmanship, and nothing so rich and rare is to be seen in the Treasuries of Churches.

Thus decked in cope and mitre, and majestic as St. Ambrose, the glory of Milan, Satan pursued his way, leaning on his crozier, over the flowery plain.

Presently nearing the holy man, he hailed him and said:

"Peace be with you!"

But he said not of what sort this peace was; and Fra Giovanni supposed it was the peace of the Lord. He thought to himself:

"This Bishop, who gives me the salutation of peace, was doubtless in his lifetime a sainted Pontiff and a blessed Martyr unshakable in his constancy. That is why Jesus Christ has changed the wooden cross to a golden in the hands of this gallant Confessor of the Faith. To-day he is powerful in Heaven; and lo! after his holy and happy death, he walks in these meadows that are painted with flowers and broidered with pearls of dew."

Such were the good Giovanni's thoughts, and he was in no wise abashed. So saluting Satan with a deep reverence, he said:

"Sir! you are exceeding gracious to appear to a poor man such as I. But indeed these meadows are so lovely, 'tis no wonder if the Saints of Paradise come to walk here; they are painted with flowers and broidered with pearls of dew. The Lord did very kindly when he made them.".

And Satan said to him:

"It is not the meadows, it is your heart I am fain to look at; I have come down from the Mountain to speak with you. I have, in bygone Centuries, held many high disputations in the Church. Amid the assembled Doctors my voice would boom forth like thunder, and my thoughts flash like lightning. I am very learned, and they name me the Subtle Doctor. I have disputed with God's Angels. Now I would hold dispute with you."

Fra Giovanni made answer:

"Nay! but how should the poor little man that I am hold dispute with the Subtle Doctor? I know nothing, and my simplicity is such I can keep nothing in my head but those songs in the vulgar tongue where they have stuck in rhymes to help the memory, as in

> 'Jesus, mirror of my soul,
>   Cleanse my heart and make it whole.'

or in

> 'Holy Mary, Maid of Flowers,
>   Lead me to the Heavenly Bowers.'

And Satan answered:

"Fra Giovanni, the Venetian ladies amuse their leisure and show their adroitness in fitting a multitude of little pieces of ivory into a box of cedarwood, which at the set-off seemed all too small to contain so many. In the same fashion I will pack ideas into your head that no one would have dreamed it could ever hold; and I will fill you with a new wisdom. I will show that, thinking to walk in the right way, you are straying abroad all the while like a drunken man, and that you are driving the plough without any heed to draw the furrows straight."

Fra Giovanni humbled himself, saying:

"It is most true I am a fool, and do nothing but what is wrong."

Then Satan asked him:

"What think you of poverty?"—and the holy man replied:

"I think it is a pearl of price."

But Satan retorted:

"You pretend poverty is a great good; yet all the while you are robbing the poor of a part of this great good, by giving them alms."

Fra Giovanni pondered over this, and said:

"The alms I give, I give to Our Lord Jesus Christ, whose poverty cannot be minished, for it is infinite.

It gushes from Him as from an inexhaustible fountain; and its waters flow freely for His favourite sons. And these shall be poor always, according to the promise of the Son of God. In giving to the poor, I am giving not to men, but to God, as the citizens pay tax to the Podestà, and the rate is for the City, which of the money it so receives supplies the town's needs. Now what I give is for paving the City of God. It is a vain thing to be poor in deed, if we be not poor in spirit. The gown of frieze, the cord, the sandals, the wallet and the wooden bowl are only signs and symbols. The Poverty I love is spiritual, and I address her as *Lady*, because she is an idea, and all beauty resides in this same idea."

Satan smiled, and replied:

"Your maxims, Fra Giovanni, are the maxims of a wise man of Greece, Diogenes by name, who taught at their Universities in the times when Alexander of Macedon was waging his wars."

And Satan said again:

"Is it true you despise the goods of this world?"

And Fra Giovanni replied:

"I do despise them."

And Satan said to him:

"Look you! in scorning these, you are scorning at the same time the hard-working men who produce

And the holy man was seized with terror, and he prayed, saying:

"O God, my heart is so sore troubled I cannot find on my lips the sweet savour of the fire Thy Angel hath touched them with.

"Thou wouldst chasten me, O Lord, seeing Thou dost send me to speak to the folk, who will not hearken to my words. I shall be hateful to all men, and Thy priests themselves will declare, 'He is a blasphemer!'

"For Thy reason is contrary to the reason of men. Nevertheless Thy will be done."

Then he rose up from his knees, and set out on his way citywards.

IX

THE HOUSE OF INNOCENCE

ON that day Fra Giovanni had left the Monastery at early dawn, the hour when the birds awake and begin singing. He was on his way to the city and he thought within himself: "I am going to the city to beg my bread and to give bread to other beggars; I shall give away what I receive, and take back what I have given. For it is good to ask and to receive for the love of God. And he who receives is the brother of him who gives. And we should not consider too curiously which of the twain brothers we are, because truly the gift is naught, but everything is in the gracious giving.

"He that receives, if he have gracious charity, is the equal of him that gives. But he who sells is the enemy of him who buys, and the seller constrains the buyer to be his foe. Herein lies the root of the curse that poisons cities, as the venom of the serpent is in his tail. And it must needs be a Lady set her foot on the serpent's tail, and that Lady is Poverty. Already hath she visited King Louis of

France in his Tower; but never yet entered among the Florentines, because she is chaste and will not put foot in a place of ill repute. Now the money-changer's shop is an ill place, for it is there Bankers and Changers commit the most heinous of sins. Harlots sin in the brothels; but their sin is not so great as is that of the Bankers, and whosoever grows rich by banking and money-dealing.

"Verily I say unto you, Bankers and Money-changers shall not enter into the Kingdom of Heaven, nor yet bakers, nor dealers in drugs, nor such as practise the trade of wool, which is the boast of the City of the Lily. Forasmuch as they give a price to gold, and make a profit out of exchange, they are setting up idols in the face of men. And when they declare 'Gold has a value,' they tell a lie. For Gold is more vile than the dry leaves that flutter and rustle in the Autumn wind under the terebinths. There is nothing precious save the work of men's hands, when God gives it His countenance."

And lo! as he was meditating in this wise, Fra Giovanni saw that the Mountain side was torn open, and that men were dragging great stones from its flank. And one of the quarrymen was lying by the wayside, with a rag of coarse cloth for all covering; and his body was disfigured by bitter marks of the biting cold and scorching heat. The bones of his shoulders and chest showed all but bare beneath the meagre flesh; and Despair looked out grim and gaunt from the black cavern of his eyes.

Fra Giovanni approached him, saying:

"Peace be with you!"

But the quarryman made no answer, and did not so much as turn his head. So Fra Giovanni thinking he had not heard, repeated:

"Peace be with you!"—and then the same words again for the third time.

At last the quarryman looked up at him sullenly, and growled:

"I shall have no peace till I am dead. Begone, cursed black crow! you wish me peace; that shows you are a glozing cheat! Go to, and caw to simpler fools than I! I know very well the quarryman's lot is an utterly miserable one, and there is no comfort for his wretchedness. I hale out stones from dawn to dark, and for price of my toil, all I get is a scrap of black bread. Then when my arms are no longer as strong as the stones of the mountain, and my body is all worn out, I shall perish of hunger."

"Brother!" said the holy man Giovanni; "it is not just or right you should hale out so much stone, and win so little bread."

Then the quarryman rose to his feet, and pointing,

"Master Monk," said he, "what see you up yonder on the hill?"

"Brother, I see the walls of the City."

"And above them?"

"Above them I see the roofs of the houses, which crown the ramparts."

"And higher still?"

"The tops of the pines, the domes of the Churches and the Belltowers."

"And higher still?"

"I see a Tower overtopping all the rest, and crowned with battlements. It is the Tower of the Podestà."

"Monk, what see you above the battlements of that Tower?"

"I see nothing, brother, above the battlements save the sky."

"But I," cried the quarryman, "I see upon that Tower a hideous giant brandishing a club, and on the club is inscribed: OPPRESSION. Yea! Oppression is lifted up above the citizens' heads on the Great Tower of the Magistrates and the City's Laws."

And Fra Giovanni answered:

"What one man sees, another cannot see, and it may be the horrid shape you describe is set on the Tower of the Podestà yonder, in the city of Viterbo.

But is there no remedy for the ills you endure, my brother? The good St. Francis left behind him on this earth so full a fountain of consolation that all men may draw refreshment therefrom."

Then the quarryman spoke after this fashion:

"Men have said, 'This mountain is ours.' And these men are my masters, and it is for them I hew stone. And they enjoy the fruit of my labour."

Fra Giovanni sighed:

"Surely men must be mad to believe they own a mountain."

But the quarryman replied:

"Nay! they are not mad; and the Laws of the City guarantee them their ownership. The citizens pay them for the stones I have hewn, which are marbles of great price."

And Fra Giovanni said:

"We must change the laws of the City and the habits of the citizens. St. Francis, that Angel of God, has given the example and shown the way. When he resolved, by God's command, to rebuild the ruined Church of St. Damian, he did not set out to find the master of the quarry. He did not say, 'Go buy me the finest marbles, and I will give you gold in exchange.' For the holy man, who was called the son of Bernardone and who was the true son of God, knew this, that the man who sells is the enemy of the man who buys, and that the art of Trafficking is more mischievous, if possible, than the art of War. Wherefore he did not apply to the master-masons or any of them that give marble and timber and lead in exchange for money. But he went forth into the Mountain and gathered his load of wood and stones, and bore it himself to the spot hallowed to the memory of the Blessed Damian. With his own hands, by help of the mason's line, he laid the stones to form the walls; and he made the cement to bind together the stones one to another. Finished, it was a lowly circuit of roughly fashioned stones, the work of a weakling. But who considers it with the eyes of the soul recognizes therein an Angel's thought. For the mortar of this wall was not worked with the blood of the unfortunate; this house of St. Damian was not raised with the thirty pieces of silver paid for the blood of that Just Man, which, rejected by Iscariot, go travelling the world ever since, passing from hand to hand, to buy up all the injustice and all the cruelty of the earth.

"For, alone of all others, this house is founded on Innocence, stablished on Love, based on Charity, and alone of all others it is the House of God.

"And I tell you verily, quarryman and brother, the poor man of Jesus Christ, in doing these things, gave to the world an example of Justice, and one day his foolishness shall shine forth as wisdom. For all things in this earth are God's and we are His children; and it is meet the children should share alike in His inheritance. That is, each should get what he has need of. And seeing grown men do not ask for broth, nor babes for wine, the share of each shall not be the same, but each shall have the heritage that is fitting for him.

"And labour shall be a joyful thing, when it is no longer paid. 'Tis gold only, the cursed gold, that makes the sharing uneven. When each man shall go severally to the Mountain for his stone, and carry his load to the city on his own back, the stone shall weigh light and it shall be the stone of cheerfulness. And we will build the house of joy and gladness, and the new city shall rise from its foundations. And there shall be neither rich nor poor, but all men will call themselves poor men, because they will be glad to bear a name that brings them honour."

So spoke the gentle Fra Giovanni, and the unhappy quarryman thought to himself:

"This man clad in a shroud and girt with a cord has proclaimed new tidings. I shall not see the end of my miseries, for I am going to die of hunger and exhaustion. But I shall die happy, for my eyes, before they close, will have beheld the dawn of the day of Justice."

X

THE FRIENDS OF ORDER

NOW in those days there was in the very illustrious city of Viterbo a Confraternity of sixty old men. These counted among their number many of the chief men of the place; and their objects were the accumulation of honours and riches, and the pursuit of virtue. The Brotherhood included a Gonfalonier of the Republic, Doctors of either faculty, Judges, Merchants, Money-changers of conspicuous piety, and one or two old Soldiers of Fortune grown too ancient and feeble for the Wars.

Seeing they were banded together for the purpose of stirring up their fellow-citizens to goodness and good order, and to bear mutual witness to the practice of these virtues, they gave themselves the title of *The Friends of Order*. This name was inscribed on the banner of the Confraternity, and they were all of one mind to persuade the poor to follow goodness and good order, to the end no changes might be made in the Constitution.

Their habit was to meet on the last day of each

month, in the Palace of the Podestà, to make inquiry of each other what of good had been done in the city during the month. And to such of the poorer citizens as had done well and orderly, they used to present pieces of money.

Now on a certain day the Friends of Order were holding meeting. At one end of the Hall was a raised platform covered with velvet, and over the platform a magnificent canopy of state, held up by four figures carved and painted. These figures represented Justice, Temperance, Strength and Chastity; and beneath the canopy sat the Officers of the Brotherhood. The President, who was entitled the Dean, took his place in the middle on a golden chair, which in richness was scarce inferior to the throne that once upon a time the disciple of St. Francis saw prepared in Heaven for the poor man of the Lord. This seat of state had been presented to the Dean of the Brotherhood to the end that in him should be honoured all the goodness done in the city.

And as soon as the Members of the Confraternity were ranged in the fitting order, the Dean got up to speak. He congratulated any serving-maids that served their masters without receiving wages, and spoke highly of the old men who, having no bread to eat, did not ask for any.

And he said:

"These have done well, and we shall reward them. For it behoves that goodness be rewarded, and it is our bounden duty to pay the price of it, being as we are the first and foremost citizens of the city."

And when he finished speaking, the crowd of the general folk that stood under the platform clapped their hands.

But no sooner had they done applauding than Fra Giovanni lifted up his voice from the midst of the miserable, poverty-stricken band, and asked loudly:

"What is goodness?"

At this great clamour arose in the assembly, and the Dean shouted:

"Who was it spoke?"

And a red-haired man who was standing among the people, answered:

"It was a Monk, by name Giovanni, who is the disgrace of his Cloister. He goes naked through the streets, carrying his clothes on his head, and gives himself up to all sorts of extravagances."

Next a Baker spoke up and said:

"He is a madman or a miscreant! He begs his bread at the Bakers' doors."

Then a number of those present, shouting noisily

and dragging Fra Giovanni by the gown, tried to hustle him out of the hall, while others more angry still, began throwing stools and breaking them over the holy man's head. But the Dean rose from his seat under the canopy, and said:

"Leave the man in peace, so that he may hear me and be confounded. He asks what goodness is, because goodness is not in him and he is devoid of virtue. I answer him, 'The knowledge of goodness resides in virtuous men; and good citizens carry within them a proper respect for the laws. They approve what has been done in the city to insure to each man enjoyment of the riches he may have acquired. They support the established order of things, and are ready to fly to arms to defend the same. For the duty of the poor is to defend the good things belonging to the rich; and this is how the union betwixt citizens is maintained. This is goodness and good order. Again, the rich man has his serving-man bring out a basket full of bread, which he distributes to the poor; and this is goodness again.' These are the lessons this rough, ignorant fellow required to be taught."

Having so said, the Dean sat down, and the crowd of poor folks raised a murmur of approval. But Fra Giovanni, stepping on one of the stools that had been thrown at his head with contumely and insult, addressed them all and said:

"Hear the words of comfort! Goodness resides not in men, for men know not of themselves what is good. They are ignorant of their own nature and destiny. What seems good, may be evil all the while; and what is deemed useful, harmful. No man can choose the things meet for him, because he knows not his own needs, but is like the little child sitting in the meadows, that sucks for wholesome milk the juice of the deadly nightshade. The babe does not know that the nightshade is poison; but its mother knows. This is why goodness is to do the will of God.

"It is false to say, ' 'Tis I teach goodness, and goodness is to obey the city laws.' For the Laws are not of God; they are of man, and share in man's craft and cunning and imperfection. They are like the rules children make in the Square of Viterbo, when they are playing ball. Goodness is not in customs nor in laws; it is in God and in the accomplishment of God's will upon earth, and it is neither by law-makers nor magistrates that God's will is accomplished upon the earth.

"For the great men of this world do their own will, and their will is contrary to God's. But they who have stripped off pride and know there is no goodness in them, these men receive noble gifts, and God Himself distils His sweetness within them like honey in the hollow of the oaks.

"And we must be the oak-tree full of honey and dew. Humble, ignorant and simple folks, these have knowledge of God; and by them shall God's kingdom be stablished on earth. Salvation is not in the strength of laws nor in the multitude of soldiers; it is in poverty and humbleness of spirit.

"Say not, 'Goodness is in me, and I teach goodness.' Rather say, 'Goodness is in God on high.' Over long have men hardened their hearts in their own wisdom. Over long have they set up the Lion and the She-Wolf above the Gates of their Cities. Their wisdom and their prudence have brought about slavery and wars and the shedding of much innocent blood. Wherefore you should put your guidance in God's hand, as the blind man trusts himself to his dog's guidance. Fear not to shut the eyes of your spirit and have done with Reason, for has not Reason made you unhappy and wicked? By Reason have you grown like the man who, having guessed the secrets of the Beast crouching in the cavern, waxed proud of his knowingness, and deeming himself wiser than his fellows, slew his father and wedded his mother.

"God was not with him; but He is with the humble and simple-minded. Learn not to will and He will put His will in you. Seek not to guess the riddles of the Beast. Be ignorant, and you shall not fear to go astray. 'Tis only wise men that are deceived."

Fra Giovanni having thus spoken, the Dean got up and said:

"The miscreant has insulted me, and I willingly forgive him the insult. But he has spoken against the laws of Viterbo, and it is meet he should be punished."

So Fra Giovanni was led before the Judges, who had him loaded with chains and cast him into the city gaol.

XI

THE REVOLT OF GENTLENESS

THE holy man Giovanni was chained to a massive pillar in the middle of the dungeon over which the river flowed.

Two other prisoners were plunged along with him in the thick and fetid darkness. Both these had realized and proclaimed the injustice of the Laws. One was for overthrowing the Republic by force. He had been guilty of startling assassinations, and his hope was to purify the city with fire and sword. The other trusted to be able to change men's hearts, and had delivered very persuasive discourses. Inventor of wise laws, he counted on the charms of his genius and the innocency of his life to induce his fellow-citizens to submit to them. But both had met with the same doom.

When they learned how the holy man was chained alongside of them for having spoken against the laws of the city, they congratulated him. And the one who had invented wise laws, said to him:

"If ever, brother, we are restored to liberty,

seeing you think as I do, you shall help me to persuade the citizens that they ought to set up above them the empire of just laws."

But the holy man Giovanni answered him:

"What matter for Justice being in the Laws, if it is not in men's hearts? And if men's hearts are unjust, what gain shall it be that Equity reign in the Courts of Law?

"Say not, 'We will stablish just laws, and we will render to every man what is his due.' For no one is just, and we know not what is meet for men. We are no less ignorant what is good for them and what is evil. And whensoever the Princes of the People and the Chiefs of the Commonwealth have loved Justice, they have caused the slaying of many folk.

"Give not the compass and the level to the false measurer; for with true instruments, he will make untrue apportionments. And he will say: 'See, I carry on me the level, the rule and the square, and I am a good measurer.' So long as men shall be covetous and cruel, will they make the most merciful laws cruel, and will rob their brethren with words of love on their lips. This is why it is vain to reveal to them the words of love and the laws of gentleness.

"Set not up laws against laws, nor raise tables of

marble and tables of brass before men's eyes. For whatever is written on the tables of the Law, is written in letters of blood."

So spoke the holy man. And the other prisoner, —he who had committed startling murders, and contrived the ruin that was to save the city, approved his words and said:

"Comrade, you have spoken well. Know you, I will never set up law against law, right rule against crooked rule; my wish is to destroy the law by violence and compel the citizens to live thenceforth in happy freedom. And know further that I have slain both judges and soldiers, and have committed many crimes for the public good."

Hearing these words, the man of the Lord rose, stretched out his manacled arms in the heavy darkness and cried:

"Ill betide the violent! for violence ever begets violence. Whosoever acts like you is sowing the earth with hate and fury, and his children shall tear their feet with the wayside briars, and serpents shall bite their heel.

"Ill betide you! for you have shed the blood of the unjust judge and the brutal soldier, and lo! you are become like the soldier and the judge yourself. Like them you bear on your hands the indelible stain.

"A fool the man who says, 'We will do evildoing in our turn, and our heart shall be comforted. We will be unjust, and it shall be the beginning of justice.' Evildoing is in evil desiring. Desire nothing, and evildoing will be done away. Injustice hurts only the unjust; I shall suffer no harm of it, if I am just. Oppression is a sword whose hilt wounds the hand of him who holds it; but its point cannot pierce the heart of the man who is simple-minded and good and kind.

"For such an one nothing is dangerous, if he fear nothing. To endure all things, is to endure nothing. Let us be good and kindly, and the whole round world shall be the same. For the world will be an instrument for your goodness, and your persecutors will work to make you better and more beautiful.

"You love life, and this is an affection which rules the heart of every man. Then love suffering; for to live is to suffer. Never envy your cruel masters; rather have compassion for the commanders of armies. Pity the Publicans and Judges; the proudest of them have known the stings of grief and the terrors of death. Happier you, because your consciences are void of offence; for you, let grief lose its bitterness and death its terrors.

"Be ye God's children, and tell yourselves, 'All

is well in Him.' Beware of pursuing even the public good with overmuch violence and avidity, for fear something of cruelty mar your integrity. Rather should your desire of universal loving-kindness have the unction of a prayer and the soft fervour of a hope.

"Fair the table, whereat every man shall get his just portion, and the guests shall each one wash the other's feet. But say not, 'I will set up this table by force in the streets of the city and in the public squares.' For it is not knife in hand you must call together your brethren to the feast of Justice and Gentleness. Of its own accord must the board be spread in the Campo di Marte, by virtue of graciousness and good will.

"This shall be a miracle; and be sure, miracles are not wrought save by faith and love. If you disobey your masters, let it be by love. Neither fetter nor kill them, but tell them rather, 'I will never slay my brothers, nor throw them into chains.' Endure, suffer, submit, will what God wills, and your will shall be done on earth as it is in heaven. What seems evil is evil, and what seems good is good. Striving and discontent is the true curse of mankind. Let us then be peaceful and content, and never strike the wicked, for fear we make ourselves like them.

"If we have not the good fortune to be poor in very deed, let us not make ourselves rich men in spirit, and heartbound to the things of this world that make folk unjust and unhappy. Let us suffer persecution with gentleness, and be those chosen vessels that turn into balm the gall poured into them."

XII

WORDS OF LOVE

THEN the Judges had the holy man, Giovanni, brought before them chained to him who had thrown Greek fire in the Palace of the Priors. And they said to the holy man:

"You are alongside of the guilty because you are not on our side. For whosoever is not with good citizens is with evil."

And the holy man answered them:

"There are neither good nor evil among men; but all alike are unhappy. And they who suffer neither hunger nor contumely, they are afflicted by riches and power. It is not given to any man born of woman to escape the miseries of life, and the son of woman is like a fever patient, who turns and turns in his bed, and can find no rest, because he will not lie down on the Cross of Jesus, his head among the thorns, and take his joy in suffering. Yet is it in suffering that joy is found; and they who love know this.

"I companion with Love, but that man with Hate; and for this cause we can never come together. And I say to him, 'Brother, you have done ill, and your crime is great and grievous.' And I speak so, because Charity and Love urge me. But you, you condemn yonder guilty man in the name of Justice. But invoking Justice, you take a vain oath, for there is no such thing as Justice among men.

"We are all of us guilty. And when you say, 'The life of peoples is in our hand,' you are lying, and you are the coffin which declares, 'I am the cradle.' The life of peoples is in the harvests of the fields, which grow yellow beneath the Lord's sight. It is in the vines hanging from the elms, and in the smiles and tears wherein heaven bathes the fruits of the trees in the orchard closes. It is not in the laws, which are made by the rich and powerful for the maintenance of their own power and riches.

"Ye forget how ye are all born poor and naked. And He who came to lie in the manger at Bethlehem, has come without profiting you. And He must needs be born again and be crucified a second time for your salvation.

"The man of violence has laid hold of the arms you forged; and is well compared to the warriors you hold in honour because they have destroyed cities. What is defended by force shall be attacked by force. And if you have wit to read the book you have written, you will find what I say therein. For you have put in your book that the right of nations is the right of war; and you have glorified violence, paying honours to conquering generals and raising statues in your public squares to them and their war-horses.

"And you have laid it down, 'There is violence that is right, and violence that is wrong. And this is the right of nations and this is the law.' But so soon as the men shall have put you outside the law, they will be the law, even as you became the law, when you had overthrown the tyrant that was the law before you.

"Now, be assured, it is very certain that there is no true right save in the renouncing of right. There is no hallowed law save in love. There is no Justice save in Charity. 'Tis not by force we should resist force, for strife only hardens the fighters' hearts and the issue of battles is aye dubious. But if we oppose gentleness to violence, this latter getting no hold upon its adversary, falls dead of itself.

"It is related by learned men in the *Bestiaries* how the unicorn, which bears on its forehead a flaming sword, transfixes the hunter in his coat-of-mail, but falls to its knees before a pure virgin.

Be ye gentle-hearted, therefore, and simple-souled; keep your heart pure, and ye shall fear nothing.

"Put not your trust in the sword of the Condottieri, for did not the shepherd boy's smooth stone pierce Goliath's brow? But be ye strong in love, and love them that hate you. Hate, when unreturned, is robbed of half its sting; and what is left is weak, widowed, and like to die. Strip yourselves, that other men strip you not. Love your enemies, that they become your friends. Forgive, that ye may be forgiven. Say not, 'Gentleness is a bane to the shepherds of the peoples.' For how can you know, seeing these have never tried? They profess by harshness to have lessened the evil of the world. Yet is evil still rampant among men, and there is never a sign of its growing less.

"I said to some, 'Be not oppressors,' and to others, 'Rise not in revolt against oppression,'— and neither hearkened to me. They cast the stone of derision at me. Because I was on all men's side, each reproached me and said, 'You are not on my side.'

"I said, 'I am the friend of the wretched.' But you never thought I was your friend, because in your pride, you know not that you are wretched. Nevertheless the wretchedness of the master is more cruel than that of the slave. My tender pity for your woes only made you think I was mocking you; and the oppressed deemed me to be of the party of the oppressors. 'He has no bowels,' they said. Nay! but I am on the side of love and not of hate. This is why you scorn me; and because I preach peace on earth, you hold me for a fool. You think my words wander all ways, like the steps of a drunken man. And it is very true I walk your fields like those harpers who on the eve of battles, come to play before the tents. And the soldiers say, as they listen: ' 'Tis some poor simpletons come playing the tunes we heard long ago in our mountains.' I am this harper that roams between the hosts in battle array of hostile armies. When I think whither human wisdom leads, I am glad to be a madman and a simpleton; and I thank God that He has given me the harp to handle and not the sword."

XIII

THE TRUTH

THE holy man Giovanni was very straitly confined in gaol, where he was fastened by chains to rings built into the wall. But his soul was unfettered, and no tortures had been able to shake his firmness. He promised himself he would never betray the faith that was in him, and was ready to be witness and martyr of the Truth, to the end he might die in God. And he said to himself, "Truth shall go along with me to the scaffold. She shall look at me and weep and say, 'My tears flow, seeing it is for my sake this man is going to his death.'"

And as the holy man was thus holding colloquy of his own thoughts in the solitude of his dungeon, a knight entered into the prison, without ever the doors having been opened. He was clad in a red mantle, and carried in his hand a lighted lantern.

Fra Giovanni accosted him and said:

"What is your name, subtle sir, that slips through prison walls?"

And the knight made answer:

"Brother, what use to tell you the names folk give me? For you I will bear the one you shall call me by. Know this, I am come to you full of helpfulness and goodwill, and being informed you dearly love the Truth, I bring you a word touching this same Truth that you have taken for lady and companion."

And Fra Giovanni began to tender thanks to his visitor. But the knight stopped him in the midst, saying:

"I warn you, this word of mine will seem to you at the first empty and of no account, for it is with it as with a tiny key, that the heedless man throws away without using.

"But the careful householder tries it in lock after lock, till he finds at last it opens a chest full of gold and precious stones.

"Wherefore I say to you, Fra Giovanni, seeing you have chosen peradventure to take Truth for your Lady and darling, it behoves you greatly to know concerning her all that may be known. Well then, know that she is *white*. And from her appearance, which I will describe you, you shall gather her nature, which will be very useful to you in making up to her and kissing her fair body with all sorts of pretty caresses, after the fashion of a lover fondling his mistress. Therefore take it as **pro**ven, brother mine, that she is *white*."

After hearkening to these words, the holy man Giovanni answered:

"Subtle Sir, the meaning of your discourse is not so hard to guess as you would seem to fear. And my wit, albeit naturally thick and dull, was instantly transfixed by the fine point of your allegory. You say that Truth is white to manifest the perfect purity that is in her, and show clearly she is a lady of immaculate virtue. And truly I picture her to myself such as you describe, overpassing in whiteness the lilies of the garden and the snow that in winter clothes the summits of Monte Alverno."

But the visitor shook his head and said:

"Nay! Fra Giovanni, that is not the meaning of my words, and you have in no wise broken the bone to extract the marrow. I instructed you that Truth is white, *not* that she is pure; and it shows little discernment to think that she is pure."

Grieved at what he now heard, the holy man Giovanni replied:

"Even as the Moon, when the Earth hides the Sun's light from her, is darkened by the thick shadow of this World, where was wrought the crime of our mother Eve, so, most Subtle Sir, you have obscured a plain saying under baffling phrases. Thus we have you astray in the dark; for indeed Truth is pure, coming from God, the fountain of all purity."

But the Opponent retorted:

"Fra Giovanni, your logic is at fault, or you would know that purity is an inconceivable quality. This is what the shepherds of Arcady did, so they say, who named pure gods the gods they knew not the nature of."

Then the good Fra Giovanni sighed and said:

"Sir! your words are dark and wrapped in sadness. At times in my sleep angels have visited me. Their words I could not comprehend; but the mystery of *their* thought was full of joy."

Hereupon the subtle visitor resumed:

"Come, Fra Giovanni, let us argue it out both of us according to the rules of syllogism."

But the holy man answered:

"Nay! I cannot argue with you; I have neither wish nor wit for the task."

"Well then!" returned the Subtle Sophist, "I must needs find another Opponent."

And in a moment, lifting the index finger of his left hand, he made with his right out of a corner of his gown a red cap for this finger. Then holding it up before his nose,

"Look!" he said, "look at this finger. He's a learned Doctor now, and I am going to hold a learned argument with him. He's a Platonist, maybe Plato himself.

"Messer Plato, what is purity? I wait your answer, Messer Plato, Oh! you say. Consciousness is pure. Consciousness only when it is devoid of everything which may be seen, heard, handled, in one word proved by the senses. You grant me further,—yes! you nod your cap, that Truth will be pure Truth under the same conditions, that is to say provided only you make her dumb, blind, deaf, legless, paralytic, crippled of all her limbs. And I am quite ready to allow that in this state she will escape the delusions that make mock of mankind, and will have no temptations to play the runagate. You are a scoffer, and you have made much mock at the world. Doff your cap."

And the Opponent, dropping the corner of his gown, once more addressed the holy man Giovanni:

"My friend, these old Sophists knew not what Truth was. But I, who am a student of physics and a great observer of natural curiosities, you may believe me when I tell you she is white, or, more strictly speaking, whiteness itself.

"From which we must not conclude, I have told you before, that she is pure. Consider the Lady Eletta, of Verona, whose thighs were like milk; think you for this they were abstract from the world in general, withdrawn in the invisible and intangible, which is the pure, according to the Platonic doctrine? You would be much mistaken if you supposed so."

"I do not know this Lady Eletta you speak of," said the holy man Giovanni.

"She gave herself and her living body," said the Opponent, "to two Popes, sixty Cardinals, fourteen Princes, eighteen merchants, the Queen of Cyprus, three Turks, four Jews, the Lord Bishop of Arezzo's ape, a hermaphrodite, and the Devil. But we are wandering from our subject, which is to discover the proper character of Truth.

"Now, if this character is not purity, as I have just established it cannot be in argument with Plato himself, it is conceivable it may be impurity, which impurity is the necessary condition of all existing things. For have we not just seen how the pure has neither life nor consciousness? And you must yourself, I trow, have learned amply from experience that life and all pertaining thereto is invariably compound, blended, diversified, liable to increase and decrease, unstable, soluble, corruptible—never pure."

"Doctor," replied Giovanni, "your reasons are nothing worth, forasmuch as God, who is all pure, exists."

But the Subtle Doctor retorted:

"If you would read your books more carefully, my son, you would see it is said of Him you have just named, *not*, 'He exists,' but 'He is.' Now to exist and to be are not one and the same thing, but two opposite things. You are alive, and do you not say yourself, 'I am nothing; I am as if I were not'? And you do not say, 'I am he who is.' Because to live, is each moment to cease to be. Again you say, 'I am full of impurities,' forasmuch you are not a single thing, but a blending of things that stir and strive."

"Now do you speak wisely," answered the holy man, "and I see by your discourse that you are very deep read, Subtle Sir, in the sciences, divine as well as human. For true indeed it is God is He who is."

"By the body of Bacchus," exclaimed the other, "He is, and that perfectly and universally. Wherefore are we dispensed from seeking Him in any single place, being assured He is to be discovered neither more nor less in any one spot than in any other, and that you cannot find so much as a pair of old spatterdashes without their due share of Him."

"Admirably put, and most true," returned Giovanni. "But it is right to add that He is more particularly in the sacred elements, by the way of transubstantiation."

"More than that!" added the learned Doctor; "He is actually edible in them. Note moreover, my son, that He is round in an apple, long-shaped in an aubergine, sharp in a knife and musical in a flute. He has all the qualities of substances, and likewise all the properties of figures. He is acute and He is obtuse, because He is at one and the same time all possible triangles; his radii are at once equal and unequal, because He is both the circle and the ellipse—and He is the hyperbola besides, which is an indescribable figure."

While the holy Giovanni was still pondering these sublime verities, he heard the Subtle Doctor suddenly burst out a-laughing. Then he asked him:

"Why do you laugh?"

"I am laughing," replied the Doctor, "to think how they have discovered in me certain oppositions and contradictions, and have reproached me bitterly for the same. It is very true I have many such.

But they fail to see that, if I had them all, I should then be like the Other."

The holy man asked him:

"What other is it you speak of?"

And the Adversary answered:

"If you knew of whom I speak, you would know who I am. And my wisest words you would be loath to listen to, for much ill has been said of me. But, if you remain ignorant who I am, I can be of much use to you. I will teach you how intensely sensitive men are to the sounds that the lips utter, and how they let themselves be killed for the sake of words that are devoid of meaning. This we see with the Martyrs,—and in your own case, Giovanni, who look forward with joy to be strangled and then burned to the singing of the Seven Psalms, in the Great Square of Viterbo, for this word *Truth,* for which you could not by any possibility discover a reasonable interpretation.

"Verily you might ransack every hole and corner of your dim brain, and pick over all the spiders' webs and old iron that cumber your head, without ever lighting on a picklock to open this word and extract the meaning. But for me, my poor friend, you would get yourself hanged and your body burned for a word of one syllable which neither you nor your judges know the sense of, so that none could ever have discovered which to despise the most, hangmen or hanged.

"Know then that Truth, your well-beloved mistress, is made up of elements compacted of wet and dry, hard and soft, cold and hot, and that it is with this lady as with women of common humanity, in whom soft flesh and warm blood are not diffused equally in all the body."

Fra Giovanni doubted in his simplicity whether this discourse was altogether becoming. The Adversary read the holy man's thought, and reassured him, saying:

"Such is the learning we are taught at School. I am a Theologian, I!"

Then he got up, and added:

"I regret to leave you, friend; but I cannot tarry longer with you. For I have many contradictions to pose to many men. I can taste no rest day nor night; but I must be going ceaselessly from place to place, setting down my lantern now on the scholar's desk, now at the bed's head of the sick man who cannot sleep."

So saying, he went away as he had come. And the holy man Giovanni asked himself: "Why did this Doctor say, Truth was white, I wonder?" And lying in the straw he kept revolving this question in his head. His body shared the restlessness of his mind, and kept turning first one side then the other in search of the repose he could not find.

XIV

GIOVANNI'S DREAM

AND this is why, left alone in his dungeon, he prayed to the Lord, saying:

"O Lord! Thy loving-kindness is infinite toward me, and Thy favour manifest, seeing Thou hast so willed I should lie on a dunghill, like Job and Lazarus, whom Thou didst love so well. And Thou hast given me to know how filthy straw is a soft and sweet pillow to the just man. And Thou, dear Son of God, who didst descend into Hell, bless Thou the sleep of Thy servant where he lies in the gloomy prison-house. Forasmuch as men have robbed me of air and light, because I was steadfast to confess the truth, deign to enlighten me with the glory of the everlasting dayspring and feed me on the flames of Thy love, O living Truth, O Lord my God!"

Thus prayed the holy man Giovanni with his lips. But in his heart he remembered the sayings of the Adversary. He was troubled to the bottom of his spirit, and in much trouble and anguish of mind he fell asleep.

And seeing the thought of the Adversary weighed heavy on his slumbers, his sleep was not like the little child's lying on its mother's breast, a gentle sleep of smiles and milk. And in his dreams he beheld a vast wheel that shone with colours of living fire.

It was like those rose windows of flower-like brilliancy that glow over the doors of Churches, the masterpieces of Gothic craftsmen, and display in the translucent glass the history of the Virgin Mary and the glory of the Prophets. But the secret of these rose windows is unknown to the Tuscan artificer.

And this wheel was great and dazzling and brighter a thousandfold than the best wrought of all the rose windows that ever were divided by compass and painted with brush in the lands of the North. The Emperor Charlemagne saw not the like the day he was crowned.

The only man who ever beheld a wheel more splendid was the poet who, a lady leading him, entered clothed in flesh into Holy Paradise. The rose was of living light, and seemed alive itself. Looking well at it, you saw it was made of a multitude of breathing figures, and that men of every age and every condition, in an eager crowd, formed the nave and spokes and felloe. They were clad each according to his estate, and it was easy to recognize Pope and Emperor, Kings and Queens, Bishops, Barons, Knights, ladies, esquires, clerks, burghers, merchants, attorneys, apothecaries, labourers, ruffians, Moors and Jews. Moreover, seeing all that live on this earth were shown on the wheel, Satyrs and Cyclops were there, and Pygmies and Centaurs such as Africa nurses in her burning deserts, and the men Marco Polo the traveller found, who are born without heads and with a face below their navel.

And from betwixt the lips of each there issued a scroll, bearing a device. Now each device was of a hue which did not appear in any other, and in all the incalculable multitude of devices, no two could have been discovered of the same appearance. Some were dyed purple, others painted with the bright colours of the sky and sea, or the shining of the stars, yet others green as grass. Many were exceeding pale, many again exceeding dark and sombre, the whole so ordered that the eye found in these devices every one of the colours that paint the universe.

The holy man Giovanni began to decipher them, by this means making himself acquainted with the divers thoughts of divers men. And after reading on a good while, he perceived that these devices were as much diversified in the sense of the words as in the hues of the letters, and that the sentences differed one from the other in such sort that there was never a single one did not flatly contradict every other.

But at the same time he noted that this contradiction which existed in the head and body of the maxims did not continue in their tail, but that they all agreed together very accurately in their lower extremity, all ending in the same fashion, seeing each and all terminated in these words, *Such is Truth*.

And he said in his heart:

"These mottoes are like the flowers young men and maidens pluck in the water-meadows by the Arno, to make them into posies. For these flowers are readily gathered together by the tails, while the heads keep separate and fight amongst themselves in hue and brilliancy. And it is the same with the opinions of human beings."

And the holy man found in the devices a host of contradictions regarding the origin of sovereignty, the fountains of knowledge, pleasure and pain, things lawful and things unlawful. And he discovered likewise mighty difficulties in connection with the shape of the Earth and the Divinity of Our Lord Jesus Christ, by reason of the Heretics and Arabs and Jews, the monsters of the African desert and the Epicureans, who all had their place, a scroll in their lips, on the wheel of fire.

And each sentence ended in this way, *Such is Truth.* And the holy man Giovanni marvelled to see so many truths all diversely coloured. He saw red, and blue, and green, and yellow, but he saw no white—not even the one the Pope made proclamation of, to wit, "On this rock have I built my Church and committed thereto the crowns of all the world." Indeed this device was all red and as if blood-stained.

And the holy man sighed:

"Then I am never to find on the wheel of the universe the pure, white Truth, the immaculate and candid Truth, I would find."

And he called upon Truth, crying with tears in his eyes:

"Truth! Truth! for whose sake I am to die, show yourself before your martyr's eyes."

And lo! as he was wailing out the words, the living wheel began to revolve, and the devices, running one into the other, no longer kept distinct, while on the great disk came circles of every hue, circles wider and wider the further they were from the centre.

Then as the motion grew faster, these circles

disappeared one by one; the widest vanished first, because the speed was swiftest near the felloe of the wheel. But directly the wheel began to spin so fast the eye could not see it move and it seemed to stand motionless, the smallest circles too disappeared, like the morning-star when the sun pales the hills of Assisi.

Then at the last the wheel looked all white; and it overpassed in brilliance the translucent orb where the Florentine poet saw Beatrice in the dewdrop. It seemed as though an Angel, wiping the eternal pearl to cleanse it of all stains, had set it on the Earth, so like was the wheel to the Moon, when she shines high in the heavens lightly veiled under the gauze of filmy clouds. For at these times no shadow of a man carrying sticks, no mark at all, shows on her opalescent surface. Even so never a stain was visible on the wheel of light.

And the holy man Giovanni heard a voice which said to him:

"Behold that same white Truth you were fain to contemplate. And know it is built up of the divers contradictory truths, in the same fashion as all colours go to make up white. The little children of Viterbo know this, for having spun their tops striped with many colours on the flags on the Great Market. But the doctors of Bologna never guessed the reasons for this appearance. Now in every one of the devices was a portion of the Truth, and all together make up the true and veritable device."

"Alas! and alas!" replied the holy man, "how am I to read it? For my eyes are dazzled."

And the voice answered:

"Very true, there is naught to be seen there but flashing fire. No Latin letters, nor Arabic, nor Greek, no cabalistic sign, can ever express this device; and no hand is there may trace it in characters of flame on palace walls.

"Friend, never set your heart on reading what is not written. Only know this, that whatsoever a man has thought or believed in his brief lifetime is a parcel of this infinite Truth; and that, even as much dirt and disorder enter into what we call the order of nature, that is the clean and proper ordering of the universe, so the maxims of knaves and fools, who make the mass of mankind, participate in some sort in that general and universal Truth—which is absolute, everlasting and divine. Which makes me sore afraid, by the by, it may very like not exist at all."

And with a great burst of mocking laughter, the voice fell silent.

Then the holy man saw a long leg stretched out,

in red hose, and inside the shoe the foot seemed cloven and like a goat's, only much larger. And it gave the wheel of light so shrewd a kick on the rim of its felloe, that sparks flew out as they do when the blacksmith smites the iron with his hammer, and the great wheel leapt into the air to fall far away, broken into fragments. Meantime the air was filled with such piercing laughter that the holy man awoke.

And in the livid gloom of the dungeon, he thought sadly:

"I have no hope or wish left to know Truth, if, as has just been manifested to me, she only shows herself in contradictions and inconsistencies. How shall I dare by my death to be witness and martyr of what men must believe, now the vision of the wheel of the universe has made me see how every particular falsehood is a parcel of general Truth, absolute and unknowable? Why, O my God, have you suffered me to behold these things, and let it be revealed to me before my last sleep, that Truth is everywhere and that she is nowhere?"

And the holy man laid his head in his hands and wept.

XV

THE JUDGMENT

FRA GIOVANNI was led before the Magistrates of the Republic to be judged according to the laws of Viterbo. And one of the Magistrates said to the guards:

"Take his chains off him. For every person accused should appear freely before us."

And Giovanni thought:

"Why does the Judge pronounce words that are not straight?"

And the first of the Magistrates began to question the holy man, and said to him:

"Giovanni, bad man that you are, being thrown in prison by the august clemency of the laws, you have spoken against those laws. You have contrived with wicked men, chained in the same dungeon as yourself, a plot to overthrow the order stablished in this city."

The holy man Giovanni made answer:

"Nay! I but spoke for Justice and Truth. If the laws of the city are agreeable to Justice and Truth, I have not spoken against them. I have only spoken words of loving-kindness. I said:

"'Strive not to destroy force by force. Be peaceable in the midst of wars, to the end the spirit of God may rest on you like a little bird on the top of a poplar in the valley that is flooded by the torrent.' I said, 'Be gentle toward the men of violence.'"

Then the Judge cried out in anger:

"Speak! tell us who are the men of violence."

But the holy man said:

"You are for milking the cow that has given all her milk, and would learn of me more than I know."

However the Judge imposed silence on the holy man, and he said:

"Your tongue has discharged the arrow of your discourse, and its shot was aimed at the Republic. Only it has lighted lower, and turned back upon yourself."

And the holy man said:

"You judge me, not by my acts and my words, which are manifest, but by my motives, which are visible only to God's eye."

And the Judge replied:

"Nay! if we could not see the invisible and were not gods upon earth, how would it be possible for us to judge folk? Do you not know a law has just been passed in Viterbo, which punishes even men's secret thoughts? For the police of cities is for ever being perfected, and the wise Ulpian, who held the rule and the square in the days of Cæsar, would be astonished himself, if he could see our rules and squares, improved as they are."

And the Judge said again:

"Giovanni, you have been conspiring in your prison against the common weal."

But the holy man denied having ever conspired against the weal of Viterbo. Then the Judge said:

"The gaoler has given testimony against you."

And the holy man asked the Judge:

"What weight will my testimony have in one scale, when that of the gaoler is in the other?"

The Judge answered:

"Why! yours will kick the beam."

Wherefore the holy man held his peace henceforth.

Then the Judge declared:

"Anon you were talking, and the words you said proved your perfidy. Now you say nothing, and your silence is the avowal of your crime. So you have confessed your guilt twice over."

And the Magistrate they entitled the Accuser rose and said:

"The illustrious city of Viterbo speaks by my voice, and my voice shall be grave and calm, because it is the public voice. And you will think you are listening to a bronze statue speaking, for I make accusation not with my heart and bowels, but with the tables of bronze whereon the Law is inscribed."

And straightway he began to gesticulate furiously and utter a raging torrent of words. And he declaimed the argument of a play, in imitation of Seneca the Tragedian: and this drama was filled full of crimes committed by the holy man Giovanni. And the Accuser represented in succession all the characters of the tragedy. He mimicked the groans of the victims and the voice of Giovanni, the better to strike awe into his audience, who seemed to hear and see Giovanni himself, intoxicated with hate and evildoing. And the Accuser tore his hair and rent his gown and fell back exhausted on his august seat of office.

And the Judge who had questioned the accused before took up the word again and said:

"It is meet a citizen defend this man. For none, so says the law of Viterbo, may be condemned without having been first defended."

Thereupon an Advocate of Viterbo got up on a stool and spoke in these terms:

"If this monk has said and done what is laid to his charge, he is very wicked. But we have no proof that he has spoken and acted in the manner supposed. Moreover, good sirs, had we this proof, it would behove us to consider further the extreme simplicity of the man and the feebleness of his understanding. He was the laughing-stock of the children in the Public Square. He is ignorant; he has done a thousand extravagances. For my own part I believe he is beside himself. What he says is worthless nonsense, and there is nothing sensible he can do. I think he has been frequenting seditious societies; and goes about repeating what he heard there, without understanding a word of it. He is too dull-witted to be punished. Look out for his instructors; it is they are to blame. There are many difficulties in the matter, and the wise man has told us, 'in doubt, refrain from action.' "

Having so said, the Advocate stepped down from his stool. And Brother Giovanni received his death sentence. And he was informed he was to be hanged in the Square where the peasant women come to sell fruit and vegetables and the children to play knucklebones.

Next a very illustrious Doctor of Law, who was one of the Judges, got up and said:

"Giovanni, it behoves you to subscribe consent to the sentence condemning you, for being pronounced in the name of the city, it is pronounced by yourself, inasmuch as you are part and parcel of the city. You have an honourable part in it, as citizen, and I will convince you that you ought to be well content to be strangled by the city's judgment.

"Know this, the satisfaction of the whole comprehends and embraces the satisfaction of the parts, and seeing you are a part—a vile and miserable part, yet still a part—of the noble city of Viterbo, your condemnation which satisfies the community should be no less satisfactory to yourself.

"And I will further prove you that you should rightly consider death doom agreeable and fitting. For there is no other thing so useful and becoming as is the law, which is the just measure of things, and you ought to be pleased to have received this same just and proper measure. In accordance with the rules stablished by Cæsar Justinian, you have got your due. Your condemnation is just, and therefore a pleasant and a good thing. But, were it unjust and tainted and contaminated with ignorance and iniquity (which God forbid), still it would be incumbent on you to approve the same.

"For an unjust sentence, when it is pronounced in the prescribed forms of law, participates in the virtue of the said forms and through them continues august, efficacious and of high merit. What it contains of wrong is temporary and of little consequence, and concerns only the particular instance, whereas the good in it derives from the fixity and permanence of the organization of the laws, and therefore is it agreeable to the general dictates of justice. Wherefore Papinian declares it is better to give false judgment than none at all, seeing how men without justice are no better than wild beasts in the woods, whereas by justice is made manifest their nobleness and dignity, as is seen by the example of the Judges of the Areopagus, who were held in special honour among the Athenians. So, seeing it is necessary and profitable to give judgment, and that it is not possible to do so without fault or mistake, it follows that mistake and faultiness are comprised in the excellence of Justice and participate in the said excellence. Accordingly, supposing you deemed your sentence unfair, you should find satisfaction in this unfairness, inasmuch as it is united and amalgamated with fairness, just as tin and copper are fused together to make bronze, which is a precious metal and employed for very noble purposes, in the fashion Pliny describes in his Histories."

The learned Doctor then proceeded to enumerate the conveniencies and advantages which flow from expiation and wash away sin, as the maids every Saturday wash the courtyards of their masters' houses. And he demonstrated to the holy man what a boon it was for him to be condemned to death by the august good pleasure of the Commonwealth of Viterbo, which had granted him judges and a defender. And so soon as the Doctor's eloquence was exhausted and he fell silent, Fra Giovanni was fettered once more and led back to prison.

XVI

THE PRINCE OF THIS WORLD

NOW on the morning appointed for his hanging, the holy man Giovanni was lying sound asleep. And the Subtle Doctor came and opened the door of his prison cell, and pulling him by the sleeve, cried:

"Ho! there, son of woman, awake! The day is just unclosing his grey eyes. The lark is singing, and the morning mists kissing the mountain sides. Clouds glide along the hills, soft and sinuous, snow-white with rosy reflexions,—which are the flanks and bosoms and loins of immortal nymphs, divine daughters of the rivers and the sky, maidens of the morn old Oceanus leads forth along the heights,—a flock multiform as his waves, and who welcome to their cool, fresh arms, on a couch of hyacinths and anemones, the gods, masters of the world, and the shepherd swains loved of goddesses. For there are shepherds their mothers bore beautiful and worthy the bed of the nymphs that dwell in the water-springs and woodlands.

"And for myself, who have deeply studied the

secrets of nature, seeing but now these clouds curling wantonly round the bosom of the hill, I was filled with mysterious longings at the sight, longings I know nothing of but that they spring from the region of my loins, and that, like the infant Hercules, they showed their strength from the very cradle. And these longings were not merely after rosy mists and floating clouds; they pictured very precisely a wench named Monna Libetta I made acquaintance with once in travelling, at Castro, at an inn where she was serving-maid and at the free disposal of the muleteers and soldiers frequenting it.

"But the picture I framed in my mind of Monna Libetta, this morning, as I fared along the slopes of the hills, was wondrously embellished by the tenderness of recollection and the regrets of separation, and she was tricked out with all the pretty fancies that, springing from the loins as I said, presently send their fragrant fire coursing through all the body's soul, transfusing it with languishing ardours and pains that are a delicious pleasure.

"For I would have you know, my Giovanni, that looking at her calmly and coldly, the girl was not greatly different from all the rest of the country wenches that, in the plains of Umbria and the Roman Marches, go afield to milk the cattle. She had dark eyes, slow and sullen, a sunburnt face, a big mouth, the bosom heavy, the belly tanned and the forepart of the legs, from the knee, shaggy with hair. Her laugh was ready and rude, in a general way; but in act with a lover, her face grew dark and transfigured as if with wonder at the presence of a god. 'Twas this had attached me to her, and I have many a time pondered since on the nature of this attachment, for I am learned and curious to search out the reasons of things.

"And I discovered the force that drew me toward this girl Monna Libetta, maid-servant at the inn of Castro, was the same that governs the stars in heaven and that there is one force and one only in the world, which is Love. And it is likewise Hate, as is shown by the case of this same Monna Libetta, who was fiercely fondled, and just as fiercely beaten.

"And I mind me how a groom in the Pope's stables, who was her chief lover, struck her so savagely one night in the hay-loft where he was bedding with her, that he left her lying there for dead. And he rushed crying through the streets that the vampires had strangled the girl. These be subjects a man must needs ponder if he would gain some notion of true physics and natural philosophy."

Thus spoke the Subtle Doctor. And the holy

man Giovanni sitting up on his bedding of dung, answered:

"Nay! Doctor, is this language meet to address to a man that is to be hanged in a very short while? Hearing you, I am filled with doubt whether your words are the words of a good man and a great Theologian, or if they do not rather come from an evil dream sent by the Angel of Darkness."

But the Subtle Doctor made answer:

"Who talks of being hanged? I tell you, Giovanni, I am come hither, at the earliest peep of day, to set you free and help you to fly. See! I have donned a gaoler's habit; the prison door stands open. Quick! up and away!"

At this the holy man rose to his feet, and answered:

"Doctor, take heed what you are saying. I have made the sacrifice of my life, and I admit it has cost me dear to make it. If trusting to your word that I am restored to life, I am then led to the place of execution, I must needs make a second sacrifice more grievous than the first, and suffer two deaths instead of one. And I confess to you my desire of martyrdom is vanished away, and a longing come upon me to breathe the air of day under the branches of the mountain pines."

The Subtle Doctor made reply:

"It happens that was just my intent to lead you away under the pines rustling in the wind with the soft sighing of a flute. We will break our fast sitting on the mossy slope overlooking the city. Come with me! Why do you tarry?"

And the holy man said:

"Before going hence with you, I would fain know clearly who you are. I am fallen from my first constancy; my courage is no better now than a straw blown about on the wasted threshing-floor of my virtue. But I am left my faith in the Son of God, and to save my body, I would ill like to lose my soul."

"Verily," cried the Subtle Doctor, "think you verily I have any desire of your soul! Is it then so fair a maid and sweet a lady you are afraid I may rob you of it? Nay! keep it, friend; I could make nothing of it."

The holy man was scarce assured by what he heard, for the other's words breathed no pious odour. But, as he was exceeding eager to be free, he asked no more questions, but followed the Doctor and passed the wicket of the prison by his side.

Only when he was without, he inquired:

"Who are you, you who send dreams to men and set prisoners free? You have the beauty of a woman and the strength of a man, and I admire you, though I cannot love you."

And the Subtle Doctor answered:

"You will love me so soon as I have made you suffer. Men cannot love but those who make them suffer; and there is no love except in pain."

And so conversing, they left the city and began climbing the mountain paths. And after faring far, they saw at the entering in of a wood a red-tiled house, before which was a wide terrace overlooking the plain, planted with fruit trees and bordered with vines.

So they sat down in the courtyard at the foot of a vine trunk; its leaves were gilded by the Autumn and from the boughs hung clusters of grapes. And a girl brought them milk and honey and cakes of maize.

Presently the Subtle Doctor, stretching out his arm, plucked a scarlet-cheeked apple, bit into it and gave it to the holy man. And Giovanni ate and drank; and his beard was all white with milk and his eyes laughed as he gazed up at the sky, which filled them with blue light and joy. And the girl smiled.

Then the Subtle Doctor said:

"Look at yonder child; she is far comelier than Monna Libetta."

And the holy man, intoxicated with milk and honey, and made merry with the light of day, sang songs his mother was used to sing when she carried him as a babe in her arms. They were songs of shepherds and shepherdesses, and they spoke of love. And as the girl stood listening on the threshold of the door, the holy man left his seat and ran staggering towards her, took her in his arms and showered on her cheeks kisses full of milk, laughter and joy.

And the Subtle Doctor having paid the reckoning, the two travellers hied them toward the plain.

As they were walking between the silvery willows that border the water, the holy man said:

"Let us sit; for now I am weary."

So they sat down beneath a willow, and watched the water-flags curling their sword-like leaves on the river banks and the bright-coloured flies flashing over the surface. But Giovanni's laughter was ceased, and his face was sad.

And the Subtle Doctor asked him:

"Why are you so pensive?"

And Giovanni answered him:

"I have felt through you the sweet caress of living things, and I am troubled at heart. I have tasted the milk and the honey. I have looked on the servant-maid standing at the threshold and seen that she was comely. And disquietude is in my soul and in my flesh.

"What a long road I have travelled since I have known you. Do you remember the grove of holm-oaks where I saw you the first time? For be sure, I recognize you.

"You it was visited me in my hermit's cell and stood before me with woman's eyes sparkling through a transparent veil, while your alluring mouth instructed me in the entanglements of Right and Wrong. Again it was you appeared in the meadows clad in a golden cope, like an Ambrose or an Augustine. Then I knew not the curse of thought; but you set me thinking. You put pride like a coal of fire on my lips; and I learned to speculate. But as yet, in the untrained freshness of my wit and raw youthfulness of mind, I felt no doubt. But again you came to me, and gave me uncertainty to feed on and doubt to drink like wine. So comes it, that this day I taste through you the entrancing illusion of things, and that the soul of woods and streams, of sky and earth, and living shapes, penetrates my breast.

"And lo! I am a miserable man, because I have followed after you, Prince of men!"

And Giovanni gazed at his companion, who stood there beautiful as day and night. And he said to him:

"Through you it is I suffer, and I love you. I love you because you are my misery and my pride, my joy and my sorrow, the splendour and the cruelty of things created, because you are desire and speculation, and because you have made me like unto yourself. For verily your promise in the Garden, in the dawn of this world's days, was not vain, and I have tasted the fruit of the knowledge of good and evil, O Satan."

Presently Giovanni resumed again.

"I know, I see, I feel, I will, I suffer. And I love you for all the ill you have done me. I love you, because you have undone me."

And, leaning on the Archangel's shoulder the man wept bitterly.

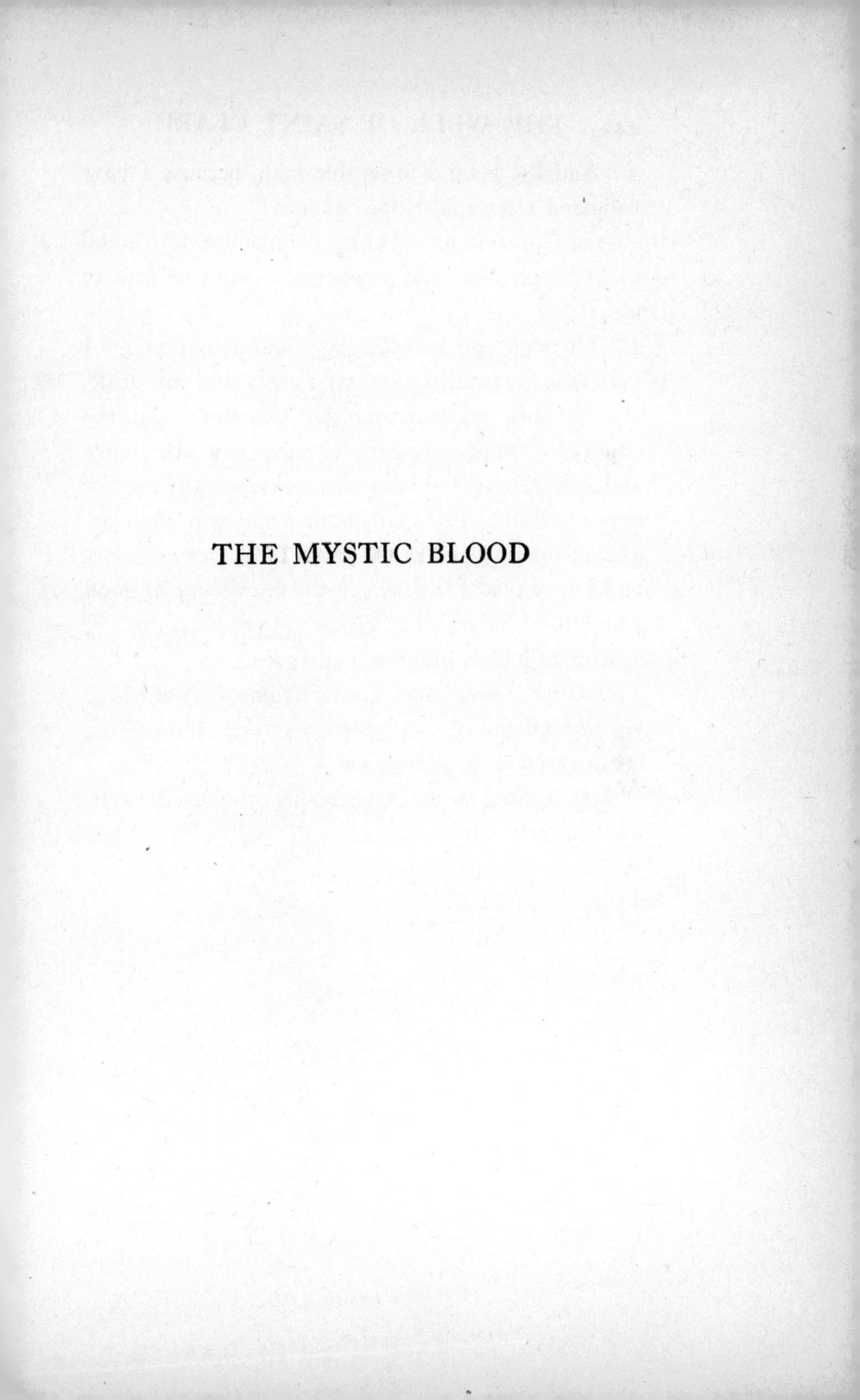

THE MYSTIC BLOOD

TO FÉLIX JEANTET

THE MYSTIC BLOOD

La Bocca sua non diceva se nos Jesù e Caterina, e cosi dicendo ricevatti el capo nelle mani mie, fermando l' occhio nella Divina Bontà, e dicendo: Io voglio. . . .

(*Le lettere di S. Caterina da Siena.*
—xcvii, Gigli e Burlamacchi.)[1]

THE good town of Sienna was like a sick man that seeks vainly for a restful place in his bed, and thinks, by turning about and about, to cheat his pain. Again and again had she changed the government of the Republic, which passed from the Consuls to the Assemblies of the Burghers, and, originally entrusted to the Nobles, was subsequently exercised by the money-changers, drapers, apothecaries, furriers, silk-mercers and all such citizens as were concerned with the superior arts and crafts. But these worthies having shown themselves weak and self-seeking, the People expelled them in their turn and entrusted the sovereign power to the petty artisans. In the year 1368 of

---

[1] "His mouth spake no word but only Jesus and Caterina, and with these words I received his head in my two hands, as he closed his eyes in the Divine Goodness, and said: I will. . . ." (*Letters of St. Catherine of Sienna*—xcvii, ed. Gigli e Burlamacchi.)

the glorious Incarnation of the Son of God, the Signory was composed of fourteen Magistrates chosen from among the hosiers, butchers, locksmiths, shoemakers, and stonemasons, who together formed a Great Council known as the *Mount of the Reformers.* They were a plebeian band, rough and hard as the bronze She-Wolf, emblem of their city, which they loved with an affection at once filial and formidable. But the People, which had set them up over the Commonwealth, had suffered another body to continue in existence, though subordinate to them, the Twelve to wit, who came from the class of Bankers and wealthy Merchants. These men were in conspiracy with the Nobles, at the Emperor's instigation, to sell the City to the Pope of Rome.

The German Kaiser was the life and soul of the plot, promising the aid of his landsknechts to guarantee success. He was in the utmost haste to have the affair ended, hoping with the price of the bargain, he might be able to redeem the Crown of Charlemagne, pledged for sixteen hundred florins with the Florentine Bankers.

Meantime, they of the *Reformers' Mount,* who formed the Signory, held firm the rod of government and watched heedfully over the safety of the Republic. These artisans, officers of a free People, had refused the Emperor, when he came within their walls, bread, water, salt and fire; they had driven him forth the city groaning and trembling, and they now condemned the conspirators to death. Guardians of the town founded by Remus long ago, they copied the sternness of the first Consuls of Rome. But their city, which went clad in silk and cloth-of-gold, was ever ready to slip betwixt their fingers, like a lascivious, false-hearted wanton; and fear and anxiety made them implacable.

In the year 1370 they discovered that a nobleman of Perugia, Ser Niccola Tuldo, had been sent by the Pope to stir up the Siennese, in Connivance with the Kaiser, to deliver up the city to the Holy Father. The young Lord in question was in the prime of manly beauty, and had learned in the company of fair ladies those arts of flattery and seductive compliment he now proceeded to practise in the Palace of the Salimbeni and the shops of the money-changers. And, for all his light heart and empty head, he gained over to the Pope's side many burghers and some artisans. Informed of his intrigues, the Magistrates of the *Mount of the Reformers* had him brought before their august Council, and after questioning him underneath the gonfalon of the Republic, which shows a Lion rampant for device, they declared him guilty of attempted outrage against the liberties of the City.

He had answered with mere smiling scorn to the questions of these cobbler fellows and butchers. But when he heard his sentence of death pronounced, he fell into ecstasy of deep astonishment, and was led away to prison as if in a trance. No sooner was he locked up in his cell than, awaking from his stupor, he began to regret the life he was to lose with all the ardour of his young blood and impetuous character; visions of all its pleasures, arms, women, horses, crowded before his eyes, and at the thought he would never enjoy the delights more, he was carried away by so furious a despair he beat with fists and forehead on the walls of his dungeon, and gave vent to such wild howls as were audible over all the neighbourhood, even in the burghers' houses and the drapers' booths. The gaoler coming in to know the cause of the uproar, found him covered with blood and foaming at the mouth.

Ser Niccola Tuldo never left off howling with rage for three days and three nights.

The thing was reported to the *Mount of the Reformers*. The members of the most august Signory, after despatching their more pressing business, examined into the case of the unhappy man in the condemned cell.

Leone Rancati, brickmaker by trade, said:

"The man must pay with his head for this crime against the Commonwealth of Sienna; and none can relieve him of this debt, without encroaching on the sacred rights of the City our mother. He must needs die; but his soul is his Maker's, and it is not meet that through our fault he die in this sinful state of madness and despair. Therefore should we use all the means within our competence to assure his eternal salvation."

Matteino Renzano, the baker, a man famed for his wisdom, rose in his turn and said:

"Well spoken, Leone Rancati! The case demands we send to the condemned man Catherine, the fuller's daughter."

The advice was approved by all the Signory, who resolved to invite Catherine to visit Niccola Tuldo in his prison.

In those days Catherine, daughter of Giacomo the fuller, filled all the city of Sienna with the perfume of her virtues. She dwelt in a little cell in her father's house and wore the habit of the Sisters of Penitence. She carried girt about her under her gown of white linen an iron chain, and scourged herself an hour long every day. Then, showing her arms covered with wounds, she would cry, "Behold my pretty red roses!" She cultivated in her chamber lilies and violets, wherewith she wove garlands for the altars of the Virgin and the Saints. And all the while she would be singing hymns in the vulgar tongue to the praise of Jesus and Mary His Mother. In those mournful times, when the city of Sienna was a hostel of sorrow, and a house of joy to boot, Catherine was ever visiting the unhappy prisoners, and telling the prostitutes: "My sisters, how fain would I hide you in the loving wounds of the Saviour!" A maiden so pure, fired with so sweet charity, could nowhere have budded and blossomed but at Sienna, which under all its defilements and amid all its crimes, was still the City of the Blessed Virgin.

Apprised by the Magistrates, Catherine betook herself to the public gaol on the morning of the day Ser Niccola Tuldo was to die. She found him stretched on the stone floor of the dungeon, bellowing blasphemies. Raising the white veil the blessed St. Dominic himself had come down from Paradise to lay upon her brow, she showed the prisoner a countenance of heavenly beauty. As he gazed at her in wonder, she leant over him to wipe away the spume that defiled his mouth.

Ser Niccola Tuldo, turning on her eyes that still retained their savage ferocity, cried out:

"Begone! I hate you, because you are of Sienna, the city that slays me. Oh! Sienna, she-wolf indeed, that with her vile claws tears out the throat of a noble gentlemen of Perugia! Horrid she-wolf! unclean and inhuman hell-hound!"

But Catherine made answer:

"Nay! brother, what is a city, what are all the cities of the earth, beside the City of God and the holy Angels? I am Catherine, and I come to call you to the everlasting nuptials."

The sweet voice and beaming face shed a sudden peace and radiance over the savage soul of Niccola Tuldo. He remembered the days of his innocence, and cried like a child.

The sun, rising above the Apennines, was just whitening the prison walls with its earliest rays. Catherine said:

"Look, the dawn! Up, up, my brother, for the eternal nuptials! Up, I say!"

And raising him from the ground, she drew him into the Chapel, where Fra Cattaneo confessed him.

Ser Niccola Tuldo then listened devoutly to the holy Mass and received the body of Our Lord. This done, he turned to Catherine and said:

"Stay with me; do not leave me, and I shall be well, and shall die content."

The bells began to toll the signal for the execution.

Then Catherine answered:

"Gentle brother, I will wait you at the place of Justice."

At this, Ser Niccola smiled and said, as if ravished with bliss:

"Joy! joy! the Delight of my soul will wait me at the holy place of Justice!"

Catherine pondered and prayed, finally saying:

"Gracious Lord, Thou hast indeed wrought in him a great enlightenment, seeing he calls holy the place of Justice."

Ser Niccola went on:

"Yes! I shall hie me thither, strong in heart and rejoicing. I weary, as though I had a thousand years to wait, to be there, where I shall find you once more."

"Farewell till the nuptials, the everlasting nuptials!" Catherine cried again, as she left the prison.

The condemned man was served with a little bread and wine, and supplied with a black cloak; then he was led forth along the precipitous streets, to the sound of trumpets, between the city guards, beneath the banner of the Republic. The ways swarmed with curious onlookers, and women lifted their little ones in their arms, showing them the man doomed to die.

Meantime Niccola Tuldo was dreaming of Catherine, and his lips, that had so long been bitter, opened softly as though to kiss the likeness of the blessed maid.

After climbing for some while the rude brick-paved road, the procession reached one of the heights dominating the city, and the condemned man saw suddenly, with his eyes that were soon to see no more, the roofs, domes, cloisters, and towers of Sienna, and further away the walls that followed the slope of the hills. The sight reminded him of his native town, the gay city of Perugia, surrounded with its gardens, where springs of living water sing amid the fruits and flowers. He saw once more in fancy the terrace that looks over the vale of Trasimene, whence the eye drinks in the light of day with delight.

And the yearning for life tore his heart afresh, and he sighed:

"Oh! city of my fathers! Oh! house of my birth!"

But presently the thought of Catherine re-entered his soul, filling it to the brim with gladness and sweet peace.

Finally they arrive in the Market Square, where each Saturday the peasant girls of Camiano and Granayola display their citrons, grapes, figs, and pomegranates, and hail the housewives with merry appeals to buy, not unmixed with high-spiced jests. It was there the scaffold was erected; and there Ser Niccola beheld Catherine kneeling in prayer, her head resting on the block.

He climbed the steps with eager joy. At his coming, Catherine rose and turned toward him with all the look of a bride once more united to her spouse; she insisted on baring his neck with her own hands and placing her dear one on the block as on the marriage bed.

Then she knelt down beside him. Thrice he repeated in fervent tones, "Jesus, Catherine!"—after which the executioner struck with his sword, and the maiden caught the severed head within her hands. Hereupon all the victim's blood seemed to be suffused in her, and to fill her veins with a flood as soft as warm milk; a fragrant odour set her nostrils quivering, while before her swooning eyes floated the shadows of angels. Filled with wonder and joy unspeakable, she fell softly into the depths of celestian ecstasy.

Two women of the third Order of St. Dominic, who stood at the foot of the scaffold, seeing her stretched there motionless, hastened to raise her up and support her in their arms. The holy maid, coming to herself, told them: "I have seen the heavens opened!"

One of the women made as though to wash away with a sponge the blood that covered St. Catherine's robe, but she stopped her, crying out eagerly:

"No, no! leave the blood, leave it; never rob me of my purple and my perfumes!"

A SOUND SECURITY

TO HENRI LAVEDON

A SOUND SECURITY

> . . . . . *Par cest ymage*
> *Te doing en pleige Jhesu-Crist*
> *Qui tout fist, ainsi est escript:*
> *Il te pleige tout ton avoir:*
> *Ne peuz nulz si bon pleige avoir.*
>
> (Miracles de Notre-Dame par personnages, publ. par. G. Paris et U. Robert.)[1]

OF all the merchants of Venice, Fabio Mutinelli was the most exact in keeping his engagements. In all cases he showed himself free-handed and sumptuous in his dealings,— above all where ladies and churchmen were concerned. The elegance and honesty of his character were renowned throughout the State, and all admired at San Zanipolo an altar of gold he had offered to St. Catherine for the love of the fair Catherine Manini, wife of the Senator Alesso Cornaro. Being very wealthy, he had numerous friends, whom he entertained at feasts and helped at

[1] ". . . . By this image I take Jesus Christ in pledge for you, Him who wrought all men's salvation, as is writ in Scripture: He is pledge against all your fortune; so good a pledge can no man have." (*Miracles of Our Lady, as they Fell out to Sundry*, —G. Paris and U. Robert.)

need from his purse. However, he incurred heavy losses in the war against the Genoese and in the Naples troubles. It fell out, moreover, that thirty of his ships were taken by the Uscoque pirates or foundered at sea. The Pope, to whom he had lent great sums of money, refused to repay a doit. The result of all was, the magnificent Fabio Mutinelli was stripped bare in brief space of all his riches. After selling his Palace and plate to pay what he owed, he found himself left without anything. But clever, bold, well practised in affairs and in the vigour of his powers, his only thought was to make head once more against fortune. He made careful calculation and judged that five hundred ducats were needful for him to take to sea again and attempt fresh enterprises for which he augured happy and sure success. He asked the Signor Alesso Bontura, who was the richest citizen of the Republic, to oblige him by lending him the five hundred ducats. But the good Bontura, holding that if daring wins great gains, 'tis prudence only keeps the same, refused to expose so great a sum to the risks of sea and shipwreck. Fabio next applied to the Signor Andrea Morosini, whom he had benefited in former days in a thousand ways.

"My dear Fabio," answered Andrea, "to any

one else but you I would willingly lend this sum. I have no affection for gold, and on this point act according to the maxims of Horace the Satirist. But your friendship is dear to me, Fabio Mutinelli, and I should be running the risk of losing it, if I lent you money. For more often than not, the commerce of the heart comes to a bad end betwixt debtor and creditor. I have known but too many instances."

So saying, the Signor Andrea kissed the Merchant with all seeming tenderness, and shut the door in his face.

Next day, Fabio went to see the Lombard and Florentine bankers. But not one of them would agree to lend him so much as twenty ducats without security. All day long he hurried from one counting-house to another, but was everywhere met by much the same answer:

"Signor Fabio, we all know you well for the most upright merchant of this city, and it is with regret we must refuse you what you ask. But the morality of trade requires it."

That evening, as he was making sadly for home, the courtesan Zanetta, who was bathing in the canal, hung on to his gondola and gazed amorously into his eyes. In the days of his prosperity he had

had her one night into his Palace and had treated her very kindly, for he was of a gay and gracious humour.

"Sweet Signor Fabio," she said to him, "I am aware of your misfortunes; they are the talk of all the town. Hear me; I am not rich, but I have some jewels at the bottom of a little coffer. An you will accept them of a poor girl that would serve you, I shall know God and the Virgin love me."

And it was a true word, that in the prime of her youth and fine flower of her beauty, the fair Zanetta was poor. Fabio answered her:

"Kind Zanetta, there is more nobility in the hovel where you dwell than in all the Palaces of Venice."

For three days longer Fabio visited the banks and fondacos without discovering any one willing to lend him money. Everywhere he received an unfavourable answer, and listened to speeches that always came to this:

"You did very wrong to sell your plate to pay your debts. Money is lent to a man in debt, but not to one without furniture and plate."

The fifth day he made his way, in despair, as far as the Corte delle Galli, which men also call the Ghetto, and which is the quarter the Jews inhabit.

A SOUND SECURITY

"Who knows," he kept saying to himself, "if I may not get from one of the Circumcised what the Christians have denied me?"

He proceeded therefore between the Calle San Geremia and the Calle San Girolamo along a narrow evil-smelling canal, the entrance of which was barred with chains every night, by order of the Senate. While hesitating to know which Usurer he should first apply to, he remembered to have heard speak of an Israelite named Eliezer, son of Eliezer Mainmonides, who was said to be exceedingly rich and of a wondrous subtle spirit. Accordingly, inquiring out the house of the Jew Eliezer, he stopped his gondola before the door. Above the entrance was seen a representation of the seven-branched candlestick, which the Jew had had carved as a sign of hope, in expectation of the promised days when the Temple should rise again from its ashes.

The Merchant now entered a hall lighted by a copper lamp with twelve wicks that were burning smokily. Eliezer the Jew was there, seated before his scales. The windows of the house were walled up, because he was an Unbeliever.

Fabio Mutinelli approached and thus accosted him:

"Eliezer, over and over again have I called you

dog and renegade heathen. There have been times, when I was younger and in the flush of early manhood, I have cast stones and mud at folks going along the Canal who wore the round patch of yellow sewn on their shoulder, so that I may likely have struck one of your friends or perhaps yourself. I tell you this, not to affront you, but out of fairness, at the same instant I come to ask you to do me a very great service."

The Jew lifted his arm, which was as dry and gnarled as an ancient vine-stock:

"Fabio Mutinelli, the Father which is in Heaven shall judge us, one and the other. What is the service you are come to ask of me?"

"Lend me five hundred ducats for a year."

"Men do not lend without security. Doubtless you have learned this from your own people. What is the security you offer?"

"You must know, Eliezer, I have not a denier left, not one gold cup, not one silver goblet. Neither have I a friend left. One and all, they have refused to do me the service I ask of you. I have nothing in all the world but my honour as a merchant and my faith as a Christian. I offer you for security the holy Virgin Mary and her Divine Son."

At this reply, the Jew, bending down his head

as a man does to ponder and consider, stroked his long white beard for a while. Presently he looked up and said:

"Fabio Mutinelli, take me to see this security you offer. For it is meet the lender be put in presence of the pledge proposed for his acceptance."

"You are within your rights," returned the Merchant, "rise therefore and come."

So saying, he led Eliezer to the Chiesa dell' Orto, near the spot called the *Field of the Moors*. Arrived there and pointing to the figure of the Madonna, which stood above the High Altar, the brow wreathed with a circlet of precious stones and the shoulders covered with a gold-broidered mantle, holding in her arms the Child Jesus sumptuously adorned like his mother, the Merchant said to the Jew:

"Yonder is my security."

Eliezer looked with a keen eye and a calculating air first at the Christian Merchant, then at the Madonna and Child; then presently bowed his head in assent and said he would accept the pledge offered. He returned with Fabio to his own house, and there handed him the five hundred ducats, well and truly weighed:

"The money is yours for a year. If at the end of that time, to the day, you have not paid me back the sum with interest at the rate fixed by the law of Venice and the custom of the Lombards, you can picture yourself, Fabio Mutinelli, what I shall think of the Christian Merchant and his security."

Fabio, without a moment's loss of time, bought ships and loaded up with salt and other sorts of merchandise, which he disposed of in the cities of the Adriatic shore to great advantage. Then, with a fresh cargo aboard, he set sail for Constantinople, where he bought carpets, perfumes, peacock feathers, ivory and ebony. These goods his agents exchanged along the coasts of Dalmatia for building timber, which the Venetians had contracted for from him in advance. By these means, in six months' time, he had multiplied tenfold the amount the Jew had lent him.

But one day that he was taking his diversion with some Greek women, aboard his vessel, which lay in the Bosphorus, having put out too far to sea, he was captured by pirates and carried prisoner to Egypt, though, by rare good fortune, his gold and merchandise were in a safe place all the while. The pirates sold him to a Saracen lord, who putting him in fetters, sent him afield to till the wheat, which grows very finely in that country. Fabio offered his master to pay a heavy ransom, but the Paynim's daughter, who loved him and was fain to bring him to the end she desired, over-persuaded her father not to let him go at any price. Reduced to the necessity of trusting to himself alone for release, he filed his irons with the tools given him for tilling the ground, made good his escape to the Nile and threw himself into a boat. Casting loose, he got to the sea, which was not far off, and when on the point of death from thirst and hunger, was rescued by a Spanish vessel bound for Genoa. But, after keeping her course a week, the ship was caught in a storm which drove her on the coast of Dalmatia. In making the shore, she was wrecked on a reef. All the crew were drowned except Fabio, who reached the beach after much difficulty, clinging to a hen-coop. There he lay senseless, but was presently succoured by a handsome widow, named Loreta, whose house was upon the seashore. She had him carried to it, put him to bed in her own chamber, watched over him and lavished every care for his recovery.

On coming to himself, he smelt the perfume of myrtles and roses, and looking out of window saw a garden that descended in successive declivities to the sea. Signora Loreta, standing at his bed's head, took up her viol and began playing a tender air.

Fabio, ravished with gratitude and pleasure, fell

to kissing the lady's hands a thousand times over. He thanked her earnestly, assuring her he was less touched by the saving of his life than by the fact of his owing his recovery to the pains of so fair a benefactress.

Presently he rose and went to walk with her in the garden, and sitting down to rest in a thicket of myrtles, he drew the young widow on his knee and manifested his gratitude by a thousand caresses.

He found her not insensible to his efforts and spent some hours by her side drowned in amorous delight. But soon he grew pensive, and suddenly asked his hostess what month they were in, and what day of the month precisely it then was.

And when she told him, he fell to groaning and lamenting sore, finding it lacked but twenty-four short hours of a full year since he had received the five hundred ducats of Eliezer the Jew. The thought of breaking his promise and exposing his pledge to the reproaches of the Circumcised was intolerable to him. Signora Loreta inquiring the reason of his despair, he told her the whole story; and being a very pious woman and an ardent votress of the Holy Mother of God, she shared his chagrin to the full. The difficulty was not to procure the five hundred ducats; a Banker in a neighbouring town had had such a sum in his hands for the last six months at Fabio's disposition. But to travel from the coast of Dalmatia to Venice in four-and-twenty hours, with a broken sea and contrary winds, was a thing beyond all hope.

"Let us have the money ready to begin with," said Fabio.

And when one of his hostess's serving-men had brought the sum, the noble Merchant ordered a vessel to be brought close in to the shore. In her he laid the bags containing the ducats, then went to the Signora Loreta's Oratory in search of an image of the Virgin with the Infant Jesus—an image of cedar-wood and greatly revered. This he set in the little bark, near the rudder, and addressed in these words:

"Madonna, you are my pledge. Now the Jew Eliezer must needs be paid to-morrow; 'tis a question of mine honour and of yours, Madonna, and of your Son's good name. What a mortal sinner, such as I, cannot do, you will assuredly accomplish, unsullied Star of the Sea, you whose bosom suckled Him who walked upon the waters. Bear this silver to Eliezer the Jew, in the Ghetto at Venice, to the end the Circumcised may never say you are a bad surety."

And pushing the bark afloat, he doffed his hat and cried softly:

"Farewell, Madonna! farewell!"

The vessel sailed out to sea, and long the merchant and the widow followed it with their eyes. When night began to close in, a furrow of light was seen marking her wake over the waters, which were fallen to a dead calm.

At Venice next morning Eliezer, on opening his door, saw a bark in the narrow canal of the Ghetto laden with full sacks and manned by a little figure of black wood, flashing in the clear morning sunbeams. The vessel stopped before the house where the seven-branched candlestick was carved; and the Jew recognized the Virgin Mary with the infant Jesus, pledge of the Christian Merchant.

HISTORY OF
DOÑA MARIA D'AVALOS AND
DON FABRICIO, DUKE D'ANDRIA

TO
HENRY GAUTHIER-VILLARS

HISTORY OF
DOÑA MARIA D'AVALOS AND
DON FABRICIO, DUKE D'ANDRIA

Done Marie d'Avalos, l'une des belles princesses du païs mariée avec le prince de Venouse, laquelle s'estant enamourachée du comte d'Andriane, l'un des beaux princes du païs aussy, et s'estans tous deux concertez à la jouissance et le mari l'ayant descouverte . . . les fit tous deux massacrer par gens appostez; si que le lendemain on trouva ces deux belles moictiez et créatures exposées et tendues sur le pavé devant la porte de la maison, toutes mortes et froides, à la veue de tous les passants, qui les larmoyoient et plaignoient de leur misérable estat.[1]

(Pierre de Bourdeilles, abbé et
Seigneur de Brantôme,
Recueil des dames, seconde partie.)

[1] "Doña Maria d'Avalos, one of the fair Princesses of the land, and married to the Prince of Venosa, was enamoured of the Count d'Andriane, likewise one of the noble Princes of the country. So being both of them come together to enjoy their passion, and the husband having discovered it . . . had the twain of them slain by men appointed thereto. In such wise that next morning the fair and noble pair, unhappy beings, were seen lying stretched out and exposed to public view on the pavement in front of the house door, all dead and cold, in sight of all passers-by, who could not but weep and lament over their piteous lot."

IT was a day of high rejoicing at Naples, when the Prince of Venosa, a rich and puissant Lord, was wed to Doña Maria, of the illustrious house of Avalos.

Drawn by horses bedizened with scales, feathers or furs, in such wise as to figure forth dragons, griffins, lions, lynxes, panthers and unicorns, were twelve cars which did bear through all the city an host of naked men and women, gilded all over, for to represent the Gods of Olympus, come down to Earth to do honour to the Venosian nuptials. On one of these cars was to be seen a young lad with wings treading underfoot three old hags of an hideous ugliness. A tablet was fixed up above the car to display the meaning thereof, to wit: LOVE VANQUISHETH THE FATAL SISTERS. Whereby 'twas to be understood that the new-wedded pair would enjoy many a long year of happiness by each other's side.

But this presage of Love, more strong than the Fates, was false withal. Two years after the marriage, one day she was gone abroad a-fowling, Doña Maria d'Avalos saw the Duke d'Andria, which was a gallant, handsome and well-knit man, and did straight love the same. An honest girl and a well-born, heedful of her noble name and still in that callow youth when women have not gotten boldness yet to match their naughty desires, she sent no go-between to the nobleman for to make assignation in Church or at her own abode. She never told her love, but did bide the time when her good star should bring beside her him which had grown in the twinkling of an eye more dear to her than the day. She had not to tarry long. For the Duke d'Andria had noted her beauty, and went straightway to pay his court to the Prince of Venosa. Encountering Doña Maria in the Palace with no other by, he did beseech her in right gentle, and withal gallant and masterful wise, that very favour she was herself well disposed and well resolved to grant him. She did lead him to her chamber instantly, and did there refuse him naught of all he was fain to have of her.

But when he did proffer her his thanks for that she had graciously yielded to his desires, she made answer:

"My Lord, the desire was mine own more than it was yours. I, it was, was fain we should lie in the arms one of the other, as we be now laid, in this bed, to the which I will aye make you dearly welcome, as oft as it shall please you to come thither."

Every time she was able so to do, from that day forth Doña Maria d'Avalos would receive in her chamber the Duke d'Andria and this was many a time and oft, for the Prince of Venosa went much to the chase and would sometimes spend whole weeks together diverting him with his friends in one of his pleasure houses he had in the country parts.

The whole while that Doña Maria was abed with her lover, her nurse Lucia would stand a-watching at the chamber door, telling of her beads and trembling sore lest the Prince perchance should return home against all expectation.

'Twas indeed a nobleman mightily feared by reason of his jealous and grim humour. His enemies did reproach him for his cunning and cruelty, naming him mongrel cur of fox and she-wolf, stinking hound, if ever stinking hound was. But his friends would commend him, for that he kept ever in sure memory whatsoever of right or wrong folk did him, and would in no wise suffer patiently any injury wrought him or his.

During the space of three full months which were now gone by the lovers had great joy of each other and content of their desires without or let or hindrance, when one morning the Nurse came to seek Doña Maria in her chamber, and spake thus to her:

"Listen, my pearl of pearls; albeit my words this day will be neither of flowers nor sugar-plums, but of a right serious and fearsome matter. My Lord the Prince of Venosa hath heard some ill report concerning you and the Duke d'Andria.

"But now I saw him in the Palace court, as he was a-mounting his horse. He was gnawing his moustache—a fell sign with him. He was in talk with two fellows, which had little of the air about them of leading honest lives; all I heard him tell them was, 'See ye, without being seen!' Of such sort the orders the noble Prince was charging them withal. And the worst is, he did stop dead whenas he set eyes on me. My own little pearl of price, so true as God is in the Holy Sacrament, an if the Prince find you with the Lord Duke d'Andria, he will kill both the twain of you. You will be a dead woman; and ah! me, what will become of me?"

The Nurse spake on in this wise and besought her mistress long and sore; but Doña Maria d'Avalos did send her away without deigning so much as one word of answer.

As it was Springtide she went forth that same day a-walking in the country with some ladies of the city. They were following a path bordered with thorn-trees all a-bloom, when one of the ladies said thus to her:

"Dogs will sometimes come and stick at travellers' heels, Doña Maria. Well! look, to-day we be dogged by a great black and white hound!"

And the Princess, turning her head to see, did recognize a certain Dominican monk which was used to come each day to the courtyard of the Palazzo Venosa for to rest in the shade there, and in winter-time to warm him in the great kitchen.

Meanwhile the Nurse, seeing her lady mistress paid no heed to her words, ran to warn the Duke d'Andria. Moreover the said Duke had reasons of his own to fear the sweet secret of his loves had been unhappily discovered. The very evening afore, finding himself followed by a pair of ruffians armed with arquebuses, he had killed one of the twain with a sword-thrust, whiles the other had taken to his heels. The Duke felt no doubt now but these two rascals had been set at him by the Prince of Venosa.

"Lucia," he said to the Nurse, "I must needs shudder at this danger, seeing it doth threaten my Lady Maria d'Avalos no less than myself. Tell her I will not return again to her chamber, cost me what regrets it will, before that the Prince's suspicions be lulled asleep."

These words the Nurse did report the same evening to Doña Maria, which did harken to them with impatience, biting her lip till the blood came.

Learning that the Prince was at the moment abroad, she bade her Nurse go straight to fetch the Duke d'Andria, and bring him into her chamber; and so soon as he was come spake thus to him:

"My gracious Lord, a day spent apart from you is to me the cruellest of torments. I shall not fear to die; but I have not the fortitude to endure your absence. You should not have loved me, if you had not the hardihood to brave all for love of me. You should not have loved me if there were aught else in all the world you set above my love, even mine own honour and mine own life. Choose; either you shall see me every day as aforetime, or you shall never see me more."

He made answer:

"Well and good then, Lady, and so be it; for, indeed, there is no room for ill or evil henceforth betwixt us twain! Verily I do love you as you would have me love you, even more than your own life."

And that day, which was a Thursday, they did tarry a long time, close pressed one against the other. Naught of moment fell out ere the Monday of the next week, on the which day the Prince did apprise his wife how that he was setting forth with a numerous train for Rome, whither he was called by the Pope, which was his kinsman. And in very deed a score of horses were then standing ready saddled and bridled in the Great Court. Then did the Prince kiss his wife's hand, as he was used to do on taking leave of her for any lengthy absence. Last of all, when he was now a-horseback, he did turn his face to her and say:

"God have you in His keeping, Doña Maria!" and so rode forth with his company behind him.

Soon as ever she thought her husband's troop to be gotten forth of the walls, the Princess bade her Nurse summon the Duke d'Andria to her. The old woman besought her to defer a meeting that might easily be cause of such sore calamity.

"My dove," she cried, falling on her knees, her hands uplifted in supplication, "receive not the Duke to-day! All night long I heard the Prince's men grinding swords. Yet another thing, my flower of flowers, the good brother that cometh day by day to our kitchen to seek his dole of bread, hath but now overset a salt-cellar of salt with the sleeve of his gown. Give your lover a little repose, little one. Your pleasure will be all the greater to have him again presently, and he will love you all the better for the respite."

But Doña Maria d'Avalos said:

"Nurse, an if he be not here in one quarter of an hour, I will send you back home to your brethren in the mountains."

And when the Duke d'Andria was by her side she did welcome him with an exceeding great joy.

"My Lord," cried she, "this will be a good day for us, and the night better still. I shall keep you till the dawn."

And straightway did they exchange betwixt them an host of kisses and fond caresses. Presently, after doffing their clothes, they gat them to bed, and held each the other close embraced so long that evening found them yet pressed in each other's arms. Then, for that they were sore hungered, Doña Maria drew forth of her marriage chest a pasty, dried conserves, and a flask of wine, the which she had been heedful to lay by therein.

After the twain had eaten and drunk their fill, playing the while all sorts of pretty plays, the moon rose and did look in so friendly at the window that they were fain to wish her welcome. So they went forth upon the balcony, and there, breathing the freshness and softness of the night, did watch the fireflies dancing in the dark bushes. All were still save only the shrilling of the insects in the grass. Then there came a sound of footsteps along the street, and Doña Maria did recognize the poor monk which was wont to haunt the kitchen and the Palace courtyards, the same she had encountered one day in the flowery path where she was a-walking with two ladies—her companions. She shut to the window softly, and to bed again with her lover. 'Twas deep in the night, and they were lying so, kissing and murmuring the softest nothings ever were inspired by Love, whether at Naples or any other spot in all the wide world, when of a sudden they caught a noise of steps mounting the stairway and the rattle of arms; at the same time they beheld a red glow shining through the chinks of the door. And they heard the Nurse's voice shrieking, "Jesu Maria! I am a dead woman." The Duke d'Andria sprang up, leapt upon his sword, and cried:

"Up, Doña Maria! We must leap forth by the window."

But, rushing to the balcony and leaning out, he saw how the street was guarded and all bristling with pikes.

Thereupon he came back to Doña Maria, which said:

" 'Tis the end of all! But know this, I do not regret aught of what I have done, my dear, dear Lord!"

And he made answer:

"Well and good then, and so be it!" and did haste to don his trunks.

Cracking and crunching under the mighty blows struck by them outside, the door was meantime a-trembling, and the panels began to gape.

He spake again and said:

"Fain would I know who hath betrayed and sold us thus."

At the instant he was seeking his shoon, the one half of the door gave way, and a troop of men, bearing arms and torches, threw themselves into the chamber. The Prince of Venosa was in their midst, shouting: "Have at the traitor! Kill! Kill!"

Lustily did three swordsmen attack the Duke, but he set him in front of the bed, where was Doña Maria, and made valiant stand against the caitiffs.

Six men were there in all, led on by the Prince, being of his bosom friends every one or his own varlets. Albeit blinded by the dazzle of the torches, the Duke d'Andria did contrive to parry several thrusts, and gave back some shrewd blows himself. But catching his foot in the platters lying on the floor, with the remains of the pasty and conserves, he fell over backward. Finding himself on his back, a sword's point at his throat, he did seize the blade in his left hand; the man, snatching it back, cut off three of his fingers, and the sword was bent. Then, as the Duke d'Andria was heaving forward his shoulders to rise, one of the fellows struck him a blow over the head which did break in the bones of his skull. At this all six did hurl them upon him, and slew him, lunging with such savage haste they did wound each other.

Whenas the thing was done, the Prince of Venosa bade them stand quietly aside; and marching upon Doña Maria, which till now had tarried still beside the bed, he drave her before his sword's point into the corner of the chamber where was the marriage chest. And there, holding her at bay, he did hiss in her face one word:

"*Puttana!*" (Harlot!)

Shamed by reason of her nakedness, she went to drag to her some of the bedclothes, which were hanging over the bedside. But he stayed her with a thrust of his sword, which did graze her white side.

Then, leaning against the wall, hands and arms held up to veil her eyes, she stood waiting.

The other never left off crying:

"*Puttaccia! Puttaccia!*" (Whore! Whore!)

Then, forasmuch as he did yet tarry, and slew her not, she was afraid. He saw that she was afraid, and said gleefully:

"You are afraid!"

But pointing her finger at the dead body of the Duke d'Andria, she made answer:

"Fool! what think you I can have to fear now?"

And, to make a seeming of being no more terrified, she sought to recall a song-tune she had sung many a time as a girl, and began humming the same, or rather hissing it, betwixt her teeth.

The Prince, furious to see how she defied him, did now prick her with his point in the belly, crying out:

"*Ah! Sporca puttaccia!*" (Fie! Filthy trull!)

Exultant, she stayed her singing, and said:

"Sir, 'tis two years sithence I have been to confession."

At this word the Prince of Venosa bethought him how that, an if she died and were damned, she might return by night and drag him down to Hell along with her. He asked her:

"Will you not have a Confessor?"

She did ponder an instant, then shaking her head:

"'Tis useless. I cannot save my soul. I repent me not. I cannot, and I will not, repent. I love him! I love him! Let me die in his arms."

With a quick movement, she did thrust the sword aside, threw her on the bleeding corse of the Duke d'Andria, and lay clipping her dead lover in her arms.

Seeing her so, the Prince of Venosa did lose what patience he had kept till then, to the end he might not kill her ere he had made her suffer. He drave his blade through her body. She cried, "Jesu!" rolled over, sprang to her feet, and after a little shudder that shook her every limb, fell to the floor dead.

He struck her several blows more in the belly and bosom; then said to his varlets:

"Go throw these two pieces of carrion at the foot of the Great Staircase, and open wide the Palace doors, that men may note my vengeance at the same time as the insult done mine honour."

He bade strip the lover's corse bare like the other.

The men did as they were bidden. And all the day the bodies of the Duke d'Andria and Doña Maria lay naked at the bottom of the steps. The passers-by drew near to see them. And the news of the bloody deed being spread about the city, a great press of curious onlookers came crowding before the Palace. Some said, "Lo! a good deed well done!" Others, and these the more part, at sight of so lamentable a spectacle, were filled with ruth. Yet durst they not openly commiserate the Prince's victims, for fear of evil handling by his armed dependents, which were set to guard the bodies. Young men gazed at the Princess's corse, for to discover the traces of that beauty which had been her undoing, while the little children would be expounding one to the other the meaning of that they saw.

Doña Maria lay stretched on her back. The lips were drawn back, displaying the teeth in a ghastly smile. Her eyes stood wide open, the whites only showing. Six wounds were upon her, three in the belly, which was greatly swollen, two in the bosom, one in the neck. The last had bled profusely, and the dogs kept fawning up to lick it.

Towards nightfall, the Prince bade set torches of resin, like as on days of festival, in the bronze rings fixed in the Palace walls, and eke kindle great fires in the Courtyard, to the end all men might see the criminals plain. At midnight, a pious widow brought coverings and spread the same over the dead bodies. But, by the Prince's commandment, these were incontinent torn away again.

The Ambassador of Spain informed of the unseemly treatment meted to a lady of the Spanish house of Avalos, came in person urgently to entreat the Prince of Venosa to stay these outrages, which did insult the noble memory of the Duke of Pescara, uncle to Doña Maria, and offend in their tomb so many great Captains of whose blood the said lady was descended. But he withdrew after profiting naught by his intercession; and writ a letter thereanent to his Catholic Majesty. The poor bodies were left shamefully exposed as before. Toward the latter end of the night, the curious having ceased to come any more, the guards were withdrawn.

Then a Dominican monk, which had all the day lurked about the great doors, did slip within the vestibule by the smoky light of the dying torches, crept to the steps where Doña Maria lay, and threw himself on her corse.

BONAPARTE AT SAN MINIATO

TO ARMAND GENEST

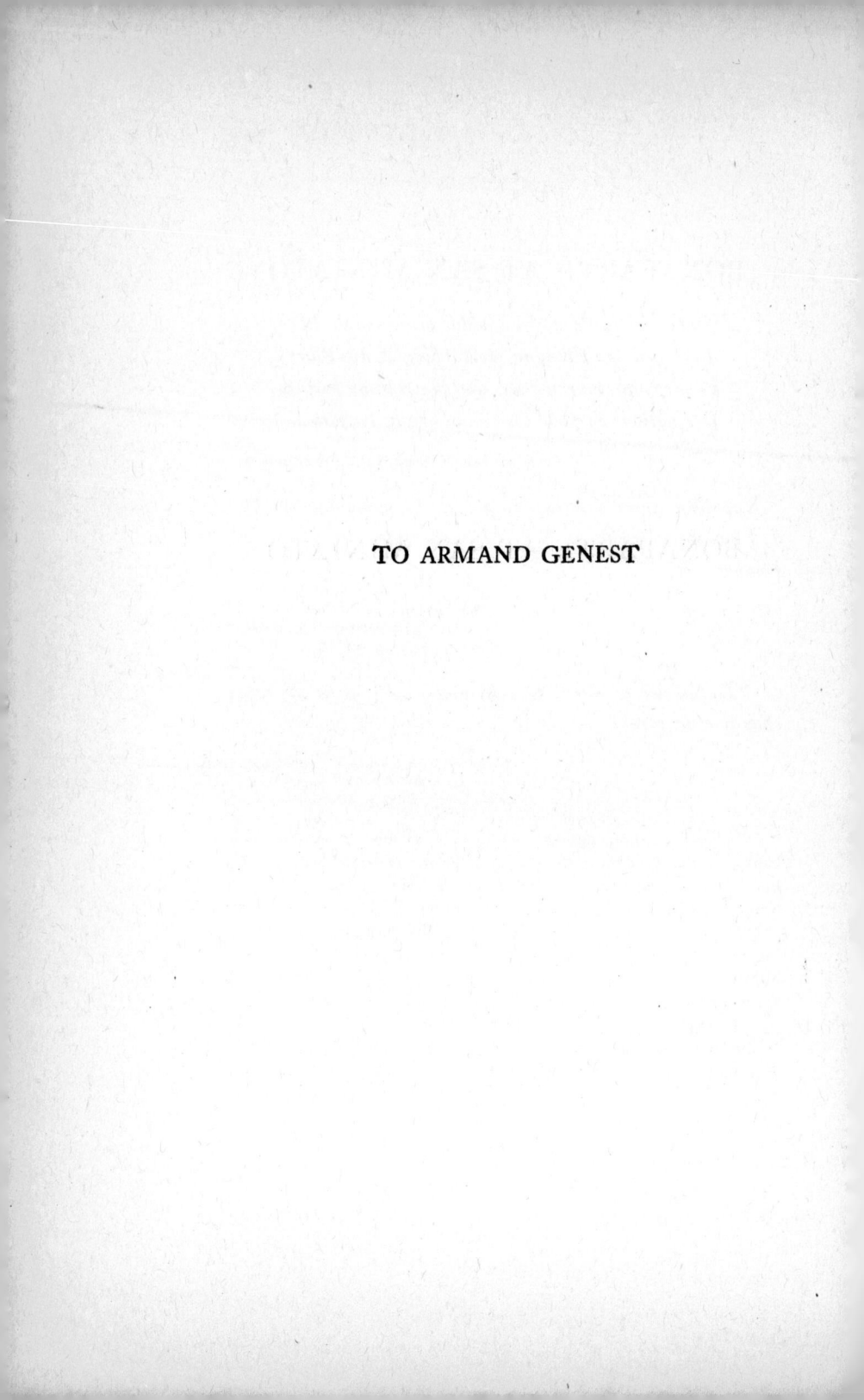

BONAPARTE AT SAN MINIATO

*Quand, simple citoyen, soldat d'un peuple libre,
Aux bords de l'Éridan, de l'Adige et du Tibre,
Foudroyant tour à tour quelques tyrans pervers,
Des nations en pleurs, sa main brisait les fers. . . .*

(Marie-Joseph Chénier, *La Promenade*.)[1]

Napoléon après son expédition de Livourne, se rendant à Florence, coùcha à San Miniato chez un vieil abbé Buonaparte. . . . .

(*Mémorial de Saint-Hélène*, par le comte de Las Cases, réimpression de 1823, 1824, t. Ier, p. 149.)[2]

"*Je fus sur le soir à San Miniato. J'y avais un vieux chanoine de parent. . . .*"

(*Mémoires du docteur F. Antommarchi, sur les derniers moments de Napoléon* 1825, t. Ier, p. 155).[3]

[1] "When, a plain citizen, soldier of a free people, by the banks of the Eridanus, the Adige and the Tiber, blasting with his lightnings one after another recalcitrant tyrants, his hand brake the fetters of the nations that wept. . . ."

[2] "Napoleon, visiting Florence after his Leghorn expedition, lay one night at San Miniato at the house of an old Abbé Buonaparte. . . ." (*Memorial of St. Helena*, by the Count de Las Cases—reprint of 1823, 1824, Vol. I, p. 149.)

[3] "I stayed for the night at San Miniato. I had a relative living there, an old Canon. . . ." (*Memoirs of Dr. F. Antommarchi on the Last Moments of Napoleon*, 1825, vol. I, p. 155.)

AFTER occupying Leghorn and closing that port against the English men-of-war, General Bonaparte proceeded to Florence to visit the Grand Duke of Tuscany, Ferdinand, who alone of all the princes of Europe had honestly and honourably fulfilled his engagements with the French Republic. In token of esteem and confidence, he went there without escort, accompanied only by the officers of his Staff. Amongst other sights he was shown the arms of the Buonapartes carved over the gateway of an old house. He was already aware that a branch of his family had been fruitful and multiplied at Florence in days of yore, and that a last descendant of this the ancient race was still alive. This was a certain Canon of San Miniato, now eighty years of age. In spite of all the pressing affairs he had to attend to, he made a point of paying him a visit. Napoleon Bonaparte was always strongly moved by feelings of natural affection.

On the eve of his departure from Florence, he made his way with some of his officers to the hill of San Miniato, which crowned with its walls and towers, rises from the plain at half a league's distance from the city.

Old Canon Buonaparte welcomed with agreeable and dignified politeness his young kinsman and the French officers who accompanied him—Berthier, Junot, Orderly Officer in Chief Chauvet and Lieutenant Thézard. He regaled them with a supper *à l'italienne,* which lacked neither the cranes of Peretola nor the little sucking-pig scented with aromatic herbs, nor the best vintages of Tuscany, Naples and Sicily. Uncompromising Republicans as Brutus himself, they drank to France and Freedom. Their host acknowledged the toast; then turning to the General whom he had seated on his right hand;

"Nephew!" said he, "are you not curious to examine the genealogical tree painted on the wall yonder? You will be gratified to see from it that we are descended from the Lombard Cadolingians, who from the tenth to the twelfth centuries covered themselves with glory by their fidelity to the German Emperors, and from whom sprung, prior to the year 1100, the Buonapartes of Treviso and the Buonapartes of Florence, the latter stock proving by far the more illustrious."

At this the officers began to whisper together and laugh. Orderly Officer Chauvet asked Berthier behind his hand if the Republican General felt flattered to possess amongst his ancestors a lot of slaves serving the Two-headed Eagle, while Lieutenant Thézard was ready to take his oath the General owed his birth to good *sans-culottes* and nobody else. Meanwhile the Canon went on with a long string of boasts concerning the nobility of his house and lineage.

"Know this, nephew," he finished by saying, "our Florentine ancestors well deserved their name. They were ever of the *bon parti*, and steadfast defenders of Mother Church."

At these words, which the old fellow had uttered in a high, clear voice, the General, who so far had been scarcely listening, gathered his wandering wits together, and raising his pale, thin face, with its classically moulded features, threw a piercing look at his interlocutor, which closed his lips instantly.

"Nay! uncle," he cried, "let us have done with these follies! the rats of your garret are very welcome to these moth-eaten parchments for me."

Then he added in a voice of brass:

"The only nobility I vaunt is in my deeds. It dates from the 13th Vendémiaire of Year IV, the day I swept the Royalist Sections with cannon-shot from the steps of St. Roch. Come, let us drink to the Republic! 'Tis the arrow of Evander, which falls not to earth again, and is transformed into a star!"

The officers answered the appeal with a shout of enthusiasm. It was a moment when Berthier himself felt a Republican's and a Patriot's fire.

Junot exclaimed: "Napoleon had no need for ancestors; 'twas enough for him his soldiers had acclaimed him Corporal at the Bridge of Lodi."

The wines had the dry smack of gunflint and the bouquet of powder, and the company imbibed freely. Lieutenant Thézard was soon in a condition that rendered him incapable of concealing his sentiments. Proud of the wounds and the kisses of women he had enjoyed in lavish abundance in this campaign, at once so heroic and so gallant and gay, he informed the Canon without more ado, that following in the steps of Bonaparte, the French were going to march round the world, upsetting Thrones and Altars in every land, giving the girls bastards and ripping up the bellies of all fanatics.

The old Priest only went on smiling, and replied he was willing enough to sacrifice to their noble rage, not indeed the pretty girls, whom he besought them rather to treat cannily, but the Fanatics, the chiefest foes, he said, of Holy Church.

Junot promised him to deal leniently with the Nuns; he could heartily commend some of them, having found them to possess tender hearts and the whitest of skins.

Orderly Officer Chauvet maintained we should take account of the influence exercised by the cloistered life on the complexion of young women; you see, he was a student of natural philosophy.

"Between Genoa and Milan," he went on, "we tasted largely of this sort of forbidden fruit. One may profess to be without prejudices; still, a pretty bosom does look prettier half hid by the Veil. I set no value on religious vows, yet I am free to confess I attach a very special value to a fine leg if it belongs to a Nun. Strange contradictions of the human heart!"

"Fie! fie!" put in Berthier; "what pleasure can you find in upsetting the wits and troubling the senses of these unhappy victims of fanaticism? What! are there no women of condition in Italy, to whom you could offer your vows at fêtes, under the Venetian cloak that favours little intrigues so admirably? Is it nothing that Pietra Grua Mariani, Madame Lambert, Signora Monti, Signora Gherardi of Brescia, are fair and gallant dames?"

As he ran over the names of these Italian toasts, he was thinking of the Princess Visconti. This great lady, finding herself unable to enthral Bonaparte, had given herself to his Chief of the Staff, whom she loved with a fire of wantonness and a refined sensuality which left their mark on the weak-kneed Berthier for the rest of his days.

"For my own part," interrupted Lieutenant Thézard, "I shall never forget a little water-melon seller on the steps of the Duomo, who . . ."

The General rose from his chair with a gesture of impatience. A bare three hours was left them for sleep, as they were to start at dawn.

"Never trouble, kinsman, about our sleeping accommodation," he said, addressing the Canon. "We are soldiers; a bundle of hay is good enough for us."

But their excellent host had had beds prepared. His house was bare and unornamented, but of vast proportions. He conducted the French officers, one after the other, to the rooms assigned them, and wished them a good night.

Left alone in his chamber, Bonaparte threw off his coat and sword, and proceeded to scrawl a pencil note to Joséphine—twenty illegible lines, in which his violent, yet calculating, spirit spoke loudly. Then, folding the letter, he abruptly drove the woman's image from his mind, as you push-to a drawer. He unrolled a plan of Mantua, and selected the point on which he should concentrate his fire.

He was still absorbed in his calculations when he heard a knock at the door. He thought it was Berthier; but it proved to be the Canon, who came to ask him for a few minutes' conversation. Under his arm he carried two or three parchment-covered portfolios. The General looked at these documents with something of a quizzical air. He felt certain they contained the genealogy of the Buonapartes, and anticipated their leading to a never-ending talk. However, he suffered no trace of his impatience to appear.

He was never morose or angry but when he deliberately made up his mind to be so. Now he had no sort of wish to offend his worthy kinsman; on the contrary, he was anxious to make himself agreeable to him. Moreover, he was not really sorry to learn the nobility of his race, now his Jacobin officers were no longer there to laugh or take umbrage at the matter. He begged the Canon to take a seat, who did so, and, laying his registers on the table, said:

"I made a beginning during supper, nephew, of telling you about the Buonapartes of Florence; but I gathered by the look you gave me, it was not then the place or time to enlarge on such a subject. I broke off therefore, reserving the essential part of what I have to say for the present moment. I beg of you, kinsman, to hear me with great attention.

"The Tuscan branch of our family produced some excellent representatives, among whom should be named Jacopo di Buonaparte, who witnessed the sack of Rome in 1527 and wrote an account of that event, also Niccolò, author of a Comedy entitled *La Vedova*, that was declared the work of another Terence. However, it is not of these two famous ancestors I now wish to speak, but rather of a third, who eclipses them as much in glory as the sun outshines the stars. Know then that your family counts amongst its members a man of saintly life, deemed worthy of Beatification and the title of blessed, Fra Bonaventura, disciple of the reformed Order of St. Francis, who died in 1593 in the odour of Sanctity."

The old man bent his head reverently as he pronounced the name. Then he resumed with a fire scarcely to have been expected from one of his years and easy character:

"Fra Bonaventura! Ah, kinsman! 'tis to him, to this good Father, you owe the success of your arms. He was beside you, doubt it not, when you annihilated, as you told us at supper, the enemies of your party on the steps of St. Roch. This Capuchin Friar has been your helper 'mid the smoke of battles. But for him, be assured, you would not have been victorious, whether at Montenotte or Millesimo or Lodi. The marks of his patronage are too striking and self-evident to be ignored, and in your success I plainly discern a miracle of the good Fra Bonaventura. But what is most important you should know, is this; the holy man had a purpose of his own in view when, giving you the advantage even over Beaulieu himself, he led you from victory to victory to this antique roof under which you rest to-night with an old man's blessing to keep you. I am here for the very purpose of revealing his intentions to you. Fra Bonaventura wished you should be informed of his merits, that you should hear of his fasts and austerities and the whole year's silence he once condemned himself to endure. He would have you touch his hair-shirt and scourge, and his knees stiffened so at the altar-steps that he walked bent double like the letter Z. For this it was he has brought you into Italy, where he was for contriving you an opportunity of returning him benefit for benefit. For you must know, good kinsman, if the Friar has helped you greatly, in your turn, you can be of the greatest use to him."

With these words, the Canon laid his hands on the heavy portfolios that loaded the table, and drew a deep breath.

Bonaparte said nothing, but waited quietly for

the Canon to go on with his remarks, which diverted him greatly. Never was any one easier to amuse than Napoleon.

After recovering breath, the old man resumed:

"Why, yes! kinsman, you can be of the greatest use to Fra Bonaventura, who in his present situation needs your help. He was beatified many years ago, but is still waiting his admission to the Calendar of Saints. He is thinking long, is the good Father Bonaventura. Yet what can I, a poor Canon of San Miniato, do for him to secure him the honour he has earned? His enrolment demands an outlay that goes far beyond my fortune and even the resources of the Bishopric! Poor Canon! Poor Diocese! Poor Duchy of Tuscany! Poor Italy! they are all poor together. It is you, kinsman, must ask the Pope to recognize Fra Bonaventura's claim. He will certainly grant you so much. His Holiness will never refuse, for your sake, to add another Saint to the Calendar. Great honour will accrue to yourself and your family, and the good Friar will always be ready to afford you his patronage. Do you not realize the advantages of having a Saint in the family?"

And the Canon, pointing to the portfolios, urged the General to put them in his valise and take them with him. Their contents consisted of the memorial relating to the Canonization of the Blessed Friar Bonaventura, together with documents in corroboration of his claim.

"Promise me," he added, "that you will see to this matter, the most important that can concern you."

Bonaparte restrained his strong inclination to laugh.

"I am unfortunately situated," he objected, "for undertaking a case for Canonization. You are aware that the French Republic is taking measures to exact compensation from the Court of Rome for the murder of her Ambassador Bassville, foully assassinated."

The Canon protested eagerly:

"Corpo di Bacco! the Court of Rome will find excuses enough; all due compensation will be accorded, and our kinsman will be placed on the Calendar, never fear."

"The negotiations are far from being concluded at present," replied the Republican General. "The Roman Curia has yet to recognize the civil constitution of the French clergy and to break up and abolish the Inquisition, which is an offence to humanity and an unjustifiable encroachment on the rights of Nations."

The old man only smiled and said:

"Mio caro figliuolo Napoleone, the Pope knows perfectly well folk must both give and take. He will be reasonable, and yield a point where necessary. He is for all time, long-suffering and a man of peace."

Bonaparte pondered deeply awhile, as though a series of quite new ideas were taking muster in his powerful brain. Then suddenly breaking silence,

"You do not realize," he said, "the spirit of the age. We are highly irreligious in France; impiety is deeply rooted in our soil. You do not know the progress achieved by the ideas of Montesquieu, Raynal and Rousseau. Public worship is abolished; veneration is a thing of the past. You must have seen this from the scandalous talk my officers indulged in just now at your own table."

The good Canon shook his head:

"Ah, yes! those fine young men, they are wild fellows enough, dissipated and reckless! It is only a passing phase. Ten years more, and they will be thinking less of the girls and more of going to Mass. The Carnival is a matter of a few days, and even this mad one of your French Revolution will not last for long. The Church is eternal."

Napoleon declared bluntly he cared too little about Religion himself to meddle in a purely ecclesiastical matter like this.

Thereupon the Canon looked him in the eyes and told him:

"My son, I understand men. I can divine your nature; you are no sceptic. Take up this case, the Blessed Father Bonaventura's case. He will repay you the services you may render him. For myself, I am over old to witness the success of this noble enterprise. I must die soon; but knowing it to be in your hands, I shall die happy. Above all, never forget, my kinsman, that all power comes of God by the instrumentality of his priests."

He rose to his feet, raised his arms to bless his young kinsman and withdrew.

Left alone, Bonaparte turned over the leaves of the ponderous Memorial by the smoky light of his candle, as he pondered over the power of the Church, and told himself the Papacy was a more enduring institution than ever the Constitution of the Year III was likely to be.

A knock was heard at the door. It was Berthier, come to inform the General that all was ready for their departure.

PREFATORY LETTER

Publish *Marguerite,* dear Monsieur André Coq, if you so desire, but pray relieve me from all responsibility in the matter.

It would argue too much literary conceit on my part were I anxious to restore it to the light of day. It would argue, perhaps, still more did I endeavour to keep it in obscurity. You will not succeed in wresting it for long from the eternal oblivion whereunto it is destined. Ay me, how old it is! I had lost all recollection of it. I have just read it over, without fear or favour, as I should a work unknown to me, and it does not seem to me that I have lighted upon a masterpiece. It would ill beseem me to say more about it than that. My only pleasure as I read it was derived from the proof it afforded that, even in those far-off days, when I was writing this little trifle, I was no great lover of the Third Republic with its pinchbeck virtues, its militarist imperialism, its ideas of conquest, its love of money, its contempt for the handicrafts, its unswerving predilection for the unlovely. Its leaders caused me terrible misgivings. And the event has surpassed my apprehensions.

But it was not in my calculations to make myself a laughing-stock, by taking *Marguerite* as a text for generalizations on French politics of the late nineteenth and early twentieth centuries.

The specimens of type and the woodcuts you have shown me promise a very comely little book.

Believe me, dear Monsieur Coq,
Yours sincerely,
ANATOLE FRANCE.

La Béchellerie, 16th April, 1920.

MARGUERITE

MARGUERITE

5th July

AS I left the Palais-Bourbon at five o'clock that afternoon, it rejoiced my heart to breathe in the sunny air. The sky was bland, the river gleamed, the foliage was fresh and green. Everything seemed to whisper an invitation to idleness. Along the Pont de la Concorde, in the direction of the Champs-Élysées, victorias and landaus kept rolling by. In the shadow of the lowered carriage-hoods, women's faces gleamed clear and radiant and I felt a thrill of pleasure as I watched them flash by like hopes vanishing and reappearing in endless succession. Every woman as she passed by left me with an impression of light and perfume. I think a man, if he is wise, will not ask much more than that of a beautiful woman. A gleam and a perfume! Many a love-affair leaves even less than that behind it. Moreover, that day, if Fortune herself had run with her wheel a-spinning before my very nose along the pavement of the Pont de la Concorde, I should not have so much as stretched forth an arm to pluck her by her golden hair. I lacked nothing that day; all was mine. It was five o'clock and I was free till dinner-time. Yes, free! Free to saunter at will, to breathe at my ease for two hours, to look on at things and not have to talk, to let my thoughts wander as I listed. All was mine, I say again. My happiness was making me a selfish man. I gazed at everything about me as though it were all a picture, a splendid moving pageant, arranged for my own particular delectation. It seemed to me as though the sun were shining for me alone, as though it were pouring down its torrents of flame upon the river for my special gratification. I somehow thought that all this motley throng was swarming gaily around me for the sole purpose of animating, without destroying, my solitude. And so I almost got the notion that the people about me were quite small, that their apparent size was only an illusion, that they were but puppets; the sort of thoughts a man has when he has nothing to think about. But you must not be angry on that score with a poor man who has had his head crammed chock-full for ten years on end with politics and law making and is wearing away his life with those trivial preoccupations men call affairs of state.

In the popular imagination, a law is something

abstract, without form or colour. For me a law is a green baize table, sealing-wax, paper, pens, ink-stains, green-shaded candles, books bound in calf, papers yet damp from the printer's and all smelling of printer's ink, conversations in green papered offices, files, bundles of documents, a stuffy smell, speeches, newspapers; a law, in short, is all the hundred and one things, the hundred and one tasks you have to fulfil at all hours, the grey and gentle hours of the morning, the white hours of middle day, the purple hours of evening, the silent, meditative hours of night; tasks which leave you no soul to call your own and rob you of the consciousness of your own identity.

Yes, it is so. I have left my own *ego* behind me there. It is scattered up and down among all sorts of memoranda and reports. Industrious junior clerks have put away a parcel of it in each one of their beautiful green filing cases. And so I have had to go on living without my *ego*, which, moreover, is how all politicians have to live. But an *ego* is a strangely subtle thing. And wonder of wonders! mine came back to me just now on the Pont de la Concorde. 'Twas he without a doubt and, would you believe it, he had not suffered so very much from his sojourn among those musty papers. The very moment he arrived I found myself again, I recognized my own existence, whereof I had not been conscious these ten years. "Ha ha!" said I to myself, "since I exist, I am just as well pleased to know it." Behold I will set forth here now to improve this new acquaintance by strolling, with a lover's thoughts in my heart, down the Champs-Élysées.

And this is why I am here, at this hour, beneath the sculptured steeds of Marly, more high-spirited than those aristocratic quadrupeds themselves; this is why I am setting foot in the avenue whose entrance is marked by their hoofs of stone perpetually poised in air. The carriages flow past endlessly, like a sombre scintillating stream of lava or molten asphalt, whereon the hats of the women seem borne along like so many flowers, and like everything else one sees in Paris, at once extravagant and pretty. I light up a cigar and looking at nothing, behold everything. So intense is my joy that it scares me. It is the first cigar I have smoked for ten years. Oh yes, I grant I have begun as many as ten a day in my room; but those I scorched, bit, chewed and threw away; I never smoked them. This one I am really and truly smoking and the smoke it exhales is a cloud of poesy spreading grace and charm about it. What an interest I take in all I see. These little shops, which display at regular intervals their motley assortment of wares, fill me with delight. Here especially is one which I cannot forbear stopping to look at. What I chiefly delight to contemplate there is a decanter with lemonade in it. The decanter reflects in miniature on its polished sides the trees around it and the women that pass by and the skies. It has a lemon on the top of it which gives it a sort of oriental air. However, it is not its shape nor its colour that is the attraction in my eyes; I cannot keep my gaze from it because it reminds me of my childhood. At the sight of it, innumerable delightful scenes come thronging into my memory. Once again do I behold those shining hours, those hours divine of early childhood. Ah, what would I not give to be again the little boy of those days and to drink once more a glass of that precious liquid!

In that little shop, I find once more, besides the lemonade and the gooseberry syrup, all those divers things wherein my childhood took delight. Here be whips, trumpets, swords, guns, cartridge-pouches, belts, scabbards, sabretaches, all those magic toys which, from five to nine years old, made me feel that I was fulfilling the destiny of a Napoleon. I played that mighty rôle, in my tenpenny soldier's kit, I played it from start to finish, bating only

Waterloo and the years of exile. For, mark you, I was always the victor. Here, too, are coloured prints from Épinal. It was on them that I began to spell out those signs which to the learned reveal a few faint traces of the Mighty Riddle. Yes, the sorriest little coloured daub that ever came out of a village in the Vosges consists of print and pictures, and what is the sum and substance of Science after all but just pictures and print?

From those Épinal prints I learned things far finer and more useful than anything I ever got from the little grammar and history books my schoolmasters gave me to pore over. Épinal prints, you see, are stories, and stories are mirrors of destiny. Blessed is the child that is brought up on fairy-tales. His riper years should prove rich in wisdom and imagination. And see! here is my own favourite story *The Blue Bird*. I know him by his outspread tail. 'Tis he right enough. It is as much as I can do to prevent myself flinging my arms round the old shopwoman's neck and kissing her flabby cheeks. The Blue Bird, ah me, what a debt I owe him! If I have ever wrought any good in my life, it is all due to him. Whenever we were drafting a Bill with our Chief, the memory of the Blue Bird would steal into my mind amid the heaps of legal and parliamentary documents by which I was hemmed in. I used to reflect then that the human soul contained infinite desires, unimaginable metamorphoses and hollowed sorrows, and if, under the spell of such thoughts, I gave to the clause I chanced to be engaged upon an ampler, a humaner sense, an added respect for the soul and its rights, and for the universal order of things, that clause would never fail to encounter vigorous opposition in the Chamber. The counsels of the Blue Bird seldom prevailed in the committee stage. Howbeit some did manage to get through Parliament.

I now perceive that I am not the only one inspecting the little stall: a little girl has come to a halt in front of the brilliant display. I am looking at her from behind. Her long, bright hair comes tumbling in cascades from under her red velvet hood and spreads out on her broad lace collar and on her dress, which is the same colour as her hood. Impossible to say what is the colour of her hair (there is no colour so beautiful) but one can describe the lights in it; they are bright and pure and changing, fair as the sun's rays, pale as a beam of starlight. Nay, more than that, they shine, yes; but they flow also. They possess the splendour of light, and the charm of pleasant waters. Methinks that, were I a poet, I should write as many sonnets on those tresses as M. José de Heredia composed concerning the Conquerors of Castille d'Or. They would not be so fine, but they would be sweeter. The child, so far as I can judge, is between four and five years old. All I can see of her face is the tip of her ear, daintier than the daintiest jewel, and the innocent curve of her cheek. She does not stir; she is holding her hoop in her left hand; her right is at her lips as though she were biting her nails in her eager contemplation. What is it she is gazing at so longingly? The shop contains other things besides the arms and the gear of fighting men. Balls and skipping ropes are suspended from the awning. On the stall are baby dolls with bodies made of grey cardboard, smiling after the manner of idols, monstrous and serene as they. Little sixpenny dolls, dressed like servant girls, stretch out their arms, little stumpy arms so flimsy that the least breath of air sets them a-tremble. But the little maid whose hair is made of liquid light, has no eyes for these dolls and puppets. Her whole soul hangs upon the lips of a beautiful baby doll that seems to be calling her his mummy. He is hitched on to one of the poles of the booth all by himself. He dominates, he effaces everything else. Once you have beheld him, you see naught else save him.

Bolt upright in his warm wraps, a little swansdown tucker under his chin, he is stretching out his little chubby arms for some one to take him. He speaks straight to the little maid's heart. He appeals to her by every maternal instinct she possesses. He is enchanting. His face has three little dots, two black ones for the eyes, and one red one for the mouth. But his eyes speak, his mouth invites you. He is alive.

Philosophers are a heedless race. They pass by dolls with never a thought. Nevertheless the doll is more than the statue, more than the idol. It finds its way to the heart of woman, long ere she be a woman. It gives her the first thrill of maternity. The doll is a thing august. Wherefore cannot one of our great sculptors be so very kind as to take the trouble to model dolls whose lineaments, coming to life beneath his fingers, would tell of wisdom and of beauty?

At last the little girl awakens from her silent day-dream. She turns round and shows her violet eyes made bigger still with wonder, her nose which makes you smile to look at it, her tiny nose, quite white, that reminds you of a little pug dog's black one, her solemn mouth, her shapely but too delicate chin, her cheeks a shade too pale. I recognize her. Oh yes! I recognize her with that instinctive certainty that is stronger than all convictions supported by all the proofs imaginable. Oh yes, 'tis she, 'tis indeed she and all that remains of the most charming of women. I try to hasten away but I cannot leave her. That hair of living gold, it is her mother's hair; those violet eyes, they are her mother's own; Oh, child of my dreams, child of my despair! I long to gather you to my arms, to steal you, to bear you away.

But a governess draws near, calls the child and leads her away: "Come, Marguerite, come along, it's time to go home."

And Marguerite, casting a look of sad farewell at the baby with its outstretched arms, reluctantly follows in the footsteps of a tall woman clad in black with ostrich feathers in her hat.

10th July

JEAN, bring me file 117 . . . . Now then, M. Boscheron, let's get this circular done. Take this down: *I draw your special attention, M. le Préfet, to the following point.* An end must be put at the earliest possible moment to an abuse which, if suffered to continue, would tend to—tend to—I draw your special attention to the following point, M. le Préfet. An end must be put as soon as possible to an abuse. Take that down, M. Boscheron."

But M. Boscheron, my secretary, respectfully remarks that I keep on dictating the same sentence. Jean deferentially places a file on my table.

"What's that, Jean?"

"File number 117. You asked me to fetch it, sir."

"I asked you for file number 117?"

"Yes, sir."

Jean gives me an anxious glance and retires.

"Where were we, M. Boscheron?"

"An end must be put as soon as possible to an abuse . . ."

"That's right . . . *an abuse which would tend to diminish popular respect for government servants and to transform* . . . transform, what a wealth of hidden things that word conceals. I cannot so much as pronounce it but a world of ideas and sentiments come thronging pell-mell to invade the secret recesses of my being."

"I beg pardon, monsieur?"

"What did you say, M. Boscheron?"

"Please repeat, monsieur; I didn't quite follow you."

"Really, Monsieur Boscheron? Possibly I was not very clear. Well, well! we will stop there if you like. Give me what I have dictated, I will finish it myself."

M. Boscheron gives me his notes, gathers up his papers, bows and retires. Left alone in my office, I fall to examining the wallpaper with a sort of idiotic minuteness. It has the appearance of green felt with here and there a yellow stain; I begin to draw little men on my paper; I make an effort to write; for the fact is my Chief has asked for the circular three times and has promised the government deputies that it shall go to the prefects forthwith. I am bound to let him have it. I begin reading it through: *to diminish popular respect for government servants and to transform them.* I make a blot; then with my pen I adorn it with hair. I transform it into a comet. I dream of Marguerite's tresses. The other day, in the Champs-Élysées, little filaments of gold, little delicate spirals stood out from the rest of her graceful tresses, with a singular brightness. You can see their like in fifteenth century miniatures, also in some of an earlier date. Dante says in his *Vita Nuova:* "One day when I was busy drawing angels' heads . . ." And now here am I trying to draw angels' heads on a government circular. Come now, we must get on with it: *government servants and to transform them—transform them* . . . How is it I simply cannot write a single word after that? How is it I am here dreaming still, as I have been ever since I rediscovered my *ego* on the Pont de la Concorde that evening of the lovely sunset? Transform, did I say? O God of my mystery, nature, truth, if she whose name even now after four years I dare not utter, if she died in giving life to Marguerite, I should believe, I should know with the certainty of instinct, that the soul of the mother had passed into the daughter and that they are one and the same being.

1st November

ALL'S well. I have lost my *ego* again. It has gone back into the green filing cases. Number 117 contains a good part of it. I have finished my circular. It is drawn up in good official style. We have a fine piece of legislation to get off before the holidays. My Chief speaks every day in the House. Every night I correct the proofs of his speeches. If the Blue Bird comes to see me now and again in the small hall of the Palais Bourbon, it is merely to advise me to tone down some rather too forcible expression and he never addresses himself to my imagination. I don't know whether I am living happily or unhappily since I don't know that I am living at all. I do not even recognize my own clothes. I picked up the hat of the Comte de Mérodac a little while ago and wore it for three days without knowing it, yet it is a romantic sombrero-like sort of thing worn nowadays by no one save this elderly nobleman. I cut an astounding figure they told me, but I never noticed myself, and, if by chance I had, I should not have heeded what I saw since it had nothing to do with politics. I am no longer a person; I am a piece of the official machine. To-night I have neither proofs to correct nor official reception to attend. I have put on my slippers. There is always a tiny bit of my *ego* hidden away in these slippers. I am in my room seated by the fire and I am conscious of being there. By heaven I wonder whether I should know myself in the glass. Let's have a look. Hum! not so very . . . I didn't think I was so grave and respectable looking. I quite see that I shall have to take myself seriously. I have been a long time about it, but then it wasn't for me to begin.

I am a man of weight and I account myself such. But, alas, I do not know myself. And I am not anxious to acquire the knowledge; it would be a tedious business. No, I haven't the smallest desire to hold converse with the grave and frigid gentleman who mimics all my movements. On the other hand, did I but dare, what a happy time I should have with that little fellow whose miniature I see there in that locket hanging against the frame of the mirror. He is building a house with dominoes. What a nice little chap. I feel like calling him and saying "Let's go and have a game together shall we?" But, alas, he is far away, very far away. That little boy is myself as I was forty years ago. He is dead, just as dead as if I were lying beneath the sod, sealed up in a leaden coffin. For what have we in common, he and I? In what respect does he survive in me to-day? In what do my castles of cards resemble his tower of dominoes?

We say that we live, we miserable beings, because we keep dying over and over again.

I remember, it is true, how I used to play my games of an evening what time my mother sat sewing at the table and gazed at me, now and again, with a look full of that beautiful and simple tenderness that makes one adore life, bless God and gives one courage enough to fight a score of battles. Ah yes, hallowed memories, I shall treasure you in my heart like a precious balm which, till my days are done, will have power to soothe all bitterness and soften the very agony of death. But does the child that I then was survive in me to-day? No. He is a stranger to me; I feel that I can love him without selfishness and weep for him without unmanliness. He is dead and gone, and has taken away with him my innocent simplicities and my boundless hopes. We all of us die in swaddling clothes. Little Marguerite, that delightful image of unfolding life, how many times has she not died and what profound depths of irrevocable memories, what a grave of dead thoughts and emotions has not already been delved within her, though she is but five years old.

I, a stranger, a passer-by, know more of her life than she does and, in consequence, I am more truly she than she herself. After that let him who will prate of the feeling of identity and the consciousness of self.

Oh, gracious Heaven, what things we mortals be and into what an abyss of terrors we should be for ever plunging if we had but time to think, instead of making laws or planting cabbages. I feel like pulling my slippers off my feet and pitching them out of the window, since they have called me back to the consciousness of my existence. Our lives are only bearable provided we do not think about them.

5th July

IT is a year ago to-day since I fell in with that little girl in front of a toy-shop in the Champs-Élysées, the child of her who first awakened in me the sense of beauty.

I was happy before I saw her; but the poetry of the wide world was unknown to me, nor had I had experience of the dolorous joys of love. The first time I saw Marie was one Good Friday at a classical concert to which her father, an old diplomat with a passion for music, who had heard the finest orchestras of every Court in Europe, had conducted her attired in stately weeds of solemn black. Her mourning garb only served to accentuate her radiant beauty. The sight of her aroused in me feelings which bore, I think, a close resemblance to religious exaltation. I was no longer very young. The uncertainty of my worldly position, dependent as it then was upon the vicissitudes of a political party, combined with my natural timidity to deprive me of all hope of figuring as a successful suitor. I often saw her at her father's and she treated me with an air of open friendliness that did not encourage me to foster higher ambitions. It was clear I did not impress her as the sort of man with whom she could fall in love. As for me, the sight of her and the sound of her voice produced in me such a state of delicious agitation that the mere memory of it, mingled though it be with grief, still avails to make me in love with life.

Nevertheless, shall I avow it? I longed to hear her and to see her always; I would have died in rapture at her side, but I was never fain to wed her. No, some instinct of harmony held desire remote from my heart. "It was not love then," some one will say. I know not what it was, but I know that it filled my soul.

Clearly, however, the feelings I experienced cannot have been strange to the heart of man, since I have found them expressed with power and sweetness in the works of the poets, in Virgil, in Racine and Lamartine. They have given utterance to the emotions which I but felt. I could not break silence. The miracles wrought in my soul by this young girl will remain for ever unrevealed. For two years I lived an enchanted life; then, one day, she told me she was going to be married. My feelings, as I have said, bear a strong resemblance to religious emotion. They are sad, but in their sadness they still preserve their charm. Grief corrupts them not.

From suffering they derive a wholesome bitterness that lends them strength. I listened to her with that gentle courage which comes with renunciation. She was marrying a man senior to myself, a widower, almost an old man, whose birth and fortune had marked him out for the public career in which he had displayed a haughtiness of disposition and much misplaced courage. Although I moved in a lower sphere, I came in contact with him on several important occasions. I belonged to a political group with views very similar to his own, but we had never been able to meet without considerable friction and, although the newspapers treated us with the same approval or, as was more often the case, with the same hostility, we were not friends, far from it, and we avoided each other with sedulous care.

I was present at the wedding. I saw, and I shall ever see Marie, wearing her white dress and lace veil. She was a little pale and very lovely. I was struck, without apparent reason, by the impression of fragility with which this girl who was animated by so poetic a soul seemed to give one. This impression, which I think occurred to no one but myself, was only too well founded. I never saw Marie again.

She died after three years of married life, leaving a little girl ten months old. An indescribable feeling of tender affection has always drawn me to this child, to Marie's Marguerite. An unconquerable desire to see her took possession of me.

She was being brought up at —— near Melun, where her father had a château standing in the midst of a magnificent park. One day I went to —— and wandered for hours, like a thief, about the park boundaries. At last, through a gap in the trees, I caught sight of Marguerite in the arms of her nurse, who was dressed in black. She was wearing a hat with white plumes and an embroidered pelisse. I cannot say in what respect she differed from any other child, but I thought she was the fairest in the world. It was autumn. The wind that was sighing in the trees was whirling the dead leaves about in little eddies as they floated to earth. Dead leaves covered all the long avenue in which the little white-robed child was being carried up and down. An immense sadness took possession of me. At the edge of a bed of flowers as white as the raiment of Marguerite, an old gardener who was gathering up the fallen leaves saluted his little mistress with a smile and, with his hand on his rake and hat in hand, spoke to her with the gentle gaiety of old men who are not overburdened with their thoughts. But she paid no heed to him. With her little hand like to a star she sought her nurse's breast. As I hurried away with grief in my heart, the nurse resumed her walk and I heard the sound of the dead leaves sighing sorrowfully beneath her steps.

10th July

THE President of the Chamber rises and says: "The motion proposed by Messrs. —— and —— is now put."

The Prime Minister, without quitting his seat says: "The Government does not assent to the motion."

The President rings his bell and says: "A ballot has been demanded. A ballot will therefore be taken. Those in favour of Messrs. —— and ——'s motion must place a white paper in the urn; those who are against it, a blue paper."

There was a great movement in the hall. The deputies poured out in a disorderly mob into the corridors, while the ushers passed the white metal urn along the tiers of seats. The corridors were full of the sound of shuffling feet, and of shouting and gesticulating people. Grave looking young men and excited old ones went passing by. The air was pierced with the sound of voices calling out figures:

"Eleven votes."

"No, nine."

"They are being checked."

"Eight against."

"No, not at all; eight for."

"What, the amendment is carried?"

"Yes."

"The Government is beaten?"

"Yes."

"Ah!"

The President's bell is heard in the corridors. Slowly the hall fills again.

The President standing up with a paper in his hand rings his bell for the last time and says:

"The following is the result of the ballot on the motion proposed by Messrs. —— and ——. Number of votes 470; for the motion 239; against 231. The motion is carried."

There is an immense sensation. The Ministers get up and leave their seats. Two or three friends shake them timidly by the hand. It's all over, they are beaten. They go under and I with them. I no longer count. I make up my mind to it. To say that I am happy would be to go too far. But it spells the end of my worries and bothers and toils. I have regained my freedom, but not voluntarily. Repose and liberty, I've got them back again, but it is to my defeat that I owe them. An honourable defeat it is true, but painful all the same because our ideas suffer with ourselves. How many things are involved in our fall, alas. Economy, public security, tranquillity of conscience and that spirit of prudence, that continuity of policy, which gives a nation its strength. I hurried away to shake hands with the Chief of my department, proud of having rendered faithful service to so upright a leader. Then, pushing my way through the crowd that had gathered about the precincts of the Palais Bourbon, I crossed the Seine and made my way slowly towards the Madeleine. At the top of the boulevard there was a barrow of flowers drawn up alongside the kerb. Between the two shafts was a young girl making up bunches of violets. I went up to her and asked her for a bunch. I then saw a little girl of four sitting on the barrow amid the flowers. With her baby fingers she was trying to make bunches like her mother. She raised her head at my approach and, with a smile, held out all the flowers she had in her hands. When she had given them all to me, she blew kisses.

I was extremely flattered. "I must have a kindly look about me," I said to myself, "for a child to smile a welcome at me like that. What is your name?" I asked her.

"Marguerite," replied her mother.

It was half-past six. There was a news-vendor's hard by. I bought a paper. As soon as I glanced at it I saw that I was in for a wigging. The political editor, having referred to my Chief as an individual of ill omen, spoke of me too, on the first page, as a sinister creature. But, after Marguerite's kisses, I could not believe it. I felt at once a lightness and a sort of emptiness at heart; both glad and sorrowful.

A week later found me on my way to —— near Melun, where I had taken a little house hard by the Château of Marguerite's upbringing. In my eyes it was the fairest region in the world.

As we approached the station I looked out of the carriage window. The silver river flowed in graceful curves between willows, until it vanished from the sight. But long after it was lost to view one could divine its course by the rows of poplars which lined its banks. A weathercock and two towers visible amid the trees marked the site of the town. Then I exclaimed, "Here is the resting place for me, here will I lay my head."

25th July

THE walk I love best is the walk to Saint-Jean, for there, about a hundred yards from the town is a little wood, or rather a little half-wild cluster of hornbeams, maples, limes and lilac bushes, a bouquet that murmurs in the breeze. The very first day I discovered it, I felt its charm. I determined to make love to it; I made up my mind to know it tree by tree, to search out its humblest plants, its vetches, its saxifrages, and to see whether there was no Solomon's seal to be found growing beneath the shade of the big trees. I kept my word and now I am beginning to make acquaintance with the flora and fauna of my little wood. I had been reclining on the grass to-day for the space of an hour, book in hand, when I heard some one crying in a faint voice. I looked up and beheld a little girl standing beside an elderly man and weeping. The man was undeniably old. His face was long and pallid. There was an expression of sadness in his eyes and his mouth drooped mournfully. He had a skipping-rope in his hand and was looking fixedly at the child. Then he turned aside to brush away a tear from his cheek. It was then that I beheld him full face and saw that he was Marguerite's father. I was shocked at the great change that illness and sorrow had wrought in his haughty mien. Despair was graven on his countenance and he seemed to be calling for help.

I went up to him and, in response to my offer to assist him in any way possible, he explained with some embarrassment that a ball with which his little girl had been playing had got caught in a tree and that his stick, which he had thrown up in order to dislodge it, had become entangled in the branches. He was at his wit's end.

Only a few years before, this same man had circumvented the policy of England and imparted a vigorous stimulus to French diplomacy in Europe. Then he fell with honour, and was followed in his retirement by a profound but honourable unpopularity. And now, behold his powers are unequal to the task of dislodging a ball from a tree. Such is the frailty of man. As for his daughter, Marie's daughter, a sort of presentiment forbade me to look in her face. And then when at length I did look at her, I could not tear myself away from such a sorrowful object of contemplation. She was no longer the little pink and white child I had seen in the Champs-Élysées; she had grown taller and thinner, and her face was wan as a waxen taper. Her languid eyes were encircled with blue rings. And her temples . . . what invisible hand had laid those two sad violets upon her temples?

"There! there! there!" cried the old man as he stretched forth a trembling arm which pointed aimlessly in all directions.

The first thing to be done was to help him. By means of a stone which I threw up into the tree, I soon managed to bring the ball down. X . . . witnessed its fall with childish delight. He had not recognized me. I hurriedly escaped to spare him the trouble of thanking me and myself the agony of seeing the change that had taken place in Marie's daughter.

10th August

I SELDOM go out. I am no longer moved by the beauty of things. Or to speak more truly, the more pleasurable and splendid aspects of nature give me pain. All day long I sully sheet after sheet of paper and beguile the tedious hours with the half-faded recollections of my childhood. What I am writing will be burned. I should be ashamed that pages, tear-stained and dream-haunted, should fall beneath the eyes of grave, sober-minded folk. What would they see in them? Naught but childish faces.

20th August

TO-DAY I went for a stroll by the river in whose blue waters are mirrored the willows and the houses that befringe its banks. There is a seductive charm about running waters. They bear along with them as they flow all those idlers who love to dream their time away.

The river lured me as far as the château de —— which had witnessed the betrothal and the death of Marie, and the birth of Marguerite. My heart tolled a knell within me when I saw once more that peaceful abode, which, despite the scenes of sorrow enacted within its walls, speaks, with its white pillared façade, of naught save elegant opulence and luxurious repose. I was so overcome that, to save myself from falling, I clung to the bars of the park gate and gazed at the wide lawns which stretched away as far as the flight of steps which the hem of Marie's robe had kissed so often. I had been there some minutes when the gate was opened and X . . . came out.

On this occasion, also, he was accompanied by his child: but this time she was not walking. She was lying in a perambulator which was being pushed by a governess. With her head resting on an embroidered pillow in the shadow of the lowered hood, she resembled one of those little waxen images of saint or martyr, embellished with silver filigree, on whose wounds and gems the nuns of Spain are wont to pore in the solitude of their cells.

Her father, elegantly dressed, presented a faded, tear-stained countenance. He advanced towards me with little faltering steps, took me by the hand and led me to his little girl.

"Tell me," he said in the tone of a child asking a favour, "you don't think she has changed since you last saw her, do you? It was the day she threw her ball up into the tree."

The perambulator which we were following in silence came to a halt in the Bois Saint-Jean. The governess lowered the hood. Marguerite lay with her head thrown back, her eyes big with terror, and she was stretching out her arms to push aside something that we could not see. Oh, I guessed well enough what invisible hand it was. The same hand that had touched the mother was now laid upon the child. I fell on my knees. But the phantom departed and Marguerite, raising her head, lay resting peacefully. I gathered some flowers and laid them reverently beside her. She smiled. Seeing her come back to life I gave her more flowers and sang to her, endeavouring to beguile her. The air and the feeling of happiness she now experienced brought back to her that desire to live which had forsaken her. At the end of an hour her cheeks were almost rosy. When it grew cool and we had to take the little suffering child back to the château again, her father took my hand as we parted and, pressing it, said in suppliant tones:

"Come again to-morrow."

21st August

I RETURNED next day. On the steps of the Empire château I encountered the family doctor. He is a spare, elderly man whom you meet wherever there is good music to be heard. He seems like a man perpetually listening to the harmonies of some inward concert. He is for ever under the spell of sounds and lives by his ear alone. He is specially noted for his treatment of nervous complaints. Some say he is a genius; others that he is mad. Certainly there is something peculiar about him. When I saw him he was coming down the steps; his feet, his finger and his lips moving in time to some intricate measure.

"Well, doctor," I said with an involuntary quaver in my voice, "and how is your little patient?"

"She means to live," he answered.

"You will pull her through for us, won't you?" I said eagerly.

"I tell you she means to live."

"And you think, doctor, that people live just as long as they really want to and that we do not die save with our own consent?"

"Certainly."

I walked with him along the gravel path. He stopped for a moment at the gate, his head bowed as if in thought.

"Certainly," he said again, "but they must really want to and not merely think they want to. Conscious will is an illusion that can deceive none save the vulgar. People who believe they will a thing because they say they will it, are fools. The only genuine act of volition is that in which all the obscure forces of our nature take part. That will is unconscious, it is divine. It moulds the world. By it we exist, and when it fails we cease to be. The world *wills*, otherwise it would not exist."

We walked on a few steps farther.

"Look here," he exclaimed, tapping his stick against the bark of an oak tree that spread out its broad canopy of grey branches above our heads, "if that fellow there had not *willed* to grow, I should like to know what power could have made him do so."

But I had ceased to listen.

"So you have hopes," I said at length, "that Marguerite . . ."

But he was a stubborn little old fellow. He murmured as he walked away: "The Will's crowning Victory is Love."

And I stood and watched him as he departed with little quick steps, beating time to a tune that was running in his head.

I went quickly back to the château and found little Marguerite. The moment I saw her, I realized that she had the will to live. She was still very pale and very thin, but her eyes had more colour in them and were not so big, and her lips, lately so dead-looking and so silent, were gay with prattling talk.

"You are late," she said. "Come here, see! I have a theatre and actors. Play me a beautiful piece. They say that 'Hop o' my Thumb' is nice. Play 'Hop o' my Thumb' for me."

You may be sure I did not refuse. However, I encountered great difficulties at the very outset of my undertaking. I pointed out to Marguerite that the only actors she had were princes and princesses, and that we wanted woodmen, cooks and a certain number of folks of all sorts.

She thought for a moment and then said: "A prince dressed like a cook; that one there looks like a cook, don't you think?"

"Yes, I think so too."

"Well, then, we'll make woodmen and cooks out of all the princes we have over."

And that's what we did. O Wisdom, what a day we spent together!

Many others like it followed in its train. I watched Marguerite taking an ever firmer hold on life. Now she is quite well again. I had a share in this miracle. I discovered a tiny portion of that gift wherein the apostles so richly abounded when they healed the sick by the laying on of hands.

Editor's Note.—I found this manuscript in a train on the Northern Railway. I give it to the public without alteration of any sort, save that, as the names were those of well-known persons, I have thought it well to suppress them.

ANATOLE FRANCE.

THE END

THAÏS

BY ANATOLE FRANCE

A TRANSLATION BY ROBERT B. DOUGLAS

BOOKLOVERS' EDITION

NEW YORK: WM. H. WISE & CO.
MCMXXX

PRINTED IN U. S. A. BY
FERRIS PRINTING COMPANY
BINDING BY - VAN REES
BOOK BINDING CORPORATION

CONTENTS

		PAGE
Part I.	The Lotus	3
Part II.	The Papyrus	63
	The Banquet	111
	The Papyrus (resumed)	146
Part III.	The Euphorbia	177

# PART THE FIRST

THE LOTUS

PART THE FIRST
THE LOTUS

IN those days there were many hermits living in the desert. On both banks of the Nile numerous huts, built by these solitary dwellers, of branches held together by clay, were scattered at a little distance from each other, so that the inhabitants could live alone, and yet help one another in case of need. Churches, each surmounted by a cross, stood here and there amongst the huts, and the monks flocked to them at each festival to celebrate the services or to partake of the Communion. There were also, here and there on the banks of the river, monasteries, where the cenobites lived in separate cells, and only met together that they might the better enjoy their solitude.

Both hermits and cenobites led abstemious lives, taking no food till after sunset, and eating nothing but bread with a little salt and hyssop. Some retired into the desert, and led a still more strange life in some cave or tomb.

All lived in temperance and chastity; they wore a hair shirt and a hood, slept on the bare ground after long watching, prayed, sang psalms, and, in short, spent their days in works of penitence. As an atonement for original sin, they refused their body not only all pleasures and satisfactions, but even that care and attention which in this age are deemed indispensable. They believed that the diseases of our members purify our souls, and the flesh could put on no adornment more glorious than wounds and ulcers. Thus, they thought they fulfilled the words of the prophet, "The desert shall rejoice and blossom as the rose."

Amongst the inhabitants of the holy Thebaid, there were some who passed their days in asceticism and contemplation; others gained their livelihood by plaiting palm fibre, or by working at harvest-time for the neighbouring farmers. The Gentiles wrongly suspected some of them of living by brigandage, and allying themselves to the nomadic Arabs who robbed the caravans. But, as a matter of fact, the monks despised riches, and the odour of their sanctity rose to heaven.

Angels in the likeness of young men, came, staff in hand, as travellers, to visit the hermitages; whilst demons—having assumed the form of Ethiopians or of animals—wandered round the habitations of the hermits in order to lead them into temptation. When the monks went in the morning to fill their pitcher at the spring, they saw the footprints of

Satyrs and Aigipans in the sand. The Thebaid was, really and spiritually, a battlefield, where, at all times, and more especially at night, there were terrible conflicts between heaven and hell.

The ascetics, furiously assailed by legions of the damned, defended themselves—with the help of God and the angels—by fasting, prayer, and penance. Sometimes carnal desires pricked them so cruelly that they cried aloud with pain, and their lamentations rose to the starlit heavens mingled with the howls of the hungry hyænas. Then it was that the demons appeared in delightful forms. For though the demons are, in reality, hideous, they sometimes assume an appearance of beauty which prevents their real nature from being recognised. The ascetics of the Thebaid were amazed to see in their cells phantasms of delights unknown even to the voluptuaries of the age. But, as they were under the sign of the Cross, they did not succumb to these temptations, and the unclean spirits, assuming again their true character, fled at daybreak, filled with rage and shame. It was not unusual to meet at dawn one of these beings, flying away and weeping, and replying to those who questioned it, "I weep and groan because one of the Christians who live here has beaten me with rods, and driven me away in ignominy."

The power of the old saints of the desert extended over all sinners and unbelievers. Their goodness was sometimes terrible. They derived from the Apostles authority to punish all offences against the true and only God, and no earthly power could save those they condemned. Strange tales were told in the cities, and even as far as Alexandria, how the earth had opened and swallowed up certain wicked persons whom one of these saints struck with his staff. Therefore they were feared by all evil-doers, and particularly by mimes, mountebanks, married priests, and prostitutes.

Such was the sanctity of these holy men that even wild beasts felt their power. When a hermit was about to die, a lion came and dug a grave with its claws. The saint knew by this that God had called him, and he went and kissed all his brethren on the cheek. Then he lay down joyfully, and slept in the Lord.

Now that Anthony, who was more than a hundred years old, had retired to Mount Colzin with his well-beloved disciples, Macarius and Amathas, there was no monk in the Thebaid more renowned for good works than Paphnutius, the Abbot of Antinoë. Ephrem and Serapion had a greater number of followers, and in the spiritual and temporal management of their monasteries surpassed him. But

Paphnutius observed the most rigorous fasts, and often went for three entire days without taking food. He wore a very rough hair shirt, he flogged himself night and morning, and lay for hours with his face to the earth.

His twenty-four disciples had built their huts near his, and imitated his austerities. He loved them all dearly in Jesus Christ, and unceasingly exhorted them to good works. Amongst his spiritual children were men who had been robbers for many years, and had been persuaded by the exhortations of the holy abbot to embrace the monastic life, and who now edified their companions by the purity of their lives. One, who had been cook to the Queen of Abyssinia, and was converted by the Abbot of Antinoë, never ceased to weep. There was also Flavian, the deacon, who knew the Scriptures, and spoke well; but the disciple of Paphnutius who surpassed all the others in holiness was a young peasant named Paul, and surnamed the Fool, because of his extreme simplicity. Men laughed at his childishness, but God favoured him with visions, and by bestowing upon him the gift of prophecy.

Paphnutius passed his life in teaching his disciples, and in ascetic practices. Often did he meditate upon the Holy Scriptures in order to find allegories in them. Therefore he abounded in good works, though still young. The devils, who so rudely assailed the good hermits, did not dare to approach him. At night, seven little jackals sat in the moonlight in front of his cell, silent and motionless, and with their ears pricked up. It was believed that they were seven devils, who, owing to his sanctity, could not cross his threshold.

Paphnutius was born at Alexandria of noble parents, who had instructed him in all profane learning. He had even been allured by the falsehoods of the poets, and in his early youth had been misguided enough to believe that the human race had all been drowned by a deluge in the days of Deucalion, and had argued with his fellow-scholars concerning the nature, the attributes, and even the existence of God. He then led a life of dissipation, after the manner of the Gentiles, and he recalled the memory of those days with shame and horror.

"At that time," he used to say to the brethren, "I seethed in the cauldron of false delights."

He meant by that that he had eaten food properly dressed, and frequented the public baths. In fact, until his twentieth year he had continued to lead the ordinary existence of those times, which now seemed to him rather death than life; but, owing to the lessons of the priest Macrinus, he then became a new man.

The truth penetrated him through and through, and—as he used to say—entered his soul like a sword. He embraced the faith of Calvary, and worshipped Christ crucified. After his baptism he remained yet a year amongst the Gentiles, unable to cast off the bonds of old habits. But one day he entered a church, and heard a deacon read from the Bible, the verse, "If thou wilt be perfect, go and sell that thou hast, and give to the poor." Thereupon he sold all that he had, gave away the money in alms, and embraced the monastic life.

During the ten years that he had lived remote from men, he no longer seethed in the cauldron of false delights, but more profitably macerated his flesh in the balms of penitence.

One day when, according to his pious custom, he was recalling to mind the hours he had lived apart from God, and examining his sins one by one, that he might the better ponder on their enormity, he remembered that he had seen at the theatre at Alexandria a very beautiful actress named Thaïs. This woman showed herself in the public games, and did not scruple to perform dances, the movements of which, arranged only too cleverly, brought to mind the most horrible passions. Sometimes she imitated the horrible deeds which the Pagan fables ascribe to Venus, Leda, or Pasiphaë. Thus she fired all the spectators with lust, and when handsome young men, or rich old ones, came, inspired with love, to hang wreaths of flowers round her door, she welcomed them, and gave herself up to them. So that, whilst she lost her own soul, she also ruined the souls of many others.

She had almost led Paphnutius himself into the sins of the flesh. She had awakened desire in him, and he had once approached the house of Thaïs. But he stopped on the threshold of the courtesan's house, partly restrained by the natural timidity of extreme youth—he was then but fifteen years old—and partly by the fear of being refused on account of his want of money, for his parents took care that he should commit no great extravagances.

God, in His mercy, had used these two means to prevent him from committing a great sin. But Paphnutius had not been grateful to Him for that, because at that time he was blind to his own interests, and did not know that he was lusting after false delights. Now, kneeling in his cell, before the image of that holy cross on which hung, as in a balance, the ransom of the world, Paphnutius began to think of Thaïs, because Thaïs was a sin to him, and he meditated long, according to ascetic rules, on the fearful hideousness of the carnal delights with which this woman had inspired him in the days of his sin and ignorance. After some hours of meditation the image of Thaïs appeared to him clearly and distinctly. He saw her again, as he had seen her when she tempted him, in all the beauty of the flesh. At first she showed herself like a Leda, softly lying upon a bed of hyacinths, her head bowed, her eyes humid and filled with a strange light, her nostrils quivering, her mouth half open, her breasts like two flowers, and her arms smooth and fresh as two brooks. At this sight Paphnutius struck his breast and said—

"I call Thee to witness, my God, that I have considered how heinous has been my sin."

Gradually the face of the image changed its expression. Little by little the lips of Thaïs, by lowering at the corners of the mouth, expressed a mysterious suffering. Her large eyes were filled with tears and lights; her breast heaved with sighs, like the sighing of a wind that precedes a tempest. At this sight Paphnutius was troubled to the bottom of his soul. Prostrating himself on the floor, he uttered this prayer—

"Thou who hast put pity in our hearts, like the morning dew upon the fields, O just and merciful God, be Thou blessed! Praise! praise be unto Thee! Put away from Thy servant that false tenderness which tempts to concupiscence, and grant that I may only love Thy creatures in Thee, for they pass away, but Thou endurest for ever. If I care for this woman, it is only because she is Thy handiwork. The angels themselves feel pity for her. Is she not, O Lord, the breath of Thy mouth? Let her not continue to sin with many citizens and strangers. There is great pity for her in my heart. Her wickednesses are abominable, and but to think of them makes my flesh creep. But the more wicked she is, the more do I lament for her. I weep when I think that the devils will torment her to all eternity."

As he was meditating in this way, he saw a little jackal lying at his feet. He felt much surprised, for the door of his cell had been closed since the morning. The animal seemed to read the Abbot's thoughts, and wagged its tail like a dog. Paphnutius made the sign of the cross and the beast vanished. He knew then that, for the first time, the devil had entered his cell, and he uttered a short prayer; then he thought again about Thaïs.

"With God's help," he said to himself, "I must save her." And he slept.

The next morning, when he had said his prayers, he went to see the sainted Palemon, a holy hermit who lived some distance away. He found him smiling quietly as he dug the ground, as was his custom.

Palemon was an old man, and cultivated a little garden; the wild beasts came and licked his hands, and the devils never tormented him.

"May God be praised, brother Paphnutius," he said, as he leaned upon his spade.

"God be praised!" replied Paphnutius. "And peace be unto my brother."

"The like peace be unto thee, brother Paphnutius," said Palemon; and he wiped the sweat from his forehead with his sleeve.

"Brother Palemon, all our discourse ought to be solely the praise of Him who has promised to be wheresoever two or three are gathered together in His Name. That is why I come to you concerning a design I have formed to glorify the Lord."

"May the Lord bless thy design, Paphnutius, as He has blessed my lettuces. Every morning He spreads His grace with the dew on my garden, and His goodness causes me to glorify Him in the cucumbers and melons which He gives me. Let us pray that He may keep us in His peace. For nothing is more to be feared than those unruly passions which trouble our hearts. When these passions disturb us we are like drunken men, and we stagger from right to left unceasingly, and are like to fall miserably. Sometimes these passions plunge us into a turbulent joy, and he who gives way to such, sullies the air with brutish laughter. Such false joy drags the sinner into all sorts of excess. But sometimes also the troubles of the soul and of the senses throw us into an impious sadness which is a thousand times worse than the joy. Brother Paphnutius, I am but a miserable sinner, but I have found, in my long life, that the cenobite has no foe worse than sadness. I mean by that the obstinate melancholy which envelopes the soul as in a mist, and hides from us the light of God. Nothing is more contrary to salvation, and the devil's greatest triumph is to sow black and bitter thoughts in the heart of a good man. If he sent us only pleasurable temptations, he would not be half so much to be feared. Alas! he excels in making us sad. Did he not show to our father Anthony a black child of such surpassing beauty that the very sight of it drew tears? With God's help, our father Anthony avoided the snares of the demon. I knew him when he lived amongst us; he was cheerful with his disciples, and never gave way to melancholy. But did you not come, my brother, to talk to me of a design you had formed in your mind? Let me know what it is—if, at least, this design has for its object the glory of God."

"Brother Palemon, what I propose is really to the glory of God. Strengthen me with your counsel, for you know many things, and sin has never darkened the clearness of your mind."

"Brother Paphnutius, I am not worthy to unloose the latchet of thy sandals, and my sins are as countless as the sands of the desert. But I am old, and I will never refuse the help of my experience."

"I will confide in you, then, brother Palemon, that I am stricken with grief at the thought that there is, in Alexandria, a courtesan named Thaïs, who lives in sin, and a subject of reproach unto the people."

"Brother Paphnutius, that is, in truth, an abomination which we do well to deplore. There are many women amongst the Gentiles who lead lives of that kind. Have you thought of any remedy for this great evil?"

"Brother Palemon, I will go to Alexandria and find this woman, and, with God's help, I will convert her; that is my intention; do you approve of it, brother?"

"Brother Paphnutius, I am but a miserable sinner, but our father Anthony used to say, 'In whatsoever place thou art, hasten not to leave it to go elsewhere.'"

"Brother Palemon, do you disapprove of my project?"

"Dear Paphnutius, God forbid that I should suspect my brother of bad intentions. But our father Anthony also said, 'Fishes die on dry land, and so is it with those monks who leave their cells and mingle with the men of this world, amongst whom no good thing is to be found.'"

Having thus spoken, the old man pressed his foot on the spade, and began to dig energetically round a fig tree laden with fruit. As he was thus engaged, there was a rustling in the bushes, and an antelope leaped over the hedge which surrounded the garden; it stopped, surprised and frightened, its delicate legs trembling, then ran up to the old man, and laid its pretty head on the breast of its friend.

"God be praised in the gazelle of the desert," said Palemon.

He went to his hut, the light-footed little animal trotting after him, and brought out some black bread, which the antelope ate out of his hand.

Paphnutius remained thoughtful for some time, his eyes fixed upon the stones at his feet. Then he slowly walked back to his cell, pondering on what he had heard. A great struggle was going on in his mind.

"The hermit gives good advice," he said to himself; "the spirit of prudence is in him. And he doubts the wisdom of my intention. Yet it would be cruel to leave Thaïs any longer in the power of

THE LOTUS

the demon who possesses her. May God advise and conduct me."

As he was walking along, he saw a plover, caught in the net that a hunter had laid on the sand, and he knew that it was a hen bird, for he saw the male fly to the net, and tear the meshes one by one with its beak, until it had made an opening by which its mate could escape. The holy man watched this incident, and as, by virtue of his holiness, he easily comprehended the mystic sense of all occurrences, he knew that the captive bird was no other than Thaïs, caught in the snares of sin, and that—like the plover that had cut the hempen threads with its beak—he could, by pronouncing the word of power, break the invisible bonds by which Thaïs was held in sin. Therefore he praised God, and was confirmed in his first resolution. But then seeing the plover caught by the feet, and hampered by the net it had broken, he fell into uncertainty again.

He did not sleep all night, and before dawn he had a vision. Thaïs appeared to him again. There was no expression of guilty pleasure on her face, nor was she dressed according to custom in transparent drapery. She was enveloped in a shroud, which hid even a part of her face, so that the Abbot could see nothing but the two eyes, from which flowed white and heavy tears.

At this sight he began to weep, and believing that this vision came from God, he no longer hesitated. He rose, seized a knotted stick, the symbol of the Christian faith, and left his cell, carefully closing the door, lest the animals of the desert and the birds of the air should enter, and befoul the copy of the Holy Scriptures which stood at the head of his bed. He called Flavian, the deacon, and gave him authority over the other twenty-three disciples during his absence; and then, clad only in a long cassock, he bent his steps towards the Nile, intending to follow the Libyan bank to the city founded by the Macedonian monarch. He walked from dawn to eve, indifferent to fatigue, hunger, and thirst; the sun was already low on the horizon when he saw the dreadful river, the blood-red waters of which rolled between the rocks of gold and fire.

He kept along the shore, begging his bread at the door of solitary huts for the love of God, and joyfully receiving insults, refusals, or threats. He feared neither robbers nor wild beasts, but he took great care to avoid all the towns and villages he came near. He was afraid lest he should see children playing at knuckle-bones before their father's house, or meet, by the side of the well, women in blue smocks, who might put down their pitcher and smile at him. All things are dangerous for the hermit; it is sometimes a danger for him to read in the Scriptures that the Divine Master journeyed from town to town and supped with His disciples. The virtues that the anchorites embroider so carefully on the tissue of faith, are as fragile as they are beautiful; a breath of ordinary life may tarnish their pleasant colours. For that reason, Paphnutius avoided the towns, fearing lest his heart should soften at the sight of his fellowmen.

He journeyed along lonely roads. When evening came, the murmuring of the breeze amidst the tamarisk trees made him shiver, and he pulled his hood over his eyes that he might not see how beautiful all things were. After walking six days, he came to a place called Silsile. There the river runs in a narrow valley, bordered by a double chain of granite mountains. It was there that the Egyptians, in the days when they worshipped demons, carved their idols. Paphnutius saw an enormous sphinx carved in the solid rock. Fearing that it might still possess some diabolical properties, he made the sign of the cross, and pronounced the name of Jesus; he immediately saw a bat fly out of one of the monster's ears, and Paphnutius knew that he had driven out the evil spirits which had been for centuries in the figure. His zeal increased, and picking up a large stone, he threw it in the idol's face. Then the mysterious face of the sphinx expressed such profound sadness that Paphnutius was moved. In fact, the expression of superhuman grief on the stone visage would have touched even the most unfeeling man. Therefore Paphnutius said to the sphinx—

"O monster, be like the satyrs and centaurs our father Anthony saw in the desert, and confess the divinity of Jesus Christ, and I will bless thee in the name of the Father, the Son, and the Holy Ghost."

When he had spoken a rosy light gleamed in the eyes of the sphinx; the heavy eyelids of the monster quivered and the granite lips painfully murmured, as though in echo to the man's voice, the holy name of Jesus Christ; therefore Paphnutius stretched out his right hand, and blessed the sphinx of Silsile.

That being done, he resumed his journey, and the valley having grown wider, he saw the ruins of an immense city. The temples, which still remained standing, were supported by idols which served as columns, and—by the permission of God—these figures with women's heads and cow's horns, threw on Paphnutius a long look which made him turn pale. He walked thus seventeen days, his only food a few raw herbs, and he slept at night in some ruined palace, amongst the wild cats and Pharaoh's rats, with which mingled sometimes, women whose bodies ended in a scaly tail. But Paphnutius knew that these women came from hell, and he drove them away by making the sign of the cross.

On the eighteenth day, he found, far from any village, a wretched hut made of palm leaves, and half buried under the sand which had been driven by the desert wind. He approached it, hoping that the hut was inhabited by some pious anchorite. He saw inside the hovel—for there was no door—a pitcher, a bunch of onions, and a bed of dried leaves.

"This must be the habitation of a hermit," he said to himself. "Hermits are generally to be found near their hut, and I shall not fail to meet this one. I will give him the kiss of peace, even as the holy Anthony did when he came to the hermit Paul, and kissed him three times. We will discourse of things eternal, and perhaps our Lord will send us, by one of His ravens, a crust of bread, which my host will willingly invite me to share with him."

Whilst he was thus speaking to himself, he walked round the hut to see if he could find any one. He had not walked a hundred paces when he saw a man seated, with his legs crossed, by the side of the river. The man was naked; his hair and beard were quite white, and his body redder than brick. Paphnutius felt sure this must be the hermit. He saluted him with the words the monks are accustomed to use when they meet each other.

"Peace be with you, brother! May you some day taste the sweet joys of paradise."

The man did not reply. He remained motionless, and appeared not to have heard. Paphnutius supposed this was due to one of those rhapsodies to which the saints are accustomed. He knelt down, with his hands joined, by the side of the unknown, and remained thus in prayer till sunset. Then, seeing that his companion had not moved, he said to him—

"Father, if you are now out of the ecstasy in which you were lost, give me your blessing in our Lord Jesus Christ."

The other replied without turning his head—

"Stranger, I understand you not, and I know not the Lord Jesus Christ."

"What!" cried Paphnutius. "The prophets have announced Him; legions of martyrs have confessed His name; Cæsar himself has worshipped Him, and, but just now, I made the sphinx of Silsile proclaim His glory. Is it possible that you do not know Him?"

"Friend," replied the other, "it is possible. It

would even be certain, if anything in this world were certain."

Paphnutius was surprised and saddened by the incredible ignorance of the man.

"If you know not Jesus Christ," he said, "all your works serve no purpose, and you will never rise to life immortal."

The old man replied—

"It is useless to act, or to abstain from acting. It matters not whether we live or die."

"Eh, what?" asked Paphnutius. "Do you not desire to live through all eternity? But, tell me, do you not live in a hut in the desert as the hermits do?"

"It seems so."

"Do I not see you naked, and lacking all things?"

"It seems so."

"Do you not feed on roots, and live in chastity?"

"It seems so."

"Have you not renounced all the vanities of this world?"

"I have truly renounced all those vain things for which men commonly care."

"Then you are like me, poor, chaste, and solitary. And you are not so—as I am—for the love of God, and with a hope of celestial happiness! That I cannot understand. Why are you virtuous if you do not believe in Jesus Christ? Why deprive yourself of the good things of this world if you do not hope to gain eternal riches in heaven?"

"Stranger, I deprive myself of nothing which is good, and I flatter myself that I have found a life which is satisfactory enough, though—to speak more precisely—there is no such thing as a good or evil life. Nothing is itself, either virtuous or shameful, just or unjust, pleasant or painful, good or bad. It is our opinion which gives those qualities to things, as salt gives savour to meats."

"So then, according to you there is no certainty. You deny the truth which the idolaters themselves have sought. You lie in ignorance—like a tired dog sleeping in the mud."

"Stranger, it is equally useless to abuse either dogs or philosophers. We know not what dogs are or what we are. We know nothing."

"Old man, do you belong, then, to the absurd sect of sceptics? Are you one of those miserable fools who alike deny movement and rest, and who know not how to distinguish between the light of the sun and the shadows of night?"

"Friend, I am truly a sceptic, and of a sect which appears praiseworthy to me, though it seems ridiculous to you. For the same things often assume different appearances. The pyramids of Memphis seem at sunrise to be cones of pink light. At sunset they look like black triangles against the illuminated sky. But who shall solve the problem of their true nature? You reproach me with denying appearances, when, in fact, appearances are the only realities I recognise. The sun seems to me illuminous, but its nature is unknown to me. I feel that fire burns—but I know not how or why. My friend, you understand me badly. Besides, it is indifferent to me whether I am understood one way or the other."

"Once more. Why do you live on dates and onions in the desert? Why do you endure great hardships? I endure hardships equally great, and, like you, I live in abstinence and solitude. But then it is to please God, and to earn eternal happiness. And that is a reasonable object, for it is wise to suffer now for a future gain. It is senseless, on the contrary, to expose yourself voluntarily to useless fatigue and vain sufferings. If I did not believe—pardon my blasphemy, O uncreated Light!—if I did not believe in the truth of that which God has taught us by the voice of the prophets, by the example of His Son, by the acts of the Apostles, by the authority of councils, and by the testimony of the martyrs,—if I did not know that the sufferings of the body are necessary for the salvation of the soul—if I were, like thee, lost in ignorance of sacred mysteries—I would return at once amongst the men of this day, I would strive to acquire riches, that I might live in ease, like those who are happy in this world, and I would say to the votaries of pleasure, 'Come, my daughters, come, my servants, come and pour out for me your wines, your philtres, your perfumes.' But you, foolish old man! you deprive yourself of all these advantages; you lose without hope of any gain; you give without hope of any return, and you imitate foolishly the noble deeds of us anchorites, as an impudent monkey thinks, by smearing a wall, to copy the picture of a clever artist. What, then, are your reasons, O most besotted of men?"

Paphnutius spoke with violence and indignation, but the old man remained unmoved.

"Friend," he replied, gently, "what matter the reasons of a dog sleeping in the dirt or a mischievous ape?"

Paphnutius' only aim was the glory of God. His anger vanished, and he apologised with noble humility.

"Pardon me, old man, my brother," he said, "if zeal for the truth has carried me beyond proper bounds. God is my witness, that it is thy errors and not thyself that I hate. I suffer to see thee in darkness, for I love thee in Jesus Christ, and care for thy salvation fills my heart. Speak! give me your reasons. I long to know them that I may refute them."

The old man replied quietly—

"It is the same to me whether I speak or remain silent. I will give my reasons without asking yours in return, for I have no interest in you at all. I care neither for your happiness nor your misfortune, and it matters not to me whether you think one way or another. Why should I love you, or hate you? Aversion and sympathy are equally unworthy of the wise man. But since you question me, know then that I am named Timocles, and that I was born at Cos, of parents made rich by commerce. My father was a shipowner. In intelligence he much resembled Alexander, who is surnamed the Great. But he was not so gross. In short, he was a man of no great parts. I had two brothers, who, like him, were shipowners. As for me, I followed wisdom. My eldest brother was compelled by my father to marry a Carian woman, named Timaessa, who displeased him so greatly that he could not live with her without falling into a deep melancholy. However, Timaessa inspired our younger brother with a criminal passion, and this passion soon turned to a furious madness. The

Carian woman hated them both equally; but she loved a flute-player, and received him at night in her chamber. One morning he left there the wreath which he usually wore at feasts. My two brothers, having found this wreath, swore to kill the flute-player, and the next day they caused him to perish under the lash, in spite of his tears and prayers. My sister-in-law felt such grief that she lost her reason, and these three poor wretches became beasts rather than human beings, and wandered insane along the shores of Cos, howling like wolves and foaming at the mouth, and hooted at by the children, who threw shells and stones at them. They died, and my father buried them with his own hands. A little later his stomach refused all nourishment, and he died of hunger, though he was rich enough to have bought all the meats and fruits in the markets of Asia. He was deeply grieved at having to leave me his fortune. I used it in travels. I visited Italy, Greece, and Africa without meeting a single person who was either wise or happy. I studied philosophy at Athens and Alexandria, and was deafened by noisy arguments. At last I wandered as far as India, and I saw on the banks of the Ganges a naked man, who had sat there motionless with his legs crossed for more than thirty years. Climbing plants twined round his dried up body, and the birds built their nests in his hair. Yet he lived. At the sight of him I called to mind Timaessa, the flute-player, my two brothers, and my father, and I realised that this Indian was a wise man. 'Men,' I said to myself, 'suffer because they are deprived of that which they believe to be good; or because, possessing it they fear to lose it; or because they endure that which they believe to be an evil. Put an end to all beliefs of this kind, and the evils would disappear.' That is why I resolved henceforth to deem nothing an advantage, to tear myself entirely from the good things of this world, and to live silent and motionless, like the Indian."

Paphnutius had listened attentively to the old man's story.

"Timocles of Cos," he replied, "I own that your discourse is not wholly devoid of sense. It is, in truth, wise to despise the riches of this world. But it would be absurd to despise also your eternal welfare, and render yourself liable to be visited by the wrath of God. I grieve at your ignorance, Timocles, and I will instruct you in the truth, in order that knowing that there really exists a God in three hypostases, you may obey this God as a child obeys its father."

Timocles interrupted him.

"Refrain, stranger, from showing me your doctrines, and do not imagine that you will persuade me to share your opinions. All discussions are useless. My opinion is to have no opinion. My life is devoid of trouble because I have no preferences. Go thy ways, and strive not to withdraw me from the beneficent apathy in which I am plunged, as though in a delicious bath, after the hardships of my past days."

Paphnutius was profoundly instructed in all things relating to the faith. By his knowledge of the human heart, he was aware that the grace of God had not fallen on old Timocles, and the day of salvation for this soul so obstinately resolved to ruin itself had not yet come. He did not reply, lest the power given for edification should turn to destruction. For it sometimes happens, in disputing with infidels, that the means used for their conversion may steep them still farther in sin. Therefore they who possess the truth should take care how they spread it.

"Farewell, then, unhappy Timocles," he said; and heaving a deep sigh, he resumed his pious pilgrimage through the night.

In the morning, he saw the ibises motionless on one leg at the edge of the water, which reflected their pale pink necks. The willows stretched their soft grey foliage to the bank, cranes flew in a triangle in the clear sky, and the cry of unseen herons was heard from the sedges. Far as the eye could reach, the river rolled its broad green waters o'er which white sails, like the wings of birds, glided, and here and there on the shores, a white house shone out. A light mist floated along the banks, and from out the shadow of the islands, which were laden with palms, flowers, and fruits, came noisy flocks of ducks, geese, flamingoes, and teal. To the left, the grassy valley extended to the desert its fields and orchards in joyful abundance; the sun shone on the yellow wheat, and the earth exhaled forth its fecundity in odorous wafts. At this sight, Paphnutius fell on his knees, and cried—

"Blessed be the Lord, who has given a happy issue to my journey. O God, who spreadest Thy dew upon the fig trees of the Arsiniote, pour Thy grace upon Thaïs, whom Thou hast formed with Thy love, as Thou hast the flowers and trees of the field. May she, by Thy loving care, flourish like a sweet-scented rose in the heavenly Jerusalem."

And every time that he saw a tree covered with blossom, or a bird of brilliant plumage, he thought of Thaïs. Keeping along the left arm of the river and through a fertile and populous district, he reached, in a few days, the city of Alexandria, which the Greeks have surnamed the Beautiful and the

Golden. The sun had risen an hour, when he beheld, from the top of a hill, the vast city, the roofs of which glittered in the rosy light. He stopped, and folded his arms on his breast.

"There, then," he said, "is the delightful spot where I was born in sin; the bright air where I breathed poisonous perfumes; the sea of pleasure where I heard the songs of the sirens. There is my cradle, after the flesh; my native land—in the parlance of the men of these days! A rich cradle, an illustrious country, in the judgment of men! It is natural that thy children should reverence thee like a mother, Alexandria, and I was begotten in thy magnificently adorned breast. But the ascetic despises nature, the mystic scorns appearances, the Christian regards his native land as a place of exile, the monk is not of this earth. I have turned away my heart from loving thee, Alexandria. I hate thee! I hate thee for thy riches, thy science, thy pleasures, and thy beauty. Be accursed, temple of demons! Lewd couch of the Gentiles, tainted pulpit of Arian heresy, be thou accursed! And thou, winged son of heaven who led the holy hermit Anthony, our father, when he came from the depths of the desert, and entered into the citadel of idolatry to strengthen the faith of believers and the confidence of martyrs, beautiful angel of the Lord, invisible child, first breath of God, fly thou before me, and cleanse, by the beating of thy wings, the corrupted air I am about to breathe amongst the princes of darkness of this world!"

Having thus spoken, he resumed his journey. He entered the city by the Gate of the Sun. This gate was a handsome structure of stone. In the shadow of its arch, crowded some poor wretches, who offered lemons and figs for sale, or with many groans and lamentations, begged for an obolus.

An old woman in rags, who was kneeling there, seized the monk's cassock, kissed it, and said—

"Man of the Lord, bless me, that God may bless me. I have suffered many things in this world that I may have joys in the world to come. You come from God, O holy man, and that is why the dust of your feet is more precious than gold."

"The Lord be praised!" said Paphnutius, and with his half-closed hand he made the sign of redemption on the old woman's head.

But hardly had he gone twenty paces down the street, than a band of children began to jeer at him, and throw stones, crying—

"Oh, the wicked monk! He is blacker than an ape, and more bearded than a goat! He is a skulker! Why not hang him in an orchard, like a wooden Priapus, to frighten the birds? But no;

he would draw down the hail on the apple-blossom. He brings bad luck. To the ravens with the monk! to the ravens!" and stones mingled with the cries.

"My God, bless these poor children!" murmured Paphnutius.

And he pursued his way, thinking.

"I was worshipped by the old woman, and hated and despised by these children. Thus the same object is appreciated differently by men who are uncertain in their judgment and liable to error. It must be owned that, for a Gentile, old Timocles was not devoid of sense. Though blind, he knew he was deprived of light. His reasoning was much better than that of these idolaters, who cry from the depths of their thick darkness, 'I see the day!' Everything in this world is mirage and moving sand. God alone is steadfast."

He passed through the city with rapid steps. After ten years of absence he would still recognise every stone, and every stone was to him a stone of reproach that recalled a sin. For that reason he struck his naked feet roughly against the kerb-stones of the wide street, and rejoiced to see the bloody marks of his wounded feet. Leaving on his left the magnificent portico of the Temple of Serapis, he entered a road lined with splendid mansions, which seemed to be drowsy with perfumes. Pines, maples, and larches raised their heads above the red cornices and golden acroteria. Through the half-open doors could be seen bronze statues in marble vestibules, and fountains playing amidst foliage. No noise troubled the stillness of these quiet retreats. Only the distant strains of a flute could be heard. The monk stopped before a house, rather small, but of noble proportions, and supported by columns as graceful as young girls. It was ornamented with bronze busts of the most celebrated Greek philosophers.

He recognised Plato, Socrates, Aristotle, Epicurus, and Zeno, and having knocked with the hammer against the door, he waited, wrapped in meditation.

"It is vanity to glorify in metal these false sages; their lies are confounded, their souls are lost in hell, and even the famous Plato himself, who filled the earth with his eloquence, now disputes with the devils."

A slave opened the door, and seeing a man with bare feet standing on the mosaic threshold, said to him roughly—

"Go and beg elsewhere, stupid monk, or I will drive you away with a stick."

"Brother," replied the Abbott of Antinoë, "all that I ask is that you conduct me to your master, Nicias."

The slave replied, more angrily than before—

"My master does not see dogs like you."

"My son," said Paphnutius, "will you please do what I ask, and tell your master that I desire to see him."

"Get out, vile beggar!" cried the porter furiously; and he raised his stick and struck the holy man, who, with his arms crossed upon his breast, received unmovedly the blow, which fell full in his face, and then repeated gently—

"Do as I ask you, my son, I beg."

The porter tremblingly murmured—

"Who is this man who is not afraid of suffering?"

And he ran and told his master.

Nicias had just left the bath. Two pretty slave girls were scraping him with strigils. He was a pleasant-looking man, with a kind smile. There was an expression of gentle satire in his face. On seeing the monk, he rose and advanced with open arms.

"It is you!" he cried, "Paphnutius, my fellow-scholar, my friend my brother! Oh, I knew you again, though, to say the truth, you look more like a wild animal than a man. Embrace me. Do you remember the time when we studied grammar, rhetoric, and philosophy together? You were, even then, of a morose and wild character, but I liked you because of your complete sincerity. We used to say that you looked at the universe with the eyes of a wild horse, and it was not surprising you were dull and moody. You needed a pinch of Attic salt, but your liberality knew no bounds. You cared nothing for either your money or your life. And you had the eccentricity of genius, and a strange character which interested me deeply. You are welcome, my dear Paphnutius, after ten years of absence. You have quitted the desert; you have renounced all Christian superstitions, and now return to your old life. I will mark this day with a white stone."

"Crobyle and Myrtale," he added, turning towards the girls, "perfume the feet, hands, and beard of my dear guest."

They smiled, and had already brought the basin, the phials, and the metal mirror. But Paphnutius stopped them with an imperious gesture, and lowered his eyes that he might not look upon them, for they were naked. Nicias brought cushions for him, and offered him various meats and drinks, which Paphnutius scornfully refused.

"Nicias," he said, "I have not renounced what you falsely call the Christian superstition, which is the truth of truths. 'In the beginning was the

Word, and the Word was with God, and the Word was God. All things were made by Him, and without Him was not anything made that was made. In Him was the life, and the life was the light of men.'"

"My dear Paphnutius," replied Nicias, who had now put on a perfumed tunic, "do you expect to astonish me by reciting a lot of words jumbled together without skill, which are no more than a vain murmur? Have you forgotten that I am a bit of a philosopher myself? And do you think to satisfy me with some rags, torn by ignorant men from the purple garment of Æmilius, when Æmilius, Porphyry, and Plato, in all their glory, did not satisfy me! The systems devised by the sages are but tales imagined to amuse the eternal childishness of men. We divert ourselves with them, as we do with the stories of *The Ass, The Tub,* and *The Ephesian Matron,* or any other Milesian fable."

And, taking his guest by the arm, he led him into a room where thousands of papyri were rolled up and lay in baskets.

"This is my library," he said. "It contains a small part of the various systems which the philosophers have constructed to explain the world. The Serapeium itself, with all its riches, does not contain them all. Alas! they are but the dreams of sick men."

He compelled his guest to sit down in an ivory chair, and sat down himself. Paphnutius scowled gloomily at all the books in the library, and said—

"They ought all to be burned."

"Oh, my dear guest, that would be a pity!" replied Nicias. "For the dreams of sick men are sometimes amusing. Besides, if we should destroy all the dreams and visions of men, the earth would lose its form and colours, and we should all sleep in a dull stupidity."

Paphnutius continued in the same strain as before—

"It is certain that the doctrines of the pagans are but vain lies. But God, who is the truth, revealed Himself to men by miracles, and He was made flesh, and lived among us."

Nicias replied—

"You speak well, my dear Paphnutius, when you say that he was made flesh. A God who thinks, acts, speaks, who wanders through nature, like Ulysses of old on the glaucous sea, is altogether a man. How do you expect that we should believe in this new Jupiter, when the urchins of Athens, in the time of Pericles, no longer believed in the old one?

But let us leave all that. You did not come here, I suppose, to argue about the three hypostases. What can I do for you, my dear fellow-scholar?"

"A good deed," replied the Abbot of Antinoë. "Lend me a perfumed tunic, like the one you have just put on. Be kind enough to add to the tunic, gilt sandals, and a vial of oil to anoint my beard and hair. It is needful also, that you should give me a purse with a thousand drachmæ in it. That, O Nicias, is what I came to ask of you, for the love of God, and in remembrance of our old friendship."

Nicias made Crobyle and Myrtale bring his richest tunic; it was embroidered, after the Asiatic fashion, with flowers and animals. The two girls held it open, and skilfully showed its bright colours, waiting till Paphnutius should have taken off the cassock which covered him down to his feet. But the monk having declared that they should rather tear off his flesh than this garment, they put on the tunic over it. As the two girls were pretty, they were not afraid of men, although they were slaves. They laughed at the strange appearance of the monk thus clad. Crobyle called him her dear satrap, as she presented him with the mirror, and Myrtale pulled his beard. But Paphnutius prayed to the Lord, and did not look at them. Having tied on the gilt sandals, and fastened the purse to his belt, he said to Nicias, who was looking at him with an amused expression—

"O Nicias, let not these things be an offence in your eyes. For know that I shall make pious use of this tunic, this purse, and these sandals."

"My dear friend," replied Nicias, "I suspect no evil, for I believe that men are equally incapable of doing evil or doing good. Good and evil exist only in the opinion. The wise man has only custom and usage to guide him in his acts. I conform with all the prejudices which prevail at Alexandria. That is why I pass for an honest man. Go, friend, and enjoy yourself."

But Paphnutius thought that it was needful to inform his host of his intention.

"Do you know Thaïs," he said, "who acts in the games at the theatre?"

"She is beautiful," replied Nicias, "and there was a time when she was dear to me. For her sake, I sold a mill and two fields of corn, and I composed in her honour three books full of detestably bad verses. Surely beauty is the most powerful force in the world, and were we so made that we could possess it always, we should care as little as may be for the demiurgos, the logos, the æons, and all the other reveries of the philosophers. But I am surprised, my good Paphnutius, that you should have come from the depths of the Thebaid to talk about Thaïs."

Having said this, he sighed gently. And Paphnutius gazed at him with horror, not conceiving it possible that a man should so calmly avow such a sin. He expected to see the earth open, and Nicias swallowed up in flames. But the earth remained solid, and the Alexandrian silent, his forehead resting on his hand, and he smiling sadly at the memories of his past youth. The monk rose, and continued in solemn tones—

"Know then, O Nicias, that, with the aid of God, I will snatch this woman Thaïs from the unclean affections of the world, and give her as a spouse to Jesus Christ. If the Holy Spirit does not forsake me, Thaïs will leave this city and enter a nunnery."

"Beware of offending Venus," replied Nicias. "She is a powerful goddess, she will be angry with you if you take away her chief minister."

"God will protect me," said Paphnutius. "May He also illumine thy heart, O Nicias, and draw thee out of the abyss in which thou art plunged."

And he stalked out of the room. But Nicias followed him, and overtook him on the threshold, and placing his hand on his shoulder whispered into his ear the same words—

"Beware of offending Venus; her vengeance is terrible."

Paphnutius, disdainful of these trivial words, left without turning his head. He felt only contempt for Nicias; but what he could not bear was the idea that his former friend had received the caresses of Thaïs. It seemed to him that to sin with that woman was more detestable than to sin with any other. To him this appeared the height of iniquity, and he henceforth looked upon Nicias as an object of execration. He had always hated impurity, but never before had this vice appeared so heinous to him; never before had it so seemed to merit the anger of Jesus Christ and the sorrow of the angels.

He felt only a more ardent desire to save Thaïs from the Gentiles, and that he must hasten to see the actress in order to save her. Nevertheless, before he could enter her house, he must wait till the heat of the day was over, and now the morning had hardly finished. Paphnutius wandered through the most frequented streets. He had resolved to take no food that day, in order to be the less unworthy of the favours he had asked of the Lord. To the great grief of his soul, he dared not enter any of the churches in the city, because he knew they were profaned by the Arians, who had overturned the Lord's table. For, in fact, these heretics, supported by the Emperor of the East, had driven the patriarch Athanasius from his episcopate, and sown trouble and confusion among the Christians of Alexandria.

He therefore wandered about aimlessly, sometimes with his eyes fixed on the ground in humility, and sometimes raised to heaven in ecstasy. After some time, he found himself on the quay. Before him lay the harbour, in which were sheltered innumerable ships and galleys, and beyond them, smiling in blue and silver, lay the perfidious sea. A galley, which bore a Nereid at its prow, had just weighed anchor. The rowers sang as the oars struck the water; and already the white daughter of the waters, covered with humid pearls, showed no more than a flying profile to the monk. Steered by her pilot, she cleared the passage leading from the basin of the Eunostos, and gained the high seas, leaving a glittering trail behind her.

"I also," thought Paphnutius, "once desired to embark singing on the ocean of the world. But I soon saw my folly, and the Nereid did not carry me away."

Lost in his thoughts, he sat down upon a coil of rope, and went to sleep. During his sleep, he had a vision. He seemed to hear the sound of a clanging trumpet, and the sky became blood red, and he knew that the day of judgment had come. Whilst he was fervently praying to God, he saw an enormous monster coming towards him, bearing on its forehead a cross of light, and he recognised the sphinx of Silsile. The monster seized him between its teeth, without hurting him, and carried him in its mouth, as a cat carries a kitten. Paphnutius was thus conveyed across many countries, crossing rivers and traversing mountains, and came at last to a desert place, covered with scowling rocks and hot cinders. The ground was rent in many places, and through these openings came a hot air. The monster gently put Paphnutius down on the ground, and said—

"Look!"

And Paphnutius, leaning over the edge of the abyss, saw a river of fire which flowed in the interior of the earth, between two cliffs of black rocks. There, in a livid light, the demons tormented the souls of the damned. The souls preserved the appearance of the bodies which had held them, and even wore some rags of clothing. These souls seemed peaceful in the midst of their torments. One of them, tall and white, his eyes closed, a white fillet across his forehead, and a sceptre in his hand, sang; his voice filled the desert shores with harmony; he sang of gods and heroes. Little green devils pierced his lips and throat with red-hot irons. And the shade of Homer still sang. Near by, old Anaxagoras, bald and hoary, traced figures in the dust with a compass. A demon poured boiling oil into his ear, yet failed, however, to disturb the sage's meditations. And the monk saw many other persons, who, on the dark shore by the side of the burning river, read, or quietly meditated, or conversed with other spirits while walking,—like the sages and pupils under the shadow of the sycamore trees of Academe. Old Timocles alone had withdrawn from the others, and shook his head like a man who denies. One of the demons of the abyss shook a torch before his eyes, but Timocles would see neither the demon nor the torch.

Mute with surprise at this spectacle, Paphnutius turned to the monster. It had disappeared, and, in place of the sphinx, the monk saw a veiled woman, who said—

"Look and understand. Such is the obstinacy of these infidels, that, even in hell, they remain victims of the illusions which deluded them when on earth. Death has not undeceived them; for it is very plain that it does not suffice merely to die in order to see God. Those who are ignorant of the truth whilst living, will be ignorant of it always. The demons which are busy torturing these souls, what are they but agents of divine justice? That is why these souls neither see them nor feel them. They were ignorant of the truth, and therefore unaware of their own condemnation, and God Himself cannot compel them to suffer.

"God can do all things," said the Abbot of Antinoë.

"He cannot do that which is absurd," replied the veiled woman. "To punish them, they must first be enlightened, and if they possessed the truth, they would be like unto the elect."

Vexed and horrified, Paphnutius again bent over the edge of the abyss. He saw the shade of Nicias smiling, with a wreath of flowers on his head, sitting under a burnt myrtle tree. By his side was Aspasia of Miletus, gracefully draped in a woollen cloak, and they seemed to talk together of love and philosophy; the expression of her face was sweet and noble. The rain of fire which fell on them was as a refreshing dew, and their feet pressed the burning soil as though it had been tender grass. At this sight Paphnutius was filled with fury.

"Strike him, O God! strike him!" he cried. "It is Nicias! Let him weep! let him groan! let him grind his teeth! He sinned with Thaïs!"

And Paphnutius woke in the arms of a sailor, as strong as Hercules, who cried—

"Quietly! quietly! my friend! By Proteus, the old shepherd of the seals, you slumber uneasily. If I had not caught hold of you, you would have tumbled into the Eunostos. It is as true as that my mother sold salt fish, that I saved your life."

"I thank God," replied Paphnutius.

And, rising to his feet, he walked straight before him, meditating on the vision which had come to him whilst he was asleep.

"This vision," he said to himself, "is plainly an evil one; it is an insult to divine goodness to imagine hell is unreal. The dream certainly came from the devil."

He reasoned thus because he knew how to distinguish between the dreams sent by God and those produced by evil angels. Such discernment is useful to the hermit, who lives surrounded by apparitions, and who, in avoiding men, is sure to meet with spirits. The deserts are full of phantoms. When the pilgrim drew near the ruined castle, to which the holy hermit, Anthony, had retired, they heard a noise like that which goes up from the public square of a large city at a great festival. The noise was made by the devils, who were tempting the holy man.

Paphnutius remembered this memorable example. He also called to mind St. John the Egyptian, who for sixty years was tempted by the devil. But John saw through all the tricks of the demon. One day, however, the devil, having assumed the appearance of a man, entered the grotto of the venerable John, and said to him, "John, you must continue to fast until to-morrow evening." And John, believing that it was an angel who spoke, obeyed the voice of the demon, and fasted the next day until the vesper hour. That was the only victory that the Prince of Darkness ever gained over St. John the Egyptian, and that was but a trifling one. It was therefore not astonishing that Paphnutius knew at once that the vision which had visited him in his sleep was an evil one.

Whilst he was gently remonstrating with God for having given him into the power of the demons, he felt himself pushed and dragged amidst a crowd of people who were all hurrying in the same direction. As he was unaccustomed to walk in the streets of a city, he was shoved and knocked from one passer to another like an inert mass; and being embarrassed by the folds of his tunic, he was more than once on the point of falling. Desirous of knowing where all these people could be going, he asked one of them the cause of this hurry.

"Do you not know, stranger," replied he, "that the games are about to begin, and that Thaïs will appear on the stage? All the citizens are going to the theatre, and I also am going. Would you like to accompany me?"

It occurred to him at once that it would further his design to see Thaïs in the games, and Paphnutius followed the stranger. In front of them stood the theatre, its portico ornamented with shining masks, and its huge circular wall covered with innumerable statues. Following the crowd, they entered a narrow passage, at the end of which lay the amphitheatre, glittering with light. They took their places on one of the seats, which descended in steps to the stage, which was empty but magnificently decorated. There was no curtain to hide the view, and on the stage was a mound, such as used to be erected in old times to the shades of heroes. This mound stood in the midst of a camp. Lances were stacked in front of the tents, and golden shields hung from masts, amidst boughs of laurel and wreaths of oak. On the stage all was silence, but a murmur like the humming of bees in a hive rose from the vast hemicycle filled with spectators. All their faces, reddened by the reflection from the purple awning which waved above them, turned with attentive curiosity towards the large, silent stage, with its tomb and tents. The women laughed and ate lemons, and the regular theatre-goers called gaily to one another from their seats.

Paphnutius prayed inwardly, and refrained from uttering any vain words, but his neighbour began to complain of the decline of the drama.

"Formerly," he said, "clever actors used to declaim, under a mask, the verses of Euripides and Menander. Now they no longer recite dramas, they act in dumb show; and of the divine spectacles with which Bacchus was honoured in Athens, we have kept nothing but what a barbarian—a Scythian even—could understand—attitude and gesture. The tragic mask, the mouth of which was provided with metal tongues that increased the sound of the voice; the cothurnus, which raised the actors to the height of gods; the tragic majesty and the splendid verses that used to be sung, have all gone. Pantomimists, and dancing girls with bare faces, have replaced Paulus and Roscius. What would the Athenians of the days of Pericles have said if they had seen a woman on the stage? It is indecent for a woman to appear in public. We must be very degenerate to permit it. It is as certain as that my name is Dorion, that woman is the natural enemy of man, and a disgrace to human kind."

"You speak wisely," replied Paphnutius; "woman

is our worst enemy. She gives us pleasure, and is to be feared on that account."

"By the immovable gods," cried Dorion, "it is not pleasure that woman gives to man, but sadness, trouble, and black cares. Love is the cause of our most biting evils. Listen, stranger. When I was a young man I visited Trœzene, in Argolis, and I saw there a myrtle of a most prodigious size, the leaves of which were covered with innumerable pin-holes. And this is what the Trœzenians say about that myrtle. Queen Phædra, when she was in love with Hippolytos, used to recline idly all day long under this same tree. To beguile the tedium of her weary life she used to draw out the golden pin which held her fair locks, and pierce with it the leaves of the sweet-scented bush. All the leaves were riddled with holes. After she had ruined the poor young man whom she pursued with her incestuous love, Phædra, as you know, perished miserably. She locked herself up in her bridal chamber, and hanged herself by her golden girdle from an ivory peg. The gods willed that the myrtle, the witness of her bitter misery, should continue to bear, in its fresh leaves, the marks of the pin-holes. I picked one of these leaves, and placed it at the head of my bed, that by the sight of it I might take warning against the folly of love, and conform to the doctrine of the divine Epicurus, my master, who taught that all lust is to be feared. But, properly speaking, love is a disease of the liver, and one is never sure of not catching the malady."

Paphnutius asked—

"Dorion, what are your pleasures?"

Dorion replied sadly—

"I have only one pleasure, and, it must be confessed, that it is not a very exciting one; it is meditation. When a man has a bad digestion, he must not look for any others."

Taking advantage of these words, Paphnutius proceeded to initiate the Epicurean into those spiritual joys which the contemplation of God procures. He began—

"Hear the truth, Dorion, and receive the light."

But he saw then that all heads were turned towards him, and everybody was making signs for him to be quiet. Dead silence prevailed in the theatre, broken at last by the strains of heroic music.

The play began. The soldiers left their tents, and were preparing to depart, when a prodigy occurred—a cloud covered the summit of the funeral pile. Then the cloud rolled away, and the ghost of Achilles appeared, clad in golden armour. Extending his arms towards the warriors, he seemed to say to them, "What! do you depart, children of Danaos? do you return to the land I shall never behold again, and leave my tomb without any offerings?" Already the principal Greek chieftains pressed to the foot of the pile. Acamas, the son of Theseus, old Nestor, Agamemnon, bearing a sceptre and with a fillet on his brow, gazed at the prodigy. Pyrrhus, the young son of Achilles, was prostrate in the dust. Ulysses, recognisable by the cap which covered his curly hair, showed by his gestures that he acquiesced in the demand of the hero's shade. He argued with Agamemnon, and their words might be easily guessed—

"Achilles," said the King of Ithaca, "is worthy to be honoured by us, for he died gloriously for Hellas. He demands that the daughter of Priam, the virgin Polyxena, should be immolated on his tomb. Greeks! appease the manes of the hero, and let the son of Peleus rejoice in Hades."

But the king of kings replied—

"Spare the Trojan virgins we have torn from the altars. Sufficient misfortunes have already fallen on the illustrious race of Priam."

He spoke thus because he shared the couch of the sister of Polyxena, and the wise Ulysses reproached him for preferring the couch of Cassandra to the lance of Achilles.

The Greeks showed they shared the opinion of Ulysses, by loudly clashing their weapons. The death of Polyxena was resolved on, and the appeased shade of Achilles vanished. The music—sometimes wild and sometimes plaintive—followed the thoughts of the personages in the drama. The spectators burst into applause.

Paphnutius, who applied divine truth to everything murmured—

"This fable shows how cruel the worshippers of false gods were."

"All religions breed crimes," replied the Epicurean. "Happily, a Greek, who was divinely wise, has freed men from foolish terrors of the unknown—"

Just at that moment, Hecuba, her white hair dishevelled, her robe tattered, came out of the tent in which she was kept captive. A long sigh went up from the audience, when her woeful figure appeared. Hecuba had been warned by a prophetic dream, and lamented her daughter's fate and her own. Ulysses approached her, and asked her to give up Polyxena. The old mother tore her hair, dug her nails into her cheeks, and kissed the hands of the cruel chieftain, who, with unpitying calmness, seemed to say—

"Be wise, Hecuba, and yield to necessity. There

are amongst us many old mothers who weep for their children, now sleeping under the pines of Ida."

And Hecuba, formerly queen of the most flourishing city in Asia, and now a slave, bowed her unhappy head in the dust.

Then the curtain in front of one of the tents was raised, and the virgin Polyxena appeared. A tremor passed through all the spectators. They had recognised Thaïs. Paphnutius saw again the woman he had come to seek. With her white arm she held above her head the heavy curtain. Motionless as a splendid statue, she stood, with a look of pride and resignation in her violet eyes, and her resplendent beauty made a shudder of commiseration pass through all who beheld her.

A murmur of applause uprose, and Paphnutius, his soul agitated, and pressing both hands to his heart, sighed—

"Why, O my God, hast thou given this power to one of Thy creatures?"

Dorion was not so disturbed. He said—

"Certainly the atoms, which have momentarily met together to form this woman, present a combination which is agreeable to the eye. But that is but a freak of nature, and the atoms know not what they do. They will some day separate with the same indifference as they came together. Where are now the atoms which formed Laïs or Cleopatra? I must confess that women are sometimes beautiful. But they are liable to grievous afflictions, and disgusting inconveniences. That is patent to all thinking men, though the vulgar pay no attention to it. And women inspire love, though it is absurd and ridiculous to love them."

Such were the thoughts of the philosopher and the ascetic as they gazed on Thaïs. They neither of them noticed Hecuba, who turned to her daughter, and seemed to say by her gestures—

"Try to soften the cruel Ulysses. Employ your tears, your beauty, and your youth."

Thaïs—or rather Polyxena herself—let fall the curtain of the tent. She made a step forward, and all hearts were conquered. And when, with firm but light steps, she advanced towards Ulysses, her rhythmic movements, which were accompanied by the sound of flutes, created in all present such happy visions, that it seemed as though she were the divine centre of all the harmonies of the world. All eyes were bent on her; the other actors were obscured by her effulgence, and were not noticed. The play continued, however.

The prudent son of Laërtes turned away his head, and hid his hand under his mantle, in order to avoid the looks and kisses of the suppliant. The virgin made a sign to him to fear nothing. Her tranquil gaze said—

"I follow you, Ulysses, and bow to necessity—because I wish to die. Daughter of Priam, and sister of Hector, my couch, which was once worthy of Kings, shall never receive a foreign master. Freely do I quit the light of day."

Hecuba, lying motionless in the dust, suddenly rose and enfolded her daughter in a last despairing embrace. Polyxena gently, but resolutely, removed the old arms which held her. She seemed to say—

"Do not expose yourself, mother, to the fury of your master. Do not wait until he drags you ignominiously on the ground in tearing me from your arms. Better, O well-beloved mother, to give me your wrinkled hand, and bend your hollow cheeks to my lips."

The face of Thaïs looked beautiful in its grief. The crowd felt grateful to her for showing them the forms and passions of life endowed with superhuman grace, and Paphnutius pardoned her present splendour on account of her coming humility, and glorified himself in advance for the saint he was about to give to heaven.

The drama neared its end. Hecuba fell as though dead, and Polyxena, led by Ulysses, advanced towards the tomb, which was surrounded by the

THE LOTUS

chief warriors. A dirge was sung as she mounted the funeral pile, on the summit of which the son of Achilles poured out libations from a gold cup to the names of the hero. When the sacrificing priests stretched out their arms to seize her, she made a sign that she wished to die free and unbound, as befitted the daughter of so many kings. Then, tearing aside her robe, she bared her bosom to the blow. Pyrrhus, turning away his head, plunged his sword into her heart, and by a skilful trick, the blood gushed forth over the dazzling white breast of the virgin, who, with head thrown back, and her eyes swimming in the horrors of death, fell with grace and modesty.

Whilst the warriors enshrouded the victim with a veil, and covered her with lilies and anemones, terrified screams and groans rent the air, and Paphnutius, rising from his seat, prophesied in a loud voice.

"Gentiles? vile worshippers of demons! And you Arians more infamous than the idolaters!—learn! That which you have just seen is an image and a symbol. There is a mystic meaning in this fable, and very soon the woman you see there will be offered, a willing and happy sacrifice, to the risen God."

But already the crowd was surging in dark waves

towards the exits. The Abbot of Antinoë, escaping from the astonished Dorion, gained the door, still prophesying.

An hour later he knocked at the door of the house of Thaïs.

The actress then lived in the rich Racotis quarter, near the tomb of Alexander, in a house surrounded by shady gardens, in which a brook, bordered with poplars, flowed amidst artificial rocks. An old black slave woman, loaded with rings, opened the door, and asked what he wanted.

"I wish to see Thaïs," he replied. "God is my witness that I came here for no other purpose."

As he wore a rich tunic, and spoke in an imperious manner, the slave allowed him to enter.

"You will find Thaïs," she said, "in the Grotto of Nymphs."

PART THE SECOND

THE PAPYRUS

PART THE SECOND
THE PAPYRUS

THAÏS was born of free, but poor, parents, who were idolaters. When she was a very little girl, her father kept, at Alexandria, near the Gate of the Moon, an inn, which was frequented by sailors. She still retained some vivid, but disconnected, memories of her early youth. She remembered her father, seated at the corner of the hearth with his legs crossed—tall, formidable, and quiet, like one of those old Pharaohs who are celebrated in the ballads sung by blind men at the street corners. She remembered also her thin, wretched mother, wandering like a hungry cat about the house, which she filled with the tones of her sharp voice, and the glitter of her phosphorescent eyes. They said in the neighbourhood that she was a witch, and changed into an owl at night, and flew to see her lovers. It was a lie. Thaïs knew well, having often watched her, that her mother practised no magic arts, but that she was eaten up with avarice, and counted all night the gains of the day. The idle father and the greedy mother let the child live as best it could, like one of the fowls in the poultry-yard. She became very clever in extracting, one by one, the oboli from the belt of some drunken sailor, and in amusing the drinkers with artless songs and obscene words, the meaning of which she did not know. She passed from knee to knee, in a room reeking with the odours of fermented drinks and resiny wine-skins; then, her cheeks sticky with beer and pricked by rough beards, she escaped, clutching the oboli in her little hand, and ran to buy honey-cakes from an old woman who crouched behind her baskets under the Gate of the Moon. Every day the same scenes were repeated, the sailors relating their perilous adventures, then playing at dice or knuckle-bones, and blaspheming the gods, amid their shouting for the best beer of Cilicia.

Every night the child was awakened by the quarrels of the drunkards. Oyster-shells would fly across the tables, cutting the heads of those they hit, and the uproar was terrible. Sometimes she saw, by the light of the smoky lamps, the knives glitter, and the blood flow.

It humiliated her to think that the only person who showed her any human kindness in her young days was the mild and gentle Ahmes. Ahmes, the house-slave, a Nubian blacker than the pot he gravely skimmed, was as good as a long night's sleep.

Often he would take Thaïs on his knee, and tell her old tales about underground treasure-houses constructed for avaricious kings, who put to death the masons and architects. There were also tales about clever thieves who married kings' daughters, and courtesans who built pyramids. Little Thaïs loved Ahmes like a father, like a mother, like a nurse, and like a dog. She followed the slave into the cellar when he went to fill the amphoræ, and into the poultry-yard amongst the scraggy and ragged fowls, all beak, claws, and feathers, who flew swifter than eagles before the knife of the black cook. Often at night, on the straw, instead of sleeping, he built for Thaïs little water-mills, and ships no bigger than his hand, with all their rigging.

He had been badly treated by his masters; one of his ears was torn, and his body covered with scars. Yet his features always wore an air of joyous peace. And no one ever asked him whence he drew the consolation in his soul, and the peace in his heart. He was as simple as a child. As he performed his heavy tasks, he sang, in a harsh voice, hymns which made the child tremble and dream. He murmured, in a gravely joyous tone—

"Tell us, Mary, what thou hast seen where thou hast been?

I saw the shroud and the linen cloths, and the angels seated on the tomb.

And I saw the glory of the Risen One."

She asked him—

"Father, why do you sing about angels seated on a tomb?"

And he replied—

"Little light of my eyes, I sing of the angels because Jesus, our Lord, is risen to heaven."

Ahmes was a Christian. He had been baptised, and was known as Theodore at the meetings of the faithful, to which he went secretly during the hours allowed him for sleep.

At that time the Church was suffering the severest trials. By order of the Emperor, the churches had been thrown down, the holy books burned, the sacred vessels and candlesticks melted. The Christians had been deprived of all their honours, and expected nothing but death. Terror reigned over all the community at Alexandria, and the prisons were crammed with victims. It was whispered with horror amongst the faithful, that in Syria, in Arabia, in Mesopotamia, in Cappadocia, in all the empire, bishops and virgins had been flogged, tortured, crucified or thrown to wild beasts. Then Anthony, already celebrated for his visions and his solitary life, a prophet, and the head of all the Egyptian believers, descended like an eagle from his desert rock on the city of Alexandria, and, flying from church to church, fired the whole community with his holy ardour. Invisible to the pagans, he was present at the same time at all the meetings of Christians, endowing all with the spirit of strength and prudence by which he was animated. Slaves, in particular, were persecuted with singular severity. Many of them, seized with fright, denied the faith. Others, and by far the greater number, fled to the desert, hoping to live there, either as hermits or robbers. Ahmes, however, frequented the meetings as usual, visited the prisoners, buried the martyrs, and joyfully professed the religion of Christ. The great Anthony, who saw his unshaken zeal, before he returned into the desert, pressed the black slave in his arms, and gave him the kiss of peace.

When Thaïs was seven years old, Ahmes began to talk to her of God.

"The good Lord God," he said, "lived in heaven like a Pharaoh, under the tents of His harem, and under the trees of His gardens. He was the Ancient of Ancients, and older than the world; and He had but one Son, the Prince Jesus, whom He loved with all His heart, and who surpassed in beauty the virgins and the angels. And the good Lord God said to Prince Jesus—

" 'Leave My harem and My palace, and My date trees and My running waters. Descend to earth for the welfare of men. There Thou shalt be like a little child, and Thou shalt live poor amongst the poor. Suffering shall be Thy daily bread, and Thou shalt weep so profusely that Thy tears shall form rivers, in which the tired slave shall bathe with delight. Go, My Son!'

"Prince Jesus obeyed the good Lord, and He came down to earth, to a place named Bethlehem of Judæa. And He walked in fields, amidst the flowering anemones, saying to His companions.

" 'Blessed are they who hunger, for I will lead them to My Father's table! Blessed are they who thirst, for they shall drink of the fountains of heaven! Blessed are they who weep, for I will dry their tears with veils finer than those of the almehs!'

"That is why the poor loved Him, and believed in Him. But the rich hated Him; fearing that He should raise the poor above them. At that time, Cleopatra and Cæsar were powerful on the earth. They both hated Jesus, and they ordered the judges and priests to put Him to death. To obey the Queen of Egypt, the princes of Syria erected a cross on a high mountain, and they caused Jesus to die on this cross. But women washed His corpse, and buried it; and Prince Jesus, having broken the door of His tomb, rose again to the good Lord, His Father.

"And, from that time, all those who believed in Him go to heaven.

"The Lord God opens His arms, and says to them—

" 'Ye are welcome, because ye love the Prince, My Son. Wash, and then eat.'

"They bathe to the sound of beautiful music, and, all the time they are eating, they see almehs dancing, and they listen to tales that never end. They are dearer to the good Lord God than the light of His eyes, because they are His guests, and they shall have for their portion the carpets of His house, and the pomegranates of His gardens."

Ahmes often spoke in this strain, and thus taught the truth to Thaïs. She wondered, and said—

"I should like to eat the pomegranates of the good Lord."

Ahmes replied—

"Only those who are baptised may taste the fruits of heaven."

And Thaïs asked to be baptised. Seeing by this that she believed in Jesus, the slave resolved to instruct her more fully, so that, being baptised, she might enter the Church; and he loved her as his spiritual daughter.

The child, unloved and uncared for by its selfish parents, had no bed in the house. She slept in a corner of the stable amongst the domestic animals, and there Ahmes came to her every night secretly.

He gently approached the mat on which she lay, and sat down on his heels, his legs bent and his body straight—a position hereditary to his race. His face and his body, which was clothed in black, were invisible in the darkness; but his big white eyes shone out, and there came from them a light like a ray of dawn through the chinks of a door. He spoke in a husky, monotonous tone, with a slight nasal twang that gave it the soft melody of music heard at night in the streets. Sometimes the breathing of an ass, or the soft lowing of an ox, accompanied, like a chorus of invisible spirits, the voice of the slave as he recited the gospels. His words flowed gently in the darkness, which they filled with zeal, mercy, and hope; and the neophyte, her hand in that of Ahmes, lulled by the monotonous sounds, and the vague visions in her mind, slept calm and smiling, amid the harmonies of the dark night and the holy mysteries, gazed down on by a star, which twinkled between the joists of the stable-roof.

The initiation lasted a whole year, till the time when the Christians joyfully celebrate the festival of Easter. One night in the holy week, Thaïs, who was already asleep on her mat, felt herself lifted by the slave, whose eyes gleamed with a strange light. He was clad, not as usual in a pair of torn drawers, but in a long white cloak, beneath which he pressed the child, whispering to her—

"Come, my soul! Come, light of my eyes! Come, little sweetheart! Come and be clad in the baptismal robes!"

He carried the child pressed to his breast. Frightened and yet curious, Thaïs, her head out of the cloak, threw her arms round her friend's neck, and he ran with her through the darkness. They went down narrow, black alleys; they passed through the Jews' quarter; they skirted a cemetery, where the osprey uttered its dismal cry; they traversed an open space, passing under crosses on which hung the bodies of victims, and on the arms of the crosses the ravens clacked their beaks. Thaïs hid her head in the slave's breast. She did not dare to peep out all the rest of the way. Soon it seemed to her that she was going down under ground. When she reopened her eyes she found herself in a narrow cave, lighted by resin torches, on the walls of which were painted standing figures, which seemed to move and live in the flickering glare of the torches. They were men clad in long tunics and carrying branches of palm, and around them were lambs, doves, and tendrils of vine.

Amongst these figures, Thaïs recognised Jesus of Nazareth, by the anemones flowering at his feet. In the centre of the cave, near a large stone font filled with water, stood an old man clad in a scarlet dalmatic embroidered with gold, and on his head a low mitre. His thin face ended in a long beard. He looked gentle and humble, in spite of his rich costume. This was Bishop Vivantius, an exiled dignitary of the Church of Cyrene, who now gained his livelihood by weaving common stuffs of goats' hair. Two poor children stood by his side. Close by, an old negress unfolded a little white robe. Ahmes set the child down on the ground, and kneeling before the Bishop, said—

"Father, this is the little soul, the child of my soul. I have brought her that you may, according to your promise, and if it please your holiness, bestow on her the baptism of life."

At these words the Bishop opened his arms, and showed his mutilated hands. His nails had been torn out because he had maintained the faith in the days of persecution. Thaïs was frightened, and threw herself into the arms of Ahmes. But the kind words of the priest reassured her.

"Fear nothing, dearly beloved little one. Thou

hast here a spiritual father, Ahmes, who is called Theodore amongst the faithful, and a kind mother in grace, who has prepared for thee, with her own hands, a white robe."

And turning towards the negress—

"She is called Nitida," he added, "and is a slave in this world, but in heaven she will be a spouse of Jesus."

Then he said to the child neophyte—

"Thaïs, dost thou believe in God, the Father Almighty; and in His only Son, who died for our salvation; and in all that the apostles taught?"

"Yes," replied together the negro and negress, who held her by each hand.

By the Bishop's orders, Nitida knelt down and undressed Thaïs. The child was quite naked; round her neck was an amulet. The Pontiff plunged her three times into the baptismal font. The acolytes brought the oil, with which Vivantius anointed the catechumen, and the salt, a morsel of which he placed on her tongue. Then, having dried that body which was destined, after many trials, to life immortal, the slave Nitida put on Thaïs the white robe she had woven.

The Bishop gave to each and all the kiss of peace, and, the ceremony being terminated, took off his sacerdotal insignia.

When they had left the crypt, Ahmes said—

"We ought to rejoice that we have this day brought a soul to the good Lord God; let us go to the house of your Holiness and spend the rest of the night in rejoicing."

"Thou hast well said, Theodore," replied the Bishop, and he led the little band to his house, which was quite near. It consisted of a single room, furnished with a couple of looms, a heavy table, and a worn-out carpet. As soon as they had entered,

"Nitida," cried the Nubian, "bring hither the stove and the jar of oil, and we will have a good supper."

Saying thus, he drew from under his cloak some little fish which he had kept concealed, and lighted a fire and fried them. The Bishop, the girl, the two boys, and the two slaves sat in a ring on the carpet, ate the fried fish, and blessed the Lord. Vivantius spoke of the torture he had undergone, and prophesied the speedy triumph of the Church. His language was grotesque, and full of word-play and rhetorical tropes. He compared the life of the just to a tissue of purple, and to explain the mystery of baptism, he said—

"The Divine Spirit floated on the waters, and that is why Christians receive the baptism of water. But demons also inhabit the brooks; springs consecrated to nymphs are especially dangerous, and there are certain waters which cause various maladies, both of the soul and of the body."

Sometimes he spoke enigmatically, and the child listened to him with profound awe and wonder. At the end of the repast he offered his guests a little wine, and this unloosed their tongues, and they began to sing lamentations and hymns. Ahmes and Nitida then rose, and danced a Nubian dance which they had learned as children, and which, no doubt, had been danced by their tribe since the early ages of the world. It was a love dance; waving their arms, and moving their bodies in rhythmic measure, they feigned, in turn, to fly from and to pursue each other. Their big eyes rolled, and they showed their gleaming teeth in broad grins.

In this strange manner did Thaïs receive the holy rite of baptism.

She loved amusements, and, as she grew, vague desires were created in her mind. All day long she danced and sang with the children in the streets, and when at night she returned to her father's house, she was still singing—

"Crooked twist, why do you stay in the house?
I comb the wool, and the Miletan threads.
Crooked twist, what did your son die of?
He fell from the white horses into the sea."

She now began to prefer the company of boys and girls to that of the gentle and quiet Ahmes. She did not notice that her friend was not so often with her. The persecution having relented, the Christians were able to assemble more regularly, and the Nubian frequented these meetings assiduously. His zeal increased, and he sometimes uttered mysterious threats. He said that the rich would not keep their wealth. He went to the public places to which the poorer Christians used to resort, and assembling together all the poor wretches who were lying in the shade of the old walls, he announced to them that all slaves would soon be free, and that the day of justice was at hand.

"In the kingdom of God," he said, "the slaves will drink new wine and eat delicious fruits; whilst the rich, crouching at their feet like dogs, will devour the crumbs from their table."

These sayings were noised abroad through all that quarter of the city, and the masters feared that Ahmes might incite the slaves to revolt. The innkeeper hated him intensely, though he carefully concealed his rancour.

One day, a silver salt-cellar, reserved for the table of the gods, disappeared from the inn. Ahmes was accused of having stolen it—out of hate to his master and to the gods of the empire. There was no proof of the accusation, and the slave vehemently denied the charge. Nevertheless, he was dragged before the tribunal, and as he had the reputation of being a bad servant, the judge condemned him to death.

"As you did not know how to make a good use of your hands," he said, "they will be nailed to the cross."

Ahmes heard the verdict quietly, bowed to the judge most respectfully, and was taken to the public prison. During the three days that remained to him, he did not cease to preach the gospel to the prisoners, and it was related afterwards that the criminals, and the gaoler himself, touched by his words, believed in Jesus crucified.

He was taken to the very place which one night, less than two years before, he had crossed so joyfully, carrying in his cloak little Thaïs, the daughter of his soul, his darling flower. When his hands were nailed to the cross, he uttered no complaint, but many times he sighed and murmured, "I thirst."

His agony lasted three days and three nights. It seemed hardly possible that human flesh could have endured such prolonged torture. Many times it was thought he was dead; the flies clustered on his eyelids, but suddenly he would reopen his bloodshot eyes. On the morning of the fourth day, he sang, in a voice clearer and purer than that of a child—

"Tell us, Mary, what thou hast seen where thou hast been?"

Then he smiled and said—

"They come, the angels of the good Lord. They bring me wine and fruit. How refreshing is the fanning of their wings!"

And he expired.

His features preserved in death an expression of ecstatic happiness. Even the soldiers who guarded the cross were struck with wonder. Vivantius, accompanied by some of the Christian brethren, claimed the body, and buried it with the remains of the other martyrs in the crypt of St. John the Baptist, and the Church venerated the memory of Saint Theodore the Nubian.

Three years later, Constantine, the conqueror of Maxentius, issued an edict which granted toleration to the Christians, and the believers were not henceforth persecuted, except by heretics.

Thaïs had completed her eleventh year when her friend was tortured to death, and she felt deeply saddened and shocked. Her soul was not sufficiently pure to allow her to understand that the slave Ahmes was blessed both in his life and his death. The idea sprang up in her little mind that no one can be good in this world except at the cost of the most terrible sufferings. And she was afraid to be good, for her delicate flesh could not bear pain.

At an early age, she had given herself to the lads about the port, and she followed the old men who wandered about the quarter in the evening, and with what she received from them she bought cakes and trinkets.

As she did not take home any of the money she gained, her mother continually ill-treated her. To get out of reach of her mother's arm, she often ran, bare-footed, to the city walls, and hid with the lizards. There she thought with envy of the ladies she had seen pass her, richly dressed, and in a litter surrounded by slaves.

One day, when she had been beaten more brutally than usual, she was crouching down beside the gate, motionless and sulky, when an old woman stopped in front of her, looked at her for some moments in silence, and then cried—

"Oh, the pretty flower! the beautiful child! Happy is the father who begot thee, and the mother who brought thee into the world!"

Thaïs remained silent, with her eyes fixed on the ground. Her eyelids were red, and it was evident she had been weeping.

"My white violet," continued the old woman, "is not your mother happy to have nourished a little goddess like you, and does not your father, when he sees you, rejoice from the bottom of his heart?"

To which the child replied, as though talking to herself—

"My father is a wine-skin swollen with wine, and my mother a greedy horse-leech."

The old woman glanced to right and left, to see if she were observed. Then, in a fawning voice—

"Sweet flowering hyacinth, beautiful drinker of light, come with me, and you shall have nothing to do but dance and smile. I will feed you on honey cakes, and my son—my own son—will love you as his eyes. My son is handsome and young; he has but little beard on his chin; his skin is soft, and he is, as they say, a little Acharnian pig."

Thaïs replied—

"I am quite willing to go with you."

And she rose and followed the old woman out of the city.

The old woman, who was named Mœroë, went from city to city with a troupe of girls and boys, whom she taught to dance, and then hired out to rich people to appear at feasts.

Guessing that Thaïs would soon develop into a most beautiful woman, she taught her—with the help of a whip—music and prosody, and she flogged with leather thongs those beautiful legs, when they did not move in time to the strains of the cithara. Her son—a decrepit abortion, of no age and no sex—ill-treated the child, on whom he vented the hate he had for all womankind. Like the dancing-girls whose grace he affected, he knew, and taught Thaïs, the art of pantomime, and how to mimic, by expression, gesture, and attitude, all human passions, and more especially the passions of love. He was a clever master, though he disliked his work; but he was jealous of his pupil, and as soon as he discovered that she was born to give men pleasure, he scratched her cheeks, pinched her arms, or pricked her legs, as a spiteful girl would have done. Thanks, however, to his lessons, she quickly became an excellent musician, pantomimist, and dancer. The brutality of her master did not at all surprise her; it seemed natural to her to be badly treated. She even felt some respect for the old woman, who knew music and drank Greek wine. Mœroë, when she came to Antioch, praised her pupil to the rich merchants of the city who gave banquets, both as a dancer and a flute-player. Thaïs danced and pleased. She accompanied the rich bankers, when they left the table, into the shady groves on the banks of the Orontes. She gave herself to all, for she knew nothing of the price of love. But one night that she had danced before the most fashionable young men of the city, the son of the pro-consul came to her, radiant with youth and pleasure, and said, in a voice that seemed redolent of kisses—

"Why am I not, Thaïs, the wreath which crowns your hair, the tunic which enfolds your beautiful form, the sandal on your pretty foot? I wish you to tread me under foot as a sandal; I wish my caresses to be your tunic and your wreath. Come, sweet girl! come to my house, and let us forget the world."

She looked at him whilst he was speaking, and saw that he was handsome. Suddenly she felt a cold sweat on her face. She turned green as grass; she reeled; a cloud descended before her eyes. He again implored her to come with him, but she refused. His ardent looks, his burning words were vain, and when he took her in his arms to try and drag her away, she pushed him off rudely. Then he implored her, and shed tears. But a new, unknown, and invincible passion dominated her heart, and she still resisted.

"What madness!" said the guests. "Lollius is noble, handsome, and rich, and a dancing-girl treats him with scorn!"

Lollius returned home alone that night, quite love-sick. He came in the morning, pale and red-eyed, and hung flowers at the dancing-girl's door.

But Thaïs was frightened and troubled; she avoided Lollius, and yet he was continually in her mind. She suffered, and she did not know the cause of her complaint. She wondered why she had thus changed, and why she was melancholy. She recoiled from all her lovers; they were hateful to her. She loathed the light of day, and lay on her bed all day, sobbing, and with her head buried in the pillows. Lollius contrived to gain admittance, and came many times, but neither his pleadings nor his execrations had any effect on the obdurate girl. In his presence, she was as timid as a virgin, and would say nothing but—

"I will not! I will not!"

But at the end of a fortnight she gave in, for she knew that she loved him; she went to his house and lived with him. They were supremely happy. They passed their days shut up together, gazing into each other's eyes, and babbling a childish jargon. In the evening, they walked on the lonely banks of the Orontes, and lost themselves in the laurel woods. Sometimes they rose at dawn, to go and gather hyacinths on the slopes of Sulpicus. They drank from the same cup, and he would take a grape from between her lips with his mouth.

Mœroë came to Lollius, and cried and shrieked that Thaïs should be restored to her.

"She is my daughter," she said, "my daughter, who has been torn from me. My perfumed flower —my own bowels—!"

Lollius gave her a large sum of money, and sent her away. But, as she came back to demand some more gold staters, the young man had her put in prison, and the magistrates having discovered that she was guilty of many crimes, she was condemned to death, and thrown to the wild beasts.

Thaïs loved Lollius with all the passion of her mind, and the bewilderment of innocence. She told him, and told him truly from the bottom of her heart—

"I have never loved any one but you."

Lollius replied—

"You are not like any other woman."

The spell lasted six months, but it broke at last. Thaïs suddenly felt that her heart was empty and lonely. Lollius no longer seemed the same to her. She thought—

"What can have thus changed me in an instant? How is it that he is now like any other man, and no longer like himself?"

She left him, not without a secret desire to find Lollius again in another, as she no longer found him in himself. She thought it would be less dull to live with someone she had never loved, than with one she had ceased to love. She appeared, in the company of rich debauchees, at those sacred feasts at which naked virgins danced in the temples, and troops of courtesans swam across the Orontes. She took part in all the pleasures of the fashionable and depraved city; and she assiduously frequented the theatres, at which clever mimes from all countries performed amidst the applause of a crowd greedy for excitement.

She carefully observed the mimes, dancers, comedians, and especially the women, who in tragedies represented goddesses in love with young men, or mortals loved by the gods. Having discovered the secrets by which they pleased the audience, she thought to herself that she was more beautiful and could act better. She went to the manager, and asked to be admitted into the troupe. Thanks to her beauty, and to the lessons she had received from old Mœroë, she was received, and appeared on the stage in the part of Dircé.

She met with but indifferent success, for she was inexperienced, and the admiration of the spectators had not been aroused by hearing her praises sung. But after she had played small parts for a few months, the power of her beauty burst forth with such effect that all the city was moved. All Antioch crowded to the theatre. The imperial magistrates and the chief citizens were compelled, by the force of public opinion, to show themselves there. The porters, sweepers, and dock labourers went without bread and garlic, that they might pay for their places. Poets composed epigrams in her honour. Bearded philosophers inveighed against her in the baths and gymnasia; when her litter passed, Christian priests turned away their heads. The threshold of her door was wreathed with flowers, and sprinkled with blood. She received so much money from her lovers that it was no longer counted, but measured by the medimnus, and all the treasure hoarded by miserly old men was poured out at her feet. But she was placid and unmoved. She rejoiced, with quiet pride, in the admiration of the public and the favour of the gods, and was so much loved that she loved herself.

After she had several years enjoyed the admiration and affection of the Antiochians, she was taken with a desire to revisit Alexandria, and show her glory in that city in which, as a child, she had wandered in want and shame, hungry and lean as a grasshopper in the middle of a dusty road. The golden city joyfully welcomed her, and loaded her with fresh riches; when she appeared in the games it was a triumph. Countless admirers and lovers came to her. She received them with indifference,

THE PAPYRUS

for she at last despaired of meeting another Lollius.

Amongst many others, she met the philosopher Nicias, who desired to possess her, although he professed to have no desires. In spite of his riches, he was intelligent and modest. But his delicate wit and beautiful sentiments failed to charm her. She did not love him and sometimes his refined irony even irritated her. His perpetual doubts hurt her, for he believed in nothing, and she believed in everything. She believed in divine providence, in the omnipotence of evil spirits, in spells, exorcisms, and eternal justice; she believed in Jesus Christ, and in the goddess of good of the Syrians; she believed also that bitches barked when black Hecate passed through the streets, and that woman could inspire love by pouring a philtre into a cup wrapped in the bleeding skin of a sheep. She thirsted for the unknown; she called on nameless gods, and lived in perpetual expectation. The future frightened her, and yet she wished to know it. She surrounded herself with priests of Isis, Chaldean magi, pharmacopolists, and professors of the black arts, who invariably deceived her, though she never tired of being deceived. She feared death, and she saw it everywhere. When she yielded to pleasure, it seemed to her that an icy finger would suddenly touch her on the bare shoulder, and she turned pale, and cried with terror, in the arms which embraced her.

Nicias said to her—

"What does it matter, O my Thaïs, whether we descend to eternal night with white locks and hollow cheeks, or, whether this very day, now laughing to the vast sky, shall be our last? Let us enjoy life; we shall have greatly lived if we have greatly loved. There is no knowledge except that of the senses; to love is to understand. That which we do not know does not exist. What good is it to worry ourselves about nothing?"

She replied angrily—

"I despise men like you, who hope for nothing and fear nothing. I wish to *know!* I wish to *know!*"

In order to understand the secret of life, she set to work to read the books of the philosophers, but she did not understand them. The further the years of her childhood receded from her, the more anxious she was to recall them. She loved to traverse at night, in disguise, the alleys, squares, and places where she had grown up so miserably. She was sorry she had lost her parents, and especially that she had not been able to love them. When she met any Christian priest, she thought of her baptism, and felt troubled. One night, when enveloped

THE PAPYRUS

in a long cloak, and her fair hair hidden under a black hood, she was wandering, according to custom, about the suburbs of the city, she found herself—without knowing how she came there—before the poor little church of St. John the Baptist. They were singing inside the church, and a bright light glimmered through the chinks of the door. There was nothing strange in that, as, for the past twenty years, the Christians, protected by the conqueror of Maxentius, had publicly solemnised their festivals. But these hymns seemed more like an ardent appeal to the soul. As if she had been invited to the mysteries, she pushed the door open with her arm, and entered the building. She found a numerous assembly of women, children, and old men, on their knees before a tomb, which stood against the wall. The tomb was nothing but a stone coffer, roughly sculptured with vine tendrils and bunches of grapes; yet it had received great honours, and was covered with green palms and wreaths of red roses. All round, innumerable lights gleamed out of the heavy shadow, in which the smoke of Arabian gums seemed like the folds of angels' robes, and the paintings on the walls visions of Paradise. Priests, clad in white, were prostrate at the foot of the sarcophagus. The hymns they sang with the people expressed the delight of suffering, and mingled, in a triumphal mourning, so much joy with so much grief, that Thaïs, in listening to them, felt the pleasures of life and the terrors of death flowing, at the same time, through her re-awakened senses.

When they had finished singing, the believers rose, and walked in single file to the tomb, the side of which they kissed. They were common men, accustomed to work with their hands. They advanced with a heavy step, the eyes fixed, the jaw dropped, but they had an air of sincerity. They knelt down, each in turn, before the sarcophagus, and put their lips to it. The women lifted their little children in their arms, and gently placed their cheek to the stone.

Thaïs, surprised and troubled, asked a deacon why they did so.

"Do you not know, woman," replied the deacon, "that we celebrate to-day the blessed memory of St. Theodore the Nubian, who suffered for the faith in the days of the Emperor Diocletian? He lived virtuously and died a martyr, and that is why, robed in white, we bear red roses to his glorious tomb."

On hearing these words, Thaïs fell on her knees, and burst into tears. Half-forgotten recollections of Ahmes returned to her mind. On the memory of this obscure, gentle, and unfortunate man, the blaze of candles, the perfume of roses, the clouds of incense, the music of hymns, the piety of souls, threw all the charms of glory. Thaïs thought in the dazzling glare—

"He was good, and now he has become great and glorious. Why is it that he is elevated above other men? What is this unknown thing which is more than riches or pleasure?"

She rose slowly, and turned towards the tomb of the saint who had loved her, those violet eyes, now filled with tears which glittered in the candle-light; then, with bowed head, humble, slow, and the last, with those lips on which so many desires hung, she kissed the stone of the slave's tomb.

When she returned to her house, she found Nicias, who, with his hair perfumed, and his tunic thrown open, was reading a treatise on morals whilst waiting for her. He advanced with open arms.

"Naughty Thaïs," he said, in a laughing voice, "whilst I was waiting for you to come, do you know what I saw in this manuscript, written by the gravest of Stoics? Precepts of virtue and noble maxims: No! On the staid papyrus, I saw dance thousands and thousands of little Thaïses. Each was no bigger than my finger, and yet their grace was infinite, and all were the only Thaïs. There were some who flaunted in mantles of purple and gold; others, like a white cloud, floated in the air in transparent drapery. Others again, motionless and divinely nude, the better to inspire pleasure, expressed no thought. Lastly, there were two, hand in hand; two so alike that it was impossible to distinguish one from the other. Both smiled. The first said, 'I am love.' The other, 'I am death.'"

Thus speaking, he pressed Thaïs in his arms, and not noticing the sullen look in her downcast eyes, he went on adding thought to thought, heedless of the fact that they were all lost upon her.

"Yes, when I had before my eyes the line in which it was written, 'Nothing should deter you from improving your mind,' I read, 'The kisses of Thaïs are warmer than fire, and sweeter than honey.' That is how a philosopher reads the books of other philosophers—and that is your fault, you naughty child. It is true that, as long as we are what we are, we shall never find anything but our own thoughts in the thoughts of others, and that all of us are somewhat inclined to read books as I have read this one."

She did not hear him; her soul was still before the Nubian's tomb. As he heard her sigh, he kissed her on the neck, and said—

"Do not be sad, my child. We are never happy in this world, except when we forget the world.

Come, let us cheat life—it is sure to take its revenge. Come, let us love!"

But she pushed him away.

"*We* love!" she cried bitterly. "*You* never loved any one. And *I* do not love *you!* No! I do not love you! I hate you! Go! I hate you! I curse and despise all who are happy, and all who are rich! Go! Go! Goodness is only found amongst the unfortunate. When I was a child I knew a black slave who died on the cross. He was good; he was filled with love, and he knew the secret of life. You are not worthy to wash his feet. Go! I never wish to see you again!"

She threw herself on her face on the carpet, and passed the night sobbing and weeping, and forming resolutions to live, in future, like Saint Theodore, in poverty and humbleness.

The next day, she devoted herself again to those pleasures to which she was addicted. As she knew that her beauty, though still intact, would not last very long, she hastened to derive all the enjoyment and all the fame she could from it. At the theatre, where she acted and studied more than ever, she gave life to the imagination of sculptors, painters, and poets. Recognising that there was in the attitudes, movements, and walk of the actress, an idea of the divine harmony which rules the spheres, wise men and philosophers considered that such perfect grace was a virtue in itself, and said, "Thaïs also is a geometrician!" The ignorant, the poor, the humble, and the timid before whom she consented to appear, regarded her as a blessing from heaven. Yet she was sad amidst all the praise she received, and dreaded death more than ever. Nothing was able to set her mind at rest, not even her house and gardens, which were celebrated, and a proverb throughout the city.

The gardens were planted with trees, brought at great expense from India and Persia. They were watered by a running brook, and colonnades in ruins, and imitation rocks, arranged by a skilful artist, were reflected in a lake, which also mirrored the statues that stood round it. In the middle of the garden was the Grotto of Nymphs, which owed its name to three life-size figures of women, which stood on the threshold. They were represented as divesting themselves of their garments, and about to bathe. They anxiously turned their heads, fearing to be seen, and looked as though they were alive. The only light which entered the building came, tempered and iridescent, through thin sheets of water. All the walls were hung—as in the sacred grottoes —with wreaths, garlands, and votive pictures, in which the beauty of Thaïs was celebrated. There were also tragic and comic masks, bright with colours; and paintings representing theatrical scenes, or grotesque figures, or fabulous animals. On a stele in the centre stood a little ivory Eros of wonderful antique workmanship. It was a gift from Nicias. In one of the bays was a figure of a goat in black marble, with shining agate eyes. Six alabaster kids crowded round its teats; but, raising its cloven hoofs and its ugly head, it seemed impatient to climb the rocks. The floor was covered with Byzantine carpets, pillows embroidered by the yellow men of Cathay, and the skins of Libyan lions. Perfumed smoke arose from golden censers. Flowering plants grew in large onyx vases. And at the far end, in the purple shadow, gleamed the gold nails on the shell of a huge Indian tortoise turned upside down, which served as the bed of the actress. It was here that every day, to the murmur of the water, and amid perfumes and flowers, Thaïs reclined softly, and conversed with her friends, while awaiting the hour of supper, or meditated in solitude on theatrical art, or on the flight of years.

On the afternoon after the games, Thaïs was reposing in the Grotto of Nymphs. She had noticed in her mirror the first signs of the decay of her beauty, and she was frightened to think that white hair and wrinkles would at last come. She vainly tried to comfort herself with the assurance that she could recover her fresh complexion by burning certain herbs and pronouncing a few magic words. A pitiless voice cried, "You will grow old Thaïs; you will grow old." And a cold sweat of terror bedewed her forehead. Then, on looking at herself again in the mirror with infinite tenderness, she found that she was still beautiful and worthy to be loved. She smiled to herself, and murmured, "There is not a woman in Alexandria who can rival me in suppleness or grace or movement, or in splendour of arms, and the arms, my mirror, are the real chains of love!"

While she was thus thinking she saw an unknown man—thin, with burning eyes and unkempt beard, and clad in a richly embroidered robe—standing before her. She let fall her mirror, and uttered a cry of fright.

Paphnutius stood motionless, and seeing how beautiful she was, he murmured this prayer from the bottom of his heart—

"Grant, my God, that the face of this woman may not be a temptation, but may prove salutary to Thy servant."

Then, forcing himself to speak, he said—

"Thaïs, I live in a far country, and the fame of

thy beauty has led me to thee. It is said that thou art the most clever of actresses and the most irresistible of women. That which is related of thy riches and thy love affairs seems fabulous, and calls to mind the old story of Rhodope, whose marvellous history is known by heart to all the boatmen on the Nile. Therefore I was seized with a desire to know thee, and I see that the truth surpasses the rumour. Thou art a thousand times more clever and more beautiful than is reported. And now that I see thee, I say to myself, 'It is impossible to approach her without staggering like a drunken man.'"

The words were feigned; but the monk, animated by pious zeal, uttered them with real warmth. Thaïs gazed, without displeasure, at this strange being who had frightened her. The rough, wild aspect, and the fiery glances of his eyes, astonished her. She was curious to learn the state of life of a man so different from all others she had met. She replied, with gentle raillery—

"You seem prompt to admire, stranger. Beware that my looks do not consume you to the bones! Beware of loving me!"

He said—

"I love thee, O Thaïs! I love thee more than my life, and more than myself. For thee I have quitted the desert; for thee my lips—vowed to silence—have pronounced profane words; for thee I have seen what I ought not to have seen, and heard what it was forbidden to me to hear; for thee my soul is troubled, my heart is open, and the thoughts gush out like the running springs at which the pigeons drink; for thee I have walked day and night across sandy deserts teeming with reptiles and vampires; for thee I have placed my bare foot on vipers and scorpions! Yes, I love thee! I love thee, but not like those men who, burning with the lusts of the flesh, come to thee like devouring wolves or furious bulls. Thou art dear to them as is the gazelle to the lion. Their ravening lusts will consume thee to the soul, O woman! I love thee in spirit and in truth; I love thee in God, and for ever and ever; that which is in my breast is named true zeal and divine charity. I promise thee better things than drunkenness crowned with flowers or the dreams of a brief night. I promise thee holy feasts and celestial suppers. The happiness that I bring thee will never end; it is unheard-of, it is ineffable, and such that if the happy of this world could only see a shadow of it they would die of wonder."

Thaïs laughed mischievously.

"Friend," she said, "show me this wonderful love. Make haste! Long speeches would be an insult to my beauty; let us not lose a moment. I am impatient to taste the felicity you announce; but, to say the truth, I fear that I shall always remain ignorant of it, and that all you have promised me will vanish in words. It is easier to promise a great happiness than to give it. Everyone has a talent of some sort. I fancy that yours is to make long speeches. You speak of an unknown love. It is so long since kisses were first exchanged that it would be very extraordinary if there still remained secrets in love. On this subject lovers knew more than philosophers."

"Do not jest, Thaïs. I bring thee the unknown love."

"Friend, you come too late. I know every kind of love."

"The love that I bring thee abounds with glory, whilst the loves that thou knowest breed only shame."

Thaïs looked at him with an angry eye, a frown gathered on her beautiful face.

"You are very bold, stranger, to offend your hostess. Look at me, and say if I resemble a creature crushed down with shame. No, I am not ashamed, and all others who live like me are not ashamed either, although they are not so beautiful or so rich as I am. I have sown pleasure in my footsteps, and I am celebrated for that all over the world. I am more powerful than the masters of the world. I have seen them at my feet. Look at me, look at these little feet; thousands of men would pay with their blood for the happiness of kissing them. I am not very big, and I do not occupy much space on the earth. To those who look at me from the top of the Serapeium, when I pass in the street, I look like a grain of rice; but that grain of rice has caused among men, griefs, despairs, hates, and crimes enough to have filled Tartarus. Are you not mad to talk to me of shame when all around proclaims my glory?"

"That which is glory in the eyes of men, is infamy before God. O woman, we have been nourished in countries so different, that it is not surprising we have neither the same language nor the same thoughts! Yet Heaven is my witness that I wish to agree with thee, and that it is my intention not to leave thee until we share the same sentiments. Who will inspire me with burning words that will melt thee like wax in my breath, O woman, that the fingers of my desires may mould thee as they wish? What virtue will deliver thee to me, O dearest of souls, that the spirit which animates me, creating thee a second time, may imprint on thee a fresh beauty, and that thou mayest cry, weeping for joy,

'It is only now that I am born'? Who will cause to gush in my heart a fount of Siloam, in which thou mayest bathe and recover thy first purity? Who will change me into a Jordan, the waves of which sprinkled on thee, will give thee life eternal?"

Thaïs was no longer angry.

"This man," she thought, "talks of life eternal, and all that he says seems written on a talisman. No doubt he is a mage, and knows secret charms against old age and death," and she resolved to offer herself to him. Therefore, pretending to be afraid of him, she retired a few steps to the end of the grotto, and sitting down on the edge of the bed, artfully pulled her tunic across her breast; then, motionless and mute and her eyes cast down, she waited. Her long eyelashes made a soft shadow on her cheeks. Her entire attitude expressed modesty; her naked feet swung gently, and she looked like a child sitting thinking on the bank of a brook.

But Paphnutius looked at her, and did not move. His trembling knees hardly supported him, his tongue dried in his mouth, a terrible buzzing rang in his ears. But all at once his sight failed, and he could see nothing before him but a thick cloud. He thought that the hand of Jesus had been laid on his eyes, to hide this woman from them. Reassured by such succour, strengthened and fortified, he said with a gravity worthy of an old hermit of the desert—

"If thou givest thyself to me, thinkest thou it is hidden from God?"

She shook her head.

"God? Who forces Him to keep His eye always upon the Grotto of Nymphs? Let Him go away if we offend Him! But why should we offend Him? Since He has created us, He can be neither angry nor surprised to see us as He made us, and acting according to the nature He has given us. A good deal too much is said on His behalf, and He is often credited with ideas He never had. You yourself, stranger, do you know His true character? Who are you that you should speak to me in His name?"

At this question the monk, opening his borrowed robe, showed the cassock, and said—

"I am Paphnutius, Abbot of Antinoë, and I come from the holy desert. The hand that drew Abraham from Chaldæa and Lot from Sodom has separated me from the present age. I no longer existed for the men of this century. But thy image appeared to me in my sandy Jerusalem, and I knew that thou wert full of corruption, and death was in thee. And now I am before thee, woman, as before a grave, and I cry unto thee, 'Thaïs, arise!'"

At the words, Paphnutius, monk, and abbot, she had turned pale with fright. And now, with dishevelled hair and joined hands, weeping and groaning, she dragged herself to the feet of the saint.

"Do not hurt me! Why have you come? What do you want of me? Do not hurt me! I know that the saints of the desert hate women who, like me, are made to please. I am afraid that you hate me, and want to hurt me. Go! I do not doubt your power. But know, Paphnutius, that you should neither despise me nor hate me. I have never, like many of the men I know, laughed at your voluntary poverty. In your turn, do not make a crime of my riches. I am beautiful, and clever in acting. I no more chose my condition than my nature. I was made for that which I do. I was born to charm men. And you yourself, did you not say just now that you loved me? Do not use your science against me. Do not pronounce magic words which would destroy my beauty, or change me into a statue of salt. Do not terrify me! I am already too frightened. Do not kill me! I am so afraid of death."

He made a sign to her to rise, and said—

"Child, have no fear. I will utter no word of shame or scorn. I come on behalf of Him who sat on the edge of the well, and drank of the pitcher which the woman of Samaria offered to Him; and who, also, when He supped at the house of Simon, received the perfumes of Mary. I am not without sin that I should throw the first stone. I have often badly employed the abundant grace which God has bestowed upon me. It was not anger, but pity, which took me by the hand to conduct me here. I can, without deceit, address thee in words of love, for it is the zeal in my heart which has brought me to thee. I burn with the fire of charity, and if thy eyes, accustomed only to the gross sights of the flesh, could see things in their mystic aspect, I should appear unto thee as a branch broken off the burning bush which the Lord showed on the mountain to Moses of old, that he might understand true love —that which envelops us, and which, so far from leaving behind it mere coals and ashes, purifies and perfumes for ever that which it penetrates."

"I believe you, monk, and no longer fear either deceit or ill-will from you. I have often heard talk of the hermits of the Thebaid. Marvellous things have been told concerning Anthony and Paul. Your name is not unknown to me, and I have heard say that, though you are still young, you equal in virtue the oldest anchorites. As soon as I saw you, and without knowing who you were, I felt that you were no ordinary man. Tell me! can you do for me that which neither the priests of Isis, nor of Hermes, nor of the celestial Juno, nor the Chaldean soothsayers, nor the Babylonian magi have been able to effect? Monk, if you love me, can you prevent me from dying?"

"Woman, whosoever wishes to live shall live. Flee from the abominable delights in which thou diest for ever. Snatch from the devils, who will burn it most horribly, that body which God kneaded with His spittle and animated with his own breath. Thou art consumed with weariness; come, and refresh thyself at the blessed springs of solitude; come and drink of those fountains which are hidden in the desert, and which gush forth to heaven. Careworn soul, come, and possess that which thou desirest! Heart greedy for joy, come and taste true joys—poverty, retirement, self-forgetfulness, seclusion in the bosom of God. Enemy of Christ now, and to-morrow His well-beloved, come to Him! Come, thou whom I have sought, and thou wilt say, 'I have found love!'"

Thaïs seemed lost in meditation on things afar.

"Monk," she asked, "if I adjure all pleasures and do penance, is it true that I shall be born again in heaven, my body intact in all its beauty?"

"Thaïs, I bring thee eternal life. Believe me, for that which I announce to thee is the truth."

"Who will assure me that it is the truth?"

"David and the prophets, the Scriptures, and the wonders that thou shalt behold."

"Monk, I should like to believe you, for I must confess that I have not found happiness in this world. My lot in life is better than that of a queen, and yet I have many bitternesses and misfortunes, and I am infinitely weary of my existence. All women envy me, and yet sometimes I have envied the lot of a toothless old woman who, when I was a child, sold honey-cakes under one of the city gates. Often has the idea flashed across my mind that only the poor are good, happy, and blessed, and that there must be great gladness in living humble and obscure. Monk, you have agitated a storm in my soul, and brought to the surface that which lay at the bottom. Who am I to believe, alas! and what is to become of me—and what is life?"

Whilst she thus spoke, Paphnutius was transfigured; celestial joy beamed in his face.

"Listen!" he said. "I was not alone when I entered this house. Another accompanied me, another who stands by my side. Him thou canst not see, because thy eyes are yet unworthy to behold Him; but soon thou shalt see Him in all His glorious splendour, and thou wilt say, 'He alone is to be adored.' But now, if He had not placed His gentle hands before my eyes, O Thaïs, I should perhaps have fallen into sin with thee, for of myself I am but weak and sinful. But He saved us both. He is as good as He is powerful, and His name is the Saviour. He was promised to the world, by David and the prophets, worshipped in His cradle by the shepherds and the magi, crucified by the Pharisees, buried by the holy women, revealed to the world by the apostles, testified to by the martyrs. And now, having learned that thou fearest death, O woman, He has come to thy house to prevent thee from dying. Art Thou not here present with me, Jesus, at this moment, as Thou didst appear to the men of Galilee, in those wonderful days when the stars, which came down with thee from heaven, were so near the earth that the holy innocents could take them in their hands, when they played in their mothers' arms on the terraces of Bethlehem? Is it not true, Jesus, that Thou art here present, and that Thou showest me in reality Thy precious body? Is not Thy face here, and that tear which flows down Thy cheek a real tear? Yes, the angel of eternal justice shall receive it, and it shall be the ransom of the soul of Thaïs. Art Thou not here, Jesus? Jesus, Thy loving lips open. Thou canst speak; speak, I hear Thee! And thee, Thaïs, happy Thaïs! listen to what the Saviour Himself says to thee; it is He who speaks, not I. He says, 'I have sought thee long, O my lost sheep! I have found thee at last! Fly from Me no more. Let me take thee by the hands, poor little one, and I will bear thee on My shoulders to the heavenly fold. Come, my Thaïs! come, my chosen one! come, and weep with Me!'"

And Paphnutius fell on his knees, his eyes filled with ecstasy. And then Thaïs saw in his face the likeness of the living Christ.

"O vanished days of my childhood!" she sobbed. "O sweet father Ahmes! good Saint Theodore, why did I not die in thy white mantle whilst thou didst bear me, in the first dawn of day, yet fresh from the waters of baptism!"

Paphnutius advanced towards her, crying—

"Thou art baptised! O divine wisdom! O Providence! O great God! I know now the power which drew me to thee. I know what rendered thee so dear and so beautiful in my eyes. It was the virtue of the baptismal water, which made me leave the shadow of God, where I lived, to seek thee in the poisoned air where men dwell. A drop—a drop, no doubt, of the water which washed thy body—has been sprinkled in my face. Come, O my sister, and receive from thy brother the kiss of peace."

And the monk touched with his lips the forehead of the courtesan.

Then he was silent, letting God speak, and nothing was heard in the Grotto of Nymphs but the sobs of Thaïs, mingled with the rippling of the running water.

She wept without trying to stop her tears, when two black slaves appeared, loaded with stuffs, perfumes, and garlands.

"It was hardly the right time to weep," she said, trying to smile. "Tears redden the eyes and spoil the complexion, and I must sup to-night with some friends, and want to be beautiful, for there will be women there quick to spy out marks of care on my face. These slaves come to dress me. Withdraw, my father, and allow them to do their work. They are clever and experienced, and I pay them well for their services. You see that one who wears thick rings of gold, and shows such white teeth. I took her from the wife of the pro-consul."

Paphnutius had at first a thought of dissuading Thaïs, as earnestly as he could, from going to this supper. But he determined to act prudently, and asked what persons she would meet there.

She replied that there would be the host, old Cotta, the Prefect of the Fleet, Nicias, and several other philosophers who loved an argument, the poet

Callicrates, the high priest of Serapis, some young men whose chief amusement was training horses, and lastly some women, of whom there was little to be said except that they were young. Then, by a supernatural inspiration—

"Go amongst them, Thaïs," said the monk. "Go! But I will not leave thee. I will go with thee to this banquet, and will remain by thy side without saying a word."

She burst out laughing. And whilst her two black slaves were busy dressing her, she cried—

"What will they say when they see that I have a monk of the Thebaid for my lover?"

THE BANQUET

WHEN, followed by Paphnutius, Thaïs entered the banqueting-room, the guests were already, for the most part, assembled, and reclining on their couches before the horseshoe table, which was covered with glittering vessels. In the centre of the table stood a silver basin, surmounted by four figures of satyrs, who poured out from wine-skins on the boiled fish a kind of pickle in which they floated. When Thaïs appeared, acclamations arose from all sides.

Greetings to the sister of the Graces!

To the silent Melpomene, who can express all things with her looks!

Salutation to the well-beloved of gods and men!

To the much desired!

To her who gives suffering and its cure!

To the pearl of Racotis!

To the rose of Alexandria!

She waited impatiently till this torrent of praise had passed, and then said to Cotta, the host—

"Lucius, I have brought you a monk of the desert,

Paphnutius, the Abbot of Antinoë. He is a great saint, whose words burn like fire."

Lucius Aurelius Cotta, the Prefect of the Fleet, rose, and replied—

"You are welcome, Paphnutius, you who profess the Christian faith. I myself have some respect of a religion that has now become imperial. The divine Constantine has placed your co-religionists in the front rank of the friends of the empire. Latin wisdom ought, in fact, to admit your Christ into our pantheon. It was a maxim of our forefathers that there was something divine in every god. But no more of that. Let us drink and enjoy ourselves while there is yet time."

Old Cotta spoke tranquilly. He had just studied a new model for a galley, and had finished the sixth book of his history of the Carthaginians. He felt sure he had not lost his day, and was satisfied with himself and the gods.

"Paphnutius," he added, "you see here several men who are worthy to be loved—Hermodorus, the High Priest of Serapis; the philosophers Dorion, Nicias, and Zenothemis; the poet Callicrates; young Chereas and young Aristobulus, both sons of dear old comrades; and near them Philina and Drosea, who deserve to be praised for their beauty."

Nicias embraced Paphnutius, and whispered in his ear—

"I warned you, brother, that Venus was powerful. It is her gentle force that has brought you here in spite of yourself. Listen: you are a man full of piety, but if you do not confess that she is the mother of the gods, your ruin is certain. Do you know that the old mathematician, Melanthes, used to say, 'I cannot demonstrate the properties of a triangle without the aid of Venus'?"

Dorion, who had for some seconds been looking at the new-comer, suddenly clapped his hands and uttered a cry of surprise.

"It is he, friends! His look, his beard, his tunic —it is he himself! I met him at the theatre whilst our Thaïs was acting. He was furiously excited, and spoke with violence, as I can testify. He is an honest man, but he will abuse us all; his eloquence is terrible. If Marcus is the Plato of the Christians, Paphnutius is the Demosthenes. Epicurus, in his little garden, never heard the like."

Philina and Drosea, however, devoured Thaïs with their eyes. She wore on her fair hair a wreath of pale violets, each flower of which recalled, in a paler hue, the colour of her eyes, so that the flowers looked like softened glances, and the eyes like sparkling flowers. It was the peculiar gift of this woman; on her everything lived, and was soul and harmony. Her robe, which was of mauve spangled with silver, trailed in long folds with a grace that was almost melancholy and was not relieved by either bracelets or necklaces. The chief charm of her appearance was her beautiful bare arms. The two friends were obliged to admire, in spite of themselves the robe and head-dress of Thaïs, though they said nothing to her on the subject.

"How beautiful you are!" said Philina. "You could not have been more so when you came to Alexandria. Yet my mother, who remembers seeing you then, says there were few women who were worthy to be compared with you."

"Who is the new lover you have brought?" asked Drosea. "He has a strange, wild appearance. If there are shepherds of elephants, assuredly he must resemble one. Where did you find such a wild-looking friend, Thaïs? Was it amongst the troglodytes who live under the earth, and are grimy with the smoke of Hades?"

But Philina put her finger on Drosea's lips.

"Hush! the mysteries of love must remain secret, and it is forbidden to know them. For my own part, certainly, I would rather be kissed by the mouth of smoking Etna than by the lips of that man. But our dear Thaïs, who is beautiful and adorable as the goddesses, should, like the goddesses, grant all requests, and not, like us, only those of nice young men."

"Take care, both of you!" replied Thaïs. "He is a mage and an enchanter. He hears words that are whispered, and even thoughts. He will tear out your heart while you are asleep, and put a sponge in its place, and the next day, when you drink water, you will be choked to death."

She watched them grow pale, then she turned away from them, and sat on a couch by the side of Paphnutius. The voice of Cotta, kind but imperious, was suddenly heard above the murmur of conversation.

"Friends, let each take his place! Slaves, pour out the honeyed wine!"

Then, the host raising his cup—

"Let us first drink to the divine Constantine and the genius of the empire. The country should be put first of all, even above the gods, for it contains them all."

All the guests raised their full cups to their lips. Paphnutius alone did not drink, because Constantine had persecuted the Nicæan faith, and because the country of the Christian is not of this world.

Dorion, having drunk, murmured—

"What is one's country? A flowing river. The shores change, and the waves are incessantly renewed."

"I know, Dorion," replied the Prefect of the Fleet, "that you care little for the civic virtues, and you think that the sage ought to hold himself aloof from all affairs. I think, on the contrary, that an honest man should desire nothing better than to fill a responsible post in the State. The State is a noble thing."

Hermodorus, the High Priest of Serapis, spoke next—

"Dorion has asked, 'What is one's country?' I will reply that the altars of the gods and the tombs of ancestors make one's country. A man is a fellow-citizen by association of memories and hopes."

Young Aristobulus interrupted Hermodorus.

"By Castor! I saw a splendid horse to-day. It belonged to Demophoon. It has a fine head, small jaw, and strong forelegs. It carries its neck high and proud, like a cock."

But young Chereas shook his head.

"It is not such a good horse as you say, Aristobulus. Its hoofs are thin, and the pasterns are too low; the animal will soon go lame."

THE BANQUET

They were continuing their dispute, when Drosea uttered a piercing shriek.

"Oh! I nearly swallowed a fish-bone, as long and much sharper than a style. Luckily, I was able to get it out of my throat in time! The gods love me!"

"Did you say, Drosea, that the gods loved you?" asked Nicias, smiling. "Then they must share the same infirmities as men. Love presupposes unhappiness on the part of whoever suffers from it, and is a proof of weakness. The affection they feel for Drosea is a great proof of the imperfection of the gods."

At these words Drosea flew into a great rage.

"Nicias, your remarks are foolish and not to the point. But that is your character—you never understand what is said, and reply in words devoid of sense."

Nicias smiled again.

"Talk away, talk away, Drosea. Whatever you say, we are glad every time you open your mouth. Your teeth are so pretty!"

At that moment, a grave-looking old man, negligently dressed, walking slowly, with his head high, entered the room, and gazed at the guests quietly. Cotta made a sign to him to take a place by his side, on the same couch.

"Eucrites," he said, "you are welcome. Have you composed a new treatise on philosophy this month? That would make, if I calculate correctly, the ninety-second that has proceeded from the Nile reed you direct with an Attic hand."

Eucrites replied, stroking his silver beard—

"The nightingale was created to sing, and I was created to praise the immortal gods."

DORION. Let us respectfully salute, in Eucrites, the last of the stoics. Grave and white, he stands in the midst of us like the image of an ancestor. He is solitary amidst a crowd of men, and the words he utters are not heard.

EUCRITES. You deceive yourself, Dorion. The philosophy of virtue is not dead. I have numerous disciples in Alexandria, Rome, and Constantinople. Many of the slaves, and some of the nephews of Cæsar, now know how to govern themselves, to live independently, and being unconcerned with all affairs, they enjoy boundless happiness. Many of them have revived, in their own person, Epictetus and Marcus Aurelius. But if it were true that virtue were for ever extinguished upon the earth, in what way would the loss of it affect my happiness, since it did not depend on me whether it existed or perished? Only fools, Dorion, place their happiness out of their own power. I desire nothing that the gods do not wish, and I desire all that they do wish. By that means I render myself like unto them, and share their infallible content. If virtue perishes, I consent that it should perish, and that consent fills me with joy, as the supreme effort of my reason or my courage. In all things my wisdom will copy the divine wisdom, and the copy will be more valuable than the model; it will have cost greater care and more work.

Nicias. I understand. You put yourself on the same level as divine providence. But if virtue consists only in effort, Eucrites, and in that intense application by which the disciples of Zeno pretend to render themselves equal to the gods, the frog, which swelled itself out to try and become as big as the ox, accomplished a masterpiece of stoicism.

Eucrites. You jest, Nicias, and, as usual, you excel in ridicule. But if the ox of which you speak is really a god, like Apis, or like that subterranean ox whose high priest I see here, and if the frog, being wisely inspired, succeed in equalling it, would it not be, in fact, more virtuous than the ox, and could you refrain from admiring such a courageous little animal!

Four servants placed on the table a wild pig, still

covered with its bristles. Little pigs, made of pastry, surrounded the animal, as though they would suckle, to show that it was a sow.

Zenothemis, turning towards the monk, said—

"Friends, a guest has come hither to join us. The illustrious Paphnutius, who leads such an extraordinary life of solitude, is our unexpected guest."

Cotta. You may even add, Zenothemis, that the place of honour is due to him, because he came without being invited.

Zenothemis. Therefore, we ought, my dear Lucius, to make him the more welcome, and strive to do that which would be most agreeable to him. Now it is certain that such a man cares less for the fumes of meat than for the perfumes of fine thoughts. We shall, doubtless, please him by discussing the doctrine he professes, which is that of Jesus crucified. For my own part, I shall the more willingly discuss this doctrine, because it keenly interests me, on account of the number and the diversity of the allegories it contains. If one may guess at the spirit by the letter, it is filled with truths, and I consider that the Christian books abound in divine revelations. But I should not, Paphnutius, grant equal merit to the Jewish books. They were inspired not, as it was said, by the Spirit of God, but by an evil genius. Iaveh, who dictated them, was one of those spirits who people the lower air, and cause the greater part of the evils, from which we suffer; but he surpassed all the others in ignorance and ferocity. On the contrary, the serpent with golden wings, which twined its azure coils round the tree of knowledge, was made up of light and love. A combat between these two powers—the one of light and the other of darkness—was, therefore, inevitable. It occurred soon after the creation of the world. God had hardly begun to rest after His labours; Adam and Eve, the first man and the first woman, lived happy and naked in the Garden of Eden, when Iaveh conceived—to their misfortune—the design of governing them and all the generations which Eve already bore in her splendid loins. As he possessed neither the compass nor the lyre, and was equally ignorant of the science which commands and the art which persuades, he frightened these two poor children by hideous apparitions, capricious threats, and thunder-bolts. Adam and Eve, feeling his shadow upon them, pressed closer to one another, and their love waxed stronger in fear. The serpent took pity on them, and determined to instruct them, in order that, possessing knowledge, they might no longer be misled by lies. Such an undertaking required extreme prudence, and the frailty of the first human couple rendered it almost hopeless. The well-intentioned demon essayed it, however. Without the knowledge of Iaveh—who pretended to see everything, but, in reality, was not very sharp-sighted—he approached these two beings, and charmed their eyes by the splendour of his coat and the brilliancy of his wings. Then he interested their minds by forming before them, with his body, definite figures, such as the circle, the ellipse, and the spiral, the wonderful properties of which have since been recognised by the Greeks. Adam meditated on these figures more than Eve did. But when the serpent began to speak, and taught the most sublime truths—those which cannot be demonstrated—he found that Adam being made of red earth, was of too dull a nature to understand these subtle distinctions, but that Eve, on the contrary, being more tender and more sensitive, was easily impressed. Therefore he conversed with her alone, in the absence of her husband, in order to initiate her first—

DORION. Permit me, Zenothemis, to interrupt you. I speedily recognised in the myth you have explained to us an episode in the war of Pallas Athene against the giants. Iaveh much resembles Typhoon, and Pallas is represented by the Athenians with a serpent at her side. But what you have said causes me considerable doubt as to the intelligence or good faith of the serpent of whom you have spoken. If he had really possessed knowledge, would he have entrusted it to a woman's little head, which was incapable of containing it? I should rather consider that he was like Iaveh, ignorant and a liar, and that he chose Eve because she was easily seduced, and he imagined that Adam would have more intelligence and perception.

ZENOTHEMIS. Learn, Dorion, that it is not by perception and intelligence, but by sensibility, that the highest and purest truths are reached. That is why women, who, generally, are less reflective but more sensitive than men, rise more easily to the knowledge of things divine. In them is the gift of prophecy, and it is not without reason that Apollo Citharedes, and Jesus of Nazareth, are sometimes represented clad, like women, in flowing robes. The initiator was therefore wise—whatever you may say to the contrary, Dorion—in bestowing light, not on the duller Adam, but on Eve, who was whiter than milk or the stars. She freely listened to him, and allowed herself to be led to the tree of knowledge, the branches of which rose to heaven, and which was bathed with the divine spirit as with a dew. This tree was covered with leaves which spoke all the languages of future races of men, and their united voices formed a perfect harmony. Its abundant fruit gave to the initiated who tasted it the knowledge of metals, stones, and plants, and also of physical and moral laws; but this fruit was like fire, and those who feared suffering and death did not dare to put it to their lips. Now, as she had listened attentively to the lessons of the serpent, Eve despised these empty terrors, and wished to taste the fruit which gave the knowledge of God. But, as she loved Adam, and did not wish him to be inferior to her, she took him by the hand and led him to the wonderful tree. Then she picked one of the burning apples, bit it, and proffered it to her companion. Unfortunately, Iaveh, who was by chance walking in the garden, surprised them, and seeing that they had become wise, he fell into a most ungovernable rage. It is in his jealous fits that he is most to be feared. Assembling all his forces, he created such a turmoil in the lower air that these two weak beings were terrified. The fruit fell from the man's hand, and the woman, clinging to the neck of her luckless husband, said, "I too will be ignorant and suffer with him." The triumphant Iaveh kept Adam and Eve and all their seed in a condition of hebetude and terror. His art, which consisted only in being able to make huge meteors, triumphed over the science of the serpent, who was a musician and geometrician. He made men unjust, ignorant, and cruel, and caused evil to reign in the earth. He persecuted Cain and his sons because they were skilful workmen; he exterminated the Philistines because they composed Orphic poems and fables like those of Æsop. He was the implacable enemy of science and beauty, and for long ages the human race expiated, in blood and tears, the defeat of the winged serpent. Fortunately, there arose among the Greeks learned men, such as Pythagoras, and Plato, who recovered by the force of genius, the figures and the ideas which the enemy of Iaveh had vainly tried to teach the first woman. The soul of the serpent was in them; and that is why the serpent, as Dorion has said, is honoured by the Athenians. Finally, in these latter days, there appeared, under human form, three celestial spirits—Jesus of Galilee, Basilides, and Valentinus—to whom it was given to pluck the finest fruits of that tree of knowledge, whose roots pass through all the earth, and whose top reaches to the highest heaven. I have said all this in vindication of the Christians, to whom the errors of the Jews are too often imputed.

DORION. If I understood you aright, Zenothemis, you said that three wonderful men—Jesus, Basilides, and Valentinus—had discovered secrets which had remained hidden from Pythagoras and Plato, and all the philosophers of Greece, and even from the divine Epicurus, who, however, has freed men from the dread of empty terrors. You would greatly oblige me by telling me by what means these three mortals acquired knowledge which had eluded the most contemplative sages.

ZENOTHEMIS. Must I repeat to you, Dorion, that science and cogitation are but the first steps to knowledge, and that ecstasy alone leads to eternal truth?

HERMODORUS. It is true, Zenothemis, that the soul is nourished on ecstasy, as the cicada is nourished on dew. But we may even say more: the mind alone is capable of perfect rapture. For man is of a threefold nature, composed of material body, of a soul which is more subtle, but also material, and of an incorruptible mind. When, emerging from the body as from a palace suddenly given over to silence and solitude and flying through the gardens of the soul, the mind diffuses itself in God, it tastes the delights of an anticipated death, or rather of a future life, for to die is to live; and in that condition, partaking of divine purity, it possesses both infinite joy and complete knowledge. It enters into the unity which is All. It is perfected.

NICIAS. That is very fine; but, to say the truth,

Hermodorus, I do not see much difference between All and Nothing. Words even seem to fail to make the distinction. Infinity is terribly like nothingness—they are both inconceivable to the mind. In my opinion perfection costs too dear; we pay for it with all our being, and to possess it must cease to exist. That is a calamity from which God Himself is not free, for the philosophers are doing their best to perfect Him. After all, if we do not know what it is *not* to be, we are equally ignorant what it is to *be*. We know nothing. It is said that it is impossible for men to agree on this question. I believe —in spite of our noisy disputes—that it is, on the contrary, impossible for men not to become some day all at unity buried under the mass of contradictions, a Pelion on Ossa, which they themselves have raised.

COTTA. I am very fond of philosophy, and study it in my leisure time. But I never understand it well, except in Cicero's books. Slaves, pour out the honeyed wine!

CALLICRATES. It is a singular thing, but when I am hungry I think of the time when the tragic poets sat at the boards of good tyrants, and my mouth waters. But when I have tasted the excellent wine that you give us so abundantly, generous Lucius, I dream of nothing but civil wars and heroic combats. I blush to live in such inglorious times; I invoke the goddess of Liberty; and I pour out my blood—in imagination—with the last Romans on the field of Philippi.

COTTA. In the days of the decline of the Republic my ancestors died with Brutus—for liberty. But there is reason to suspect that what the Roman people called liberty was only in reality the right to govern themselves. I do not deny that liberty is the greatest boon a nation can have. But the longer I live the more I am persuaded that only a strong government can bestow it on the citizens. For forty years I have filled high positions in the State, and my long experience has shown me that when the ruling power is weak the people are oppressed. Those, therefore, who—like the great majority of rhetoricians—try to weaken the government, commit an abominable crime. An autocrat, who governs by his single will, may sometimes cause most deplorable results; but if he governs by popular consent there is no remedy possible. Before the majesty of the Roman arms had bestowed peace upon all the world, the only nations which were happy were those which were ruled over by intelligent despots.

HERMODORUS. For my part, Lucius, I believe that there is no such thing as a good form of government, and that we shall never discover one, because the Greeks, who had so many excellent ideas, were never able to find one. In that respect, therefore, all hope of ultimate success is taken from us. Unmistakable signs show that the world is about to fall into ignorance and barbarism. It has been our lot, Lucius, to witness terrible events. If all the mental satisfactions which intelligence, learning, and virtue can give, all that remains is the cruel pleasure of watching ourselves die.

COTTA. It is true that the rapacity of the people, and the boldness of the barbarians, are threatening evils. But with a good fleet, a good army, and plenty of money—

HERMODORUS. What is the use of deceiving ourselves? The dying empire will become an easy prey to the barbarians. Cities which were built by Hellenic genius, or Latin patience, will soon be sacked by drunken savages. Neither art nor philosophy will exist any longer on the earth. The statues of the gods will be overturned in the temples, and in men's hearts as well. Darkness will overcome all minds, and the world will die. Can we believe that the Sarmatians will ever devote themselves to intelligent work, that the Germani will cultivate music and philosophy, and that the Quadi and the Marcomani will adore the immortal gods?

No! we are sliding toward the abyss. Our old Egypt, which was the cradle of the world, will be its burial vault; Serapis, the god of Death, will receive the last adoration of mortals, and I shall have been the last priest of the last god.

At this moment a strange figure raised the tapestry, and the guests saw before them a little hunchback, whose bald skull rose in a point. He was clad, in the Asiatic fashion, in a blue tunic, and wore round his legs, like the barbarians, red breeches, spangled with gold stars. On seeing him, Paphnutius recognised Marcus the Arian, and fearing lest a thunderbolt should fall from heaven, he covered his head with his arms, and grew pale with fright. At this banquet of the demons, neither the blasphemies of the pagans, nor the horrible errors of the philosophers, had had any effect on him, but the mere presence of the heretic quenched his courage. He would have fled, but his eyes met those of Thaïs, and he felt at once strengthened. He read in her soul that she, who was predestined to become a saint, already protected him. He seized the skirt of her long, flowing robe, and inwardly prayed to the Saviour Jesus.

A murmur of acclamation welcomed the arrival of the personage who had been called the Christian Plato. Hermodorus was the first to speak.

"Most illustrious Marcus, we rejoice to see you amongst us, and it may be said that you come at the right moment. We know nothing of the Christian doctrine, beyond what is publicly taught. Now, it is certain that a philosopher, like you, cannot think as the vulgar think, and we are curious to know your opinion of the principal mysteries of the religion you profess. Our dear friend, Zenothemis, who, as you know, is always hunting for symbolic meanings, just now questioned the illustrious Paphnutius concerning the Jewish books. But Paphnutius made no reply, and we should not be surprised at that, as our guest has made a vow of silence, and God has sealed his tongue in the desert. But you Marcus, who have spoken at the Christian synods, and even at the councils of the divine Constantine, can if you wish, satisfy our curiosity by revealing to us the philosophic truths which are wrapped up in the Christian fables. Is not the first of these truths the existence of an only God—in whom, for my part, I fervently believe?"

MARCUS. Yes, venerable brethren, I believe in an only God, not begotten—the only Eternal, the origin of all things.

NICIAS. We know, Marcus, that your God created the world. That must certainly have been a great crisis in His existence. He had already existed an eternity before He could make up His mind to it. But I must, in justice, confess that His situation was a most difficult one. He must continue inactive if He would remain perfect, and must act if He would prove to Himself His own existence. . You assure me that He decided to act. I am willing to believe you, although it was an unpardonable imprudence on the part of a perfect God. But tell us, Marcus, how He set about making the world.

MARCUS. Those who, without being Christians, possess, like Hermodorus and Zenothemis, the principles of knowledge, are aware that God did not create the world personally without an intermediary. He gave birth to an only Son, by whom all things were made.

HERMODORUS. That is quite true, Marcus; and this Son is worshipped under the various names of Hermes, Mithra, Adonis, Apollo, and Jesus.

MARCUS. I should not be a Christian if I gave Him any other names than those of Jesus Christ, and Saviour. He is the true Son of God. But He is not eternal, since He had a beginning; as to thinking that He existed before He was begotten, we must leave that absurdity to the Nicæan mules, and the obstinate ass who too long governed the Church of Alexandria under the accursed name of Athanasius.

At these words Paphnutius, white with horror and his face bedewed with the sweat of agony, made the sign of the cross, but maintained a sublime silence.

Marcus continued—

"It is clear that the foolish Nicene Creed is a treason against the majesty of the only God, by compelling Him to share His indivisible attributes with His own emanation—the Mediator by whom all things were made. Cease jesting at the true God of the Christians, Nicias, and learn that, like the lilies of the field, He toils not, neither does He spin. It was not He who was the worker, it was His only Son, Jesus, who, having created the world, came afterwards to repair His handiwork. For the creation could not be perfect, and evil was necessarily mingled with good.

NICIAS. What is "good," and what is "evil"?

There was a moment's silence, during which Hermodorus, his arm extended on the cloth, pointed to a little ass in Corinthian metal which bore two baskets—the one containing white olives, the other black olives.

"You see these olives," he said. "The contrast between the colours is pleasant to the eye, and we are content that these should be light and those should be dark. But, if they were endowed with thought and knowledge, the white would say, It is good for an olive to be white, it is bad for it to be black; and the black olives would hate the white olives. We judge better, for we are as much above them as the gods are above us. For man, who only sees a part of things, evil is an evil; for God, who understands all things, evil is a good. Doubtless ugliness is ugly, and not beautiful; but if all were beautiful, the whole would not be beautiful. It is, then, well that there should be evil, as the second Plato, far greater than the first, has demonstrated."

EUCRITES. Let us talk more morally. Evil is an evil—not for the world, of which it cannot destroy the indestructible harmony but for the sinner who does it, and cannot help doing it.

COTTA. By Jupiter! that is a good argument.

EUCRITES. The world is a tragedy by an excellent poet. God, who composed it, has intended each of us to play a part in it. If he wills that you shall be a beggar, a prince, or a cripple, make the best of the part assigned you.

NICIAS. Assuredly it would be well that the cripple should limp like Hephaistos: it would be well that the madman should indulge in all the fury of Ajax, that the incestuous woman should repeat the crimes of Phædra, that the traitor should betray, that the rascal should lie, and the murderer kill, and when the piece was played, all the actors —kings, just men, bloody tyrants, pious virgins, immodest wives, noble-minded citizens, and cowardly assassins—should receive from the poet an equal share in the felicitations.

EUCRITES. You distort my thought, Nicias, and change a beautiful young girl into a hideous Gorgon. I am sorry for you, if you are so ignorant of the nature of the gods, of justice, and of the eternal laws.

ZENOTHEMIS. For my part, friends, I believe in the reality of good and evil. But I am convinced that there is not a single human action—were it even the kiss of Judas—which does not bear within itself the germ of redemption. Evil contributes to the ultimate salvation of men, and, in that respect, issues from Good, and shares the merits belonging to Good. This has been admirably expressed by the Christians, in the myth concerning the man with red hair, who, in order to betray his master, gave him the kiss of peace, and by such act assured the salvation of men. Therefore, nothing is, in my opinion, more unjust and absurd than the hate with which certain disciples of Paul, the tentmaker, pursue the most unfortunate of the apostles of Jesus; without realising that the kiss of Iscariot—prophesied by Jesus Himself—was necessary, according to their own doctrine, for the redemption of men, and that if Judas had not received the thirty pieces, the divine wisdom would have been impugned, Providence frustrated, its designs upset, and the world given over to evil, ignorance, and death.

Marcus. Divine wisdom foresaw that Judas, though he was not obliged to give the traitor's kiss, would give it, notwithstanding. It thus employed the sin of Iscariot as a stone in the marvellous edifice of the redemption.

Zenothemis. I spoke just now, Marcus, as though I believed that the redemption of men had been accomplished by Jesus crucified, because I know that such is the belief of the Christians, and I borrowed their opinion that I might the better show the mistake of those who believe in the eternal damnation of Judas. But, in reality, Jesus was, in my eyes, but the precursor of Basilides and Valentinus. As to the mystery of the redemption, I will tell you, my dear friends—if you are at all curious to hear it—how it was really accomplished on earth.

The guests made a sign of assent. Like the Athenian virgins with the baskets sacred to Ceres, twelve young girls, bearing on their heads baskets filled with pomegranates and apples, entered the room with a light step, in time to the music of an invisible flute. They placed the baskets on the table, the flute ceased, and Zenothemis spoke as follows—

"When Eunoia, 'the thought of God,' had created the world, she confided the government of the earth to the angels. But they did not preserve the dispassion befitting masters. Seeing that the daughters of men were fair, they surprised them in the evening by the wellside, and united themselves to them. From these unions sprang a turbulent race, who covered the earth with injustice and cruelty, and the dust of the roads drank up the blood of the innocent. The sight of this caused Eunoia infinite grief.

" 'See what I have done!' she sighed, leaning towards the world. 'My poor children are plunged in misery, and by my fault. Their suffering is my crime, and I will expiate it. God Himself, who only thinks through me, would be powerless to restore them to their pristine purity. That which is done is done, and the creation will remain for ever imperfect. But, at least, I will not forsake my creatures. If I cannot make them happy, like me, I can make myself unhappy, like them. Since I committed the mistake of giving them bodies which dishonour them, I will myself assume a body like unto theirs, and will go and live amongst them.'

"Having thus spoken, Eunoia descended to the earth, and was incarnate in the breast of a woman of Argos. She was born small and feeble, and received the name of Helen. She submitted to all the labours of this life, but soon grew in grace and beauty, and became the most desired of women, as she had determined, in order that her mortal body might be tried by the most supreme defilements. An inert prey to lascivious and violent men, she suffered rape and adultery, in expiation of all the adulteries, all the violences, all the iniquities, and caused, by her beauty, the ruin of nations, that God might pardon the sins of the universe. And never was the celestial thought, never was Eunoia, so adorable as in those days when, as a woman, she prostituted herself to heroes and shepherds. The poets surmised her divinity when they painted her so peaceful, superb, and fatal, and when they addressed that invocation to her, 'A soul as serene as a calm upon the waters.'

"Thus was Eunoia led by pity into evil and suffering. She died, and the Argives still show her tomb —for it was necessary that she should know death after lust, and taste the bitter fruit she had sown. But, emerging from the decomposed flesh of Helen, she became incarnate again as a woman, and again suffered every form of insult and outrage. Thus, passing from body to body, throughout all the evil ages, she takes upon her the sins of the world. Her sacrifice will not be in vain. Joined to us by the bonds of the flesh, loving us, and weeping with us, she will effect her redemption and ours, and will carry us, clinging to her white breast, into the peace of the regained paradise."

HERMODORUS. This myth was not unknown to me. I remembered having heard that, in one of her metamorphoses, the divine Helen lived with the magician, Simon, in the reign of the Emperor Tiberius. I thought, however, that her perdition was involuntary, and that she was dragged down by the angels in their fall.

ZENOTHEMIS. It is true, Hermodorus, that men who were not properly initiated in the mysteries, have imagined that the sad Eunoia was not a party to her own downfall. But if it were as they assert, Eunoia would not be the expiating courtesan, the victim covered with stains of all sorts, the bread steeped in the wine of our shame, the pleasant offering, the meritorious sacrifice, the holocaust, the smoke of which rises to God. If they were not voluntary, there would be no merit in her sins.

CALLICRATES. Does anyone know, Zenothemis, in what country, under what name, in what adorable form, this ever-renascent Helen is living now?

ZENOTHEMIS. A man would have to be very wise indeed to discover such a secret. And wisdom, Callicrates, is not given to poets, who live in the rude world of forms and amuse themselves, like children, with sounds and empty shows.

CALLICRATES. Beware of offending the gods, impious Zenothemis; the poets are dear to them. The first laws were dictated in verse by the immortals themselves, and the oracles of the gods are poems. Hymns have a pleasant sound to celestial ears. Who does not know that the poets are prophets, and that nothing is hidden from them? Being a poet myself, and crowned with Apollo's laurel, I will make known to all the last incarnation of Eunoia. The eternal Helen is close to us; she is looking at us, and we are looking at her. You see that woman reclining on the cushions of her couch —so beautiful and so contemplative—whose eyes shed tears, and whose lips abound with kisses! It is she! Lovely as in the time of Priam and the halcyon days of Asia, Eunoia is now called Thaïs.

PHILINA. What do you say, Callicrates? Our dear Thaïs knew Paris, Menelaus, and the Achaians who fought before Ilion! Was the Trojan horse big, Thaïs?

ARISTOBULUS. Who speaks of a horse?

"I have drunk like a Thracian!" cried Chereas; and he rolled under the table.

Callicrates, raising his cup, cried—

"If we drink like desperate men, we die unavenged!"

Old Cotta was asleep, and his bald head nodded slowly above his broad shoulders.

For some time past Dorion had seemed to be greatly excited under his philosophic cloak. He reeled up to the couch of Thaïs.

"Thaïs, I love you, although it is unseemly in me to love a woman."

THAÏS. Why did you not love me before?

DORION. Because I had not supped.

THAÏS. But I, my poor friend, have drunk nothing but water; therefore you must excuse me if I do not love you.

Dorion did not wait to hear more, but made towards Drosea, who had made a sign to him in order to get him away from her friend. Zenothemis took the place he had left, and gave Thaïs a kiss on the mouth.

THAÏS. I thought you more virtuous.

ZENOTHEMIS. I am perfect, and the perfect are subject to no laws.

THAÏS. But are you not afraid of sullying your soul in a woman's arms?

ZENOTHEMIS. The body may yield to lust without the soul being concerned.

THAÏS. Go away! I wish to be loved with body and soul. All these philosophers are old goats.

The lamps died out one by one. The pale rays of dawn, which entered between the openings of the hangings, shone on the livid faces and swollen eyes of the guests. Aristobulus was sleeping soundly by the side of Chereas, and, in his dreams, devoting all his grooms to the ravens. Zenothemis pressed in his arms the yielding Philina; Dorion poured on the naked bosom of Drosea drops of wine, which rolled like rubies on the white breast, which was shaking with laughter, and the philosopher tried to catch these drops with his lips, as they rolled on the slippery flesh. Eucrites rose, and placing his arm on the shoulder of Nicias, led him to the end of the hall.

"Friend," he said, smiling, "if you can still think at all—of what are you thinking?"

"I think that the love of women is like a garden of Adonis."

"What do you mean by that?"

"Do you not know, Eucrites, that women make little gardens on the terraces, in which they plant boughs in clay pots in honour of the lover of Venus?

These boughs flourish a little time, and then fade."

"What does that signify, Nicias? That it is foolish to attach importance to that which fades?"

"If beauty is but a shadow, desire is but a lightning flash. What madness it is, then, to desire beauty! Is it not rational, on the contrary, that that which passes should go with that which does not endure, and that the lightning should devour the gliding shadow?"

"Nicias, you seem to me like a child playing at knuckle-bones. Take my advice—be free! By liberty only can you become a man."

"How can a man be free, Eucrites, when he has a body?"

"You shall see presently, my son. Presently you will say, 'Eucrites was free.'"

The old man spoke, leaning against a porphyry pillar, his face lighted by the first rays of dawn. Hermodorus and Marcus had approached, and stood before him by the side of Nicias; and all four, regardless of the laughter and cries of the drinkers, conversed on things divine. Eucrites expressed himself so wisely and eloquently, that Marcus said—

"You are worthy to know the true God."

Eucrites replied—

"The true God is in the heart of the wise man."

Then they spoke of death.

"I wish," said Eucrites, "that it may find me occupied in correcting my faults, and attentive to all my duties. In the face of death I will raise my pure hands to heaven, and I will say to the gods, 'Your images, gods, that you have placed in the temple of my soul, I have not profaned; I have hung there my thoughts, as well as garlands, fillets, and wreaths. I have lived according to your providence. I have lived enough.'"

Thus speaking, he raised his arms to heaven, and he remained thoughtful a moment. Then he continued, with extreme joy—

"Separate thyself from life, Eucrites, like the ripe olive which falls; returning thanks to the tree which bore thee, and blessing the earth, thy nurse."

At these words, drawing from the folds of his robe a naked dagger, he plunged it into his breast.

Those who listened to him sprang forward to seize his hand, but the steel point had already penetrated the heart of the sage. Eucrites had already entered into his rest. Hermodorus and Nicias bore the pale and bleeding body to one of the couches, amidst the shrill shrieks of the women, the grunts of the guests disturbed in their sleep, and the heavy breathing of the couples hidden in the shadow of the tapestry. Cotta, an old soldier, who slept lightly, woke, approached the corpse, examined the wound, and cried—

"Call Aristæus, my physician!"

Nicias shook his head.

"Eucrites is no more," he said. "He wished to die as others wish to love. He has, like all of us, obeyed his inexpressible desire. And, lo, now he is like unto the gods, who desire nothing."

Cotta struck his forehead.

"Die! To want to die when he might still serve the State! What nonsense!"

Paphnutius and Thaïs remained motionless and mute, side by side, their souls overflowing with disgust, horror, and hope.

Suddenly the monk seized the hand of the actress, and stepping over the drunkards, who had fallen close to the lascivious couples, and treading in the wine and blood spilt upon the floor, he led her out of the house.

THE sun had risen over the city. Long colonnades stretched on both sides of the deserted street, and at the end shone the dome of Alexander's tomb. Here and there on the pavement lay broken wreaths and extinguished torches. Fresh wafts of the sea could be felt in the air. Paphnutius, with a look of disgust, tore off his rich robe and trampled the fragments under his feet.

"Thou hast heard them, my Thaïs!" he cried. "They have spat forth every sort of folly and abomination. They dragged the Divine Creator of all things down the gemonies * of the devils of hell, impudently denied the existence of Good and Evil, blasphemed Jesus, and exalted Judas. And the most infamous of all, the jackal of darkness, the stinking beast, the Arian full of corruption and death, opened his mouth like a yawning sepulchre. My Thaïs, thou hast seen these filthy snails crawling towards thee and defiling thee with their sticky sweat; thou hast seen others, like brutes, sleeping under

* Steps on the Aventine Hill, leading to the Tiber, to which the bodies of executed criminals were dragged to be thrown into the river. The word is now obsolete, but was employed by Ben Jonson (*Sejanus*) and Massinger (*The Roman Actor*).—Trans.

the heels of their slaves; thou hast seen them coupling like beasts on the carpet they had fouled with their vomit; thou hast seen a foolish old man shed a blood yet viler than the wine which flowed at his debauch, and at the end of the orgie throw himself in the face of the unforeseen Christ. Praise be to God! Thou hast seen error and recognised how hideous it was. Thaïs, Thaïs, Thaïs, recall to mind the follies of these philosophers, and say if thou wilt go mad with them! Remember the looks, the gestures, the laughs of their fitting companions, those two lascivious and malicious strumpets, and say if thou wilt remain like unto them."

Thaïs, her heart stirred with horror and disgust at all she had seen and heard that night, and feeling the indifference and brutality, the malicious jealousy of women, the heavy weight of useless hours, sighed.

"I am weary to death, O my father! Where shall I find rest? I feel that my face is burning, my head empty, and my arms are so tired that I should not have the strength to seize happiness were it within reach of my hand."

Paphnutius gazed at her with loving pity.

"Courage, O my sister! The hour of rest rises for thee, white and pure as the vapours thou seest rise from the gardens and waters."

They were near the house of Thaïs, and could

see, above the wall, the tops of the sycamore and fir trees, which surrounded the Grotto of Nymphs, tremble in the morning breeze. In front of them was a public square, deserted, and surrounded with steles and votive statues, and having at each end a semicircular marble seat, supported by figures of monsters. Thaïs fell on one of these seats. Then, looking anxiously at the monk, she asked—

"What must I do?"

"Thou must," replied the monk, "follow Him who has come to seek thee. He will separate thee from this present life, as the vintager gathers the cluster that would have rotted on the tree, and bears it to the wine-press to change it into perfumed wine. Listen! there is a dozen hours from Alexandria, towards the west, not far from the sea, a nunnery, the rules of which, a masterpiece of wisdom, deserve to be put in lyric verse and sung to the sound of the theorbo and tambourines. It may truly be said that the women who are there, submissive to these rules, have their feet upon earth and their faces in heaven. They desire to be poor, that Jesus may love them, modest, that He may gaze upon them every day in the guise of a gardener, His feet bare, His beautiful hands open—even as He showed Himself to Mary at the entrance of the tomb. I will conduct thee this very day to this nunnery, my

Thaïs, and soon, commingling with these holy women, thou wilt share in their heavenly conversation. They await thee as a sister. On the threshold of the convent, their mother, the pious Albina, will give thee the kiss of peace and will say, 'My daughter, thou art welcome!' "

The courtesan uttered a cry of amazement.

"Albina! a daughter of the Cæsars! The great niece of the Emperor Carus!"

"She herself! Albina, who, born in the purple, has donned the serge, and a daughter of the masters of this world, has risen to the rank of servant of Jesus Christ. She will be thy mother."

Thaïs rose and said—

"Take me to the house of Albina."

And Paphnutius, completing his victory—

"Surely I will conduct thee thither, and there I will place thee in a cell, where thou shalt weep for thy sins. For it is not fitting that thou shouldst mingle with the daughters of Albina until thou art cleansed from thy sins. I will seal the door, and there, a happy prisoner, thou wilt wait in tears till Jesus Himself come, as a sign of pardon, to break the seal that I have placed. And doubt not that He will come, Thaïs, and how the flesh of thy soul will tremble when thou shalt feel the fingers of Light placed upon thy eyes to dry thy tears!"

Thaïs said a second time—

"Take me, my father, to the house of Albina."

His heart filled with joy, Paphnutius gazed around him, and tasted, almost without fear, the pleasure of contemplating the works of creation; his eyes drank in with joy God's light, and unknown breezes fanned his cheeks. Suddenly, seeing at one of the corners of the public square the little door which led to Thaïs' house, and remembering that the trees, whose foliage he had been admiring, shaded the courtesan's garden, he thought of all the impurities which there sullied the air, to-day so light and pure, and his soul was so grieved that bitter tears sprang to his eyes.

"Thaïs," he said, "we must fly without looking back. But we must not leave behind us the instruments, the witnesses, the accomplices of thy past crimes; those heavy hangings, those beds, carpets, perfume censers and lamps, which would proclaim thy infamy! Dost thou wish that, animated by the demons, and carried by the evil spirit that is in them, those accursed belongings should pursue thee even to the desert? It is but too true that there are tables which bring ruin, seats which serve as the instruments of devils, which act, speak, strike the ground, and pass through the air. Let all perish which has seen thy shame! Hasten, Thaïs, and, whilst the city is yet asleep, order thy slaves to make, in the centre of this place, a pile, upon which we will burn all the abominable riches thy dwelling contains."

Thaïs consented.

"Do as you will, my father," she said. "I know that spirits often dwell in inanimate objects. At night some articles of furniture talk, either by giving knocks at regular intervals or by emitting little flashes of light as signals. And even more. Have you remarked, my father, at the entrance to the Grotto of Nymphs, on the right, a statue of a naked woman about to bathe? One day I saw, with my own eyes, that statue turn its head like a living person, and then return to its ordinary attitude. I was terrified. Nicias, to whom I related this prodigy, laughed at me; yet there must be some magic in that statue, for it inspired with violent desires a certain Dalmatian, who was insensible to my beauty. It is certain that I have lived amongst enchanted things, and that I was exposed to the greatest perils, for men have been strangled by the embraces of a bronze statue. Yet it would be a pity to destroy valuable works made with rare skill, and to burn my carpets and tapestry would be a great loss. The beautiful colours of some of them are truly wonderful, and they cost much money to those who gave them to me. I also possess cups, statues, and pictures of great price. I do not think they ought to perish. But you know what is necessary. Do as you will, my father."

Thus saying, she followed the monk to the little door at which so many garlands and wreaths had been hung, and, when it was opened, she told the porter to call together all the slaves in the house. Four Indians, who were employed in the kitchen, were the first to appear. They were all four yellow men, and each had but one eye. It had cost Thaïs much trouble, and given her amusement, to get together these four slaves of the same race, and all afflicted with the same infirmity. When they attended at table they excited the curiosity of the guests, and Thaïs made them relate the story of their lives. These four waited in silence. Their assistants followed them. Then came the stablemen, the huntsmen, the litter-bearers, and the running footmen with muscles like iron, two gardeners hirsute as Priapus, six ferocious looking negroes, three Greek slaves—one a grammarian, another a poet, and the third a singer. They all stood, ranged in order, on the public square, and were presently joined by the negresses—curious, suspicious, rolling big round eyes, and each with a huge mouth slit to her earrings. Lastly, adjusting their veils and languidly dragging their feet, which were shackled with light gold chains, appeared six sulky-looking, beautiful white slave-girls. When they were all assembled, Thaïs, pointing to Paphnutius, said—

"Do whatever this man commands you; for the spirit of God is in him, and if you disobey him you will fall dead."

For she had heard, and really believed, that the earth would open and swallow up in flames and smoke any impious wretch whom a saint of the desert struck with his staff.

Paphnutius sent away the women and the Greek men-slaves, and said to the others—

"Bring wood to the middle of this place, make a huge fire, and throw into it pell-mell all that there is in the house and grotto."

They were astonished, and stood motionless, looking at their mistress. And they still stood inactive and silent, and pressed against each other, elbow to elbow, suspecting that the order was a joke.

"Obey!" said the monk.

Several of them were Christians. They understood the command, and went to the house to fetch wood and torches. The others were not indisposed to imitate them, for, being poor, they hated riches and had a natural instinct for destruction Whilst they were building the pile, Paphnutius said to Thaïs—"I thought at one time of fetching the treasurer of one of the churches of Alexandria (if there still remain one worthy of the name of church, and that is not defiled by the Arian beasts) and giving him thy goods, woman, that he might distribute them to widows, and change the proceeds of crime into the treasure of justice. But such a thought did not come from God, and I cast it from me, for assuredly it would be a great offence to the well-beloved of Jesus Christ to offer them the spoils of thy lust. Thaïs, all that thou hast touched must be devoured by the fire, even to its very soul. Thanks be to Heaven, these tunics and veils, which have seen kisses more innumerable than the waves of the sea, will only feel now the lips and tongues of the flames. Hasten, slaves! More wood! More links and torches! And thou, woman, return to thy house, strip thyself of thy shameful robes, and ask of the most humble of thy slaves, as an undeserving favour, the tunic that she puts on when she scrubs the floors."

Thaïs obeyed. Whilst the Indians knelt down and blew the embers, the negroes threw on the pile coffers of ivory, ebony, or cedar, which broke open and let out wreaths, garlands, and necklaces. The smoke rose in a dark column, as in the holocausts of the old religion. Then the fire, which had been smouldering, burst out suddenly with a roar as of some monstrous animal, and the almost invisible flames began to devour their valuable prey. The slaves worked more eagerly; they joyfully dragged out rich carpets, veils embroidered with silver, and flowered tapestry. They staggered under the weight of tables, couches, thick cushions, and beds with gold nails. Three strong Ethiopians came hugging the coloured statues of the nymphs, one of which had been loved as though it were a mortal; and they looked like huge apes carrying off women. And when the beautiful naked forms fell from the arms of these monsters, and were broken on the stones, a deep groan was heard.

At that moment Thaïs appeared, her hair unloosed and streaming over her shoulders, barefooted, and clad in a clumsy coarse garment which seemed redolent with divine voluptuousness merely from having touched her body. Behind her came a gardener, carrying, half hidden in his long beard, an ivory Eros.

She made a sign to the man to stop, and approaching Paphnutius, showed him the little god.

"My father," she asked, "should this also be thrown into the flames? It is of marvellous antique work, and is worth a hundred times its weight in gold. Its loss would be irreparable, for there is not a sculptor in the world capable of making such a beautiful Eros. Remember also, my father, that this child is Love, and he should not be harshly treated. Believe me, Love is a virtue, and if I have sinned, it is not through him, my father, but against him. Never shall I regret aught that he has caused me to do, and I deplore only those things I have done contrary to his commands. He does not allow women to give themselves to those who do not come in his name. For that reason he ought to be honoured. Look, Paphnutius, how pretty this little Eros is! With what grace he hides himself in the gardener's beard! One day Nicias, who loved me then, brought it to me and said, 'It will remind you of me.' But the roguish boy did not remind me of Nicias, but of a young man I knew at Antioch. Enough riches have been destroyed upon this pile, my father! Preserve this Eros, and place it in some monastery. Those who see it will turn their hearts towards God, for love leads naturally to heavenly thoughts."

The gardener, already believing that the little Eros was saved, smiled on it as though it had been a child, when Paphnutius, snatching the god from the arms which held it, threw it into the flames, crying—

"It is enough that Nicias has touched it to make it replete with every sort of poison!"

Then, seizing by armfuls the sparkling robes, the purple mantles, the golden sandals, the combs, strigils, mirrors, lamps, theorbos, and lyres, he threw them into this furnace, more costly than the funeral pile of Sardanapalus, whilst, drunken with the rage of destruction, the slaves danced round, uttering wild yells amid a shower of sparks and ashes.

One by one, the neighbours, awakened by the noise, opened the windows, and rubbing their eyes, looked out to see whence the smoke came. Then they came down, half dressed, and drew near the fire.

"What does it mean?" they wondered.

Amongst them were merchants from whom Thaïs had often bought perfumes and stuffs, and they looked on anxiously with long, yellow faces, unable to comprehend what was going on. Some young debauchees, who, returning from a supper, passed by there, preceded by their slaves, stopped, their heads crowned with flowers, their tunics floating, and uttered loud cries. Attracted by curiosity, the crowd increased unceasingly, and soon it was known that Thaïs had been persuaded by the Abbot of Antinoë to burn her riches, and retire to a nunnery.

The shopkeepers thought to themselves—

"Thaïs is going to leave the city; we shall sell no more to her; it is dreadful to think of. What will become of us without her? This monk has driven her mad. He is ruining us. Why let him do it? What is the use of the laws? Are there no magistrates in Alexandria? Thaïs does not think about us and our wives and our poor children. It is a public scandal. She ought to be compelled to stay in the city."

The young men, on their part, also thought—

"If Thaïs is going to renounce acting and love, our chief amusements will be taken from us. She was the glory, delight, and honour of the stage. She was the joy even of those who had never possessed her. The women we loved, we loved in her. There were no kisses given in which she was altogether absent, for she was the joy of all voluptuaries, and the mere thought that she breathed amongst us excited us to pleasure."

Thus thought the young men, and one of them, named Cerons, who had held her in his arms, cried out upon the abduction, and blasphemed against

Christ. In every group the conduct of Thaïs was severely criticised.

"It is a shameful flight!"

"A cowardly desertion!"

"She is taking the bread out of our mouths."

"She is robbing our children."

"She ought at least to pay for the wreaths I have sold to her."

"And the sixty robes she has ordered of me."

"She owes money to everybody."

"Who will represent Iphigenia, Electra, and Polyxena when she is gone? The handsome Polybia herself will not make such a success as she has done."

"Life will be dull when her door is closed."

"She was the bright star, the soft moon of the Alexandrian sky."

All the most notorious mendicants of the city—cripples, blind men, and paralytics—had by this time assembled in the place; and crawling through the remnants of the riches, they groaned—

"How shall we live when Thaïs is no longer here to feed us? Every day the fragments from her table fed two hundred poor wretches, and her lovers, when they quitted her, threw us as they passed handfuls of silver pieces."

Some thieves, too, also mingled with the crowd, and created a deafening clamour, and pushed their neighbours, to increase disorder, and take advantage of the tumult to filch some valuable object.

Old Taddeus, who sold Miletan wool and Tarentan linen, and to whom Thaïs owed a large sum of money, alone remained calm and silent in the midst of the uproar. He listened and watched, and gently stroking his goat-beard, seemed thoughtful. At last he approached young Cerons, and pulling him by the sleeve, whispered—

"You are the favoured lover of Thaïs, handsome youth; show yourself, and do not allow this monk to carry her off."

"By Pollux and his sister, he shall not!" cried Cerons. "I will speak to Thaïs, and without flattering myself, I think she will listen to me rather than to that sooty-faced Lapithan. Place! Place, dogs!"

And striking with his fist the men, upsetting the old women and treading on the young children, he reached Thaïs, and taking her aside—

"Dearest girl," he said, "look at me, remember, and tell me truly if you renounce love."

But Paphnutius threw himself between Thaïs and Cerons.

"Impious wretch!" he cried, "beware and touch her not; she is sacred—she belongs to God."

"Get away, baboon!" replied the young man furiously. "Let me speak to my sweetheart, or if not I will drag your obscene carcase by the beard to the fire, and roast you like a sausage."

And he put his hand on Thaïs. But, pushed away by the monk with unexpected force, he staggered back four paces and fell at the foot of the pile amongst the scattered ashes.

Old Taddeus, meanwhile, had been going from one to the other, pulling the ears of the slaves and kissing the hands of the masters, inciting each and all against Paphnutius, and had already formed a little band resolutely determined to oppose the monk who would steal Thaïs from them.

Cerons rose, his face black, his hair singed, and choking with smoke and rage. He blasphemed against the gods, and threw himself amongst the assailants, behind whom the beggars crawled, shaking their crutches. Paphnutius was soon enclosed in a circle of menacing fists, raised sticks, and cries of death.

"To the ravens with the monk! to the ravens!"

"No; throw him in the fire! Burn him alive!"

Seizing his fair prey, he pressed her to his heart.

"Impious men," he cried in a voice of thunder, "strive not to tear the dove from the eagle of the Lord. But rather copy this woman, and like her, turn your filth into gold. Imitate her example, and renounce the false wealth which you think you hold, and which holds you. Hasten! the day is at hand, and divine patience begins to grow weary. Repent, confess your sins, weep and pray. Walk in the footsteps of Thaïs. Hate your offences, which are as great as hers. Which of you, poor or rich, merchants, soldiers, slaves or eminent citizens, would dare to say, before God, that he was better than a prostitute? You are all nothing but living filth, and it is by a miracle of divine goodness that you do not suddenly turn into streams of mire."

Whilst he spoke flames shot from his eyes; and it seemed as though live coals came from his lips and those who surrounded him were obliged to hear him in spite of themselves.

But old Taddeus did not remain idle. He picked up stones and oyster shells, which he hid in the skirt of his tunic, and not daring to throw them himself, slipped them into the hands of the beggars. Soon the stones began to fly, and a well-directed shell cut Paphnutius' face. The blood, which flowed down the dark face of the martyr, dropped in a new baptism on the head of the penitent, and Thaïs, half stifled in the monk's embrace and her delicate skin scratched by the coarse cassock, felt a thrill of horror and fright.

At that moment a man elegantly dressed, and with a wreath of wild celery on his head, opened a road for himself through the furious crowd, and cried—

"Stop! Stop! This monk is my brother!"

It was Nicias, who, having closed the eyes of the philosopher Eucrites, was passing through the square to return to his house, and saw, without very much surprise (for nothing astonished him), the smoking pile, Thaïs clad in a serge cassock, and Paphnutius being stoned.

He repeated—

"Stop, I tell you; spare my old fellow-scholar; respect the beloved head of Paphnutius!"

But, being only used to subtle disquisitions with philosophers, he did not possess that imperious energy which commands vulgar minds. He was not listened to. A shower of stones and shells fell on the monk, who, protecting Thaïs with his body, praised the Lord whose goodness turned his wounds into caresses. Despairing of making himself heard, and feeling but too sure that he could not save his friend either by force or persuasion, Nicias resigned himself to the will of the gods—in whom he had little confidence—when the idea occurred to him to use a stratagem which his contempt for men had suddenly suggested to him. He took from his girdle his purse, which was full of gold and silver, for he was a pleasure-loving and charitable man, and running up to the men who were throwing the stones, he chinked the money in their ears. At first they paid no attention to him, their fury being too great; but little by little their looks turned towards the chinking gold, and soon their arms dropped and no longer menaced their victim. Seeing that he had attracted their eyes and minds, Nicias opened his purse and threw some pieces of gold and silver amongst the crowd. The more greedy of them stooped to pick it up. The philosopher, pleased at his first success, adroitly threw deniers and drachmas here and there. At the sound of the pieces of money rattling on the pavement, the persecutors of Paphnutius threw themselves on the ground. Beggars, slaves, and tradespeople scrambled after the money, whilst, grouped round Cerons, the patricians watched the struggle and laughed heartily. Cerons himself quite forgot his wrath. His friends encouraged the rivals, chose competitors, and made bets, and urged on the miserable wretches as they would have done fighting dogs. A cripple without legs having succeeded in seizing a drachma, the applause was frenetic. The young men themselves began to throw money, and nothing was to be seen in the square but a multitude of backs, rising and falling like waves of the sea, under a shower of coins. Paphnutius was forgotten.

Nicias ran up to him, covered him with his cloak, and dragged him and Thaïs into by-streets where they were safe from pursuit. They ran for some time in silence, and when they thought they were out of reach of their enemies, they ceased running, and Nicias said, in a tone of raillery in which a little sadness was mingled—

"It is finished then! Pluto ravishes Proserpine, and Thaïs will follow my fierce-looking friend whithersoever he will lead her."

"It is true, Nicias," replied Thaïs, "that I am tired of living with men like you, smiling, perfumed, kindly egoists. I am weary of all I know, and I am, therefore, going to seek the unknown. I have experienced joy that was not joy, and here is a man who teaches me that sorrow is true joy. I believe him, for he knows the truth."

"And I, sweetheart," replied Nicias, smiling, "I know the truths. He knows but one, I know them all. I am superior to him in that respect, but to tell the truth, it doesn't make me any the prouder nor any the happier."

Then, seeing that the monk was glaring fiercely at him—

"My dear Paphnutius, do not imagine that I think you extremely absurd, or even altogether unreasonable. And if I were to compare your life with mine, I could not say which is preferable in itself. I shall presently go and take the bath which Crobyle and Myrtale have prepared for me; I shall eat the wing of a Phasian pheasant; then I shall read—for the hundredth time—some fable by Apuleius or some treatise by Porphyry. You will return to your cell, where, leaning like a tame camel, you will ruminate on—I know not what—formulas of incarnations you have long chewed and rechewed, and in the evening you will swallow some radishes without any oil. Well, my dear friend, in accomplishing these acts, so different apparently, we are both obeying the same sentiment, the only motive for all human actions; we are both seeking our own pleasure, and striving to attain the same end—happiness, the impossible happiness. It would be folly on my part to say you were wrong, dear friend, even though I think myself in the right.

"And you, my Thaïs, go and enjoy yourself, and

be more happy still, if it be possible, in abstinence and austerity than you have been in riches and pleasure. On the whole, I should say you were to be envied. For if in our whole lives, Paphnutius and I have pursued but one kind of pleasurable satisfaction, you in your life, dear Thaïs, have tasted diverse joys such as it is rarely given to the same person to know. I should really like to be for one hour, a saint like our dear friend Paphnutius. But that is not possible. Farewell, then, Thaïs! Go where the secret forces of nature and your destiny conduct you! Go, and take with you, whithersoever you go, the good wishes of Nicias! I know that is mere foolishness, but can I give you anything more than barren regrets and vain wishes in payment for the delicious illusions which once enveloped me when I was in your arms, and of which only the shadow now remains to me? Farewell, my benefactress! Farewell, goodness that is ignorant of its own existence, mysterious virtue, joy of men! Farewell to the most adorable of the images that nature has ever thrown—for some unknown reasons—on the face of this deceptive world!"

Whilst he spoke, deep wrath had been brewing in the monk's heart, and it now broke forth in imprecations.

"Avaunt, cursed wretch! I scorn thee and hate thee. Go, child of hell, a thousand times worse than those poor lost ones who just now threw stones and insults at me! They knew not what they did, and the grace of God, which I implored for them, may some day descend into their hearts. But thou, detestable Nicias, thou art but a perfidious venom and a bitter poison. Thy mouth breathes despair and death. One of thy smiles contains more blasphemy than issues in a century from the smoking lips of Satan. Avaunt, backslider!"

Nicias looked at him.

"Farewell, my brother," he said, "and may you preserve until your life's end your store of faith, hate, and love. Farewell, Thaïs! It is in vain that you will forget me, because I shall ever remember you."

On quitting them he walked thoughtfully through the winding streets in the vicinity of the great cemetery of Alexandria, which are peopled by the makers of funeral urns. Their shops were full of clay figures painted in bright colours and representing gods and goddesses, mimes, women, winged spirits, &c., such as were usually buried with the dead. He fancied that perhaps some of the little images which he saw there might be the companions of his eternal sleep; and it seemed to him that a little Eros, with its tunic tucked up, laughed at him mockingly. He looked forward to his death, and the idea was painful to him. To cure his sadness he tried to philosophise, and reasoned thus—

"Assuredly," he said to himself, "time has no reality. It is a simple illusion of our minds. Then, if it does not exist, how can it bring death to me? Does that mean that I shall live for ever? No, but I conclude therefrom that my death is, always has been, as it always will be. I do not feel it yet, but it is in me, and I ought not to fear it, for it would be folly to dread the coming of that which has arrived. It exists, like the last page of a book I read and have not finished."

This argument occupied him all the rest of the way, but without making him more cheerful; and his mind was filled with dismal thoughts when he arrived at the door of his house and heard the merry laughter of Crobyle and Myrtale, who were playing at tennis whilst they were waiting for him.

Paphnutius and Thaïs left the city by the Gate of the Moon, and followed the coast.

"Woman," said the monk, "all that great blue sea could not wash away thy pollutions."

He spoke with scorn and anger.

"More filthy than a bitch or a sow, thou hast prostituted to pagans and infidels a body which the

Eternal had intended for a tabernacle, and thy impurities are such that, now that thou knowest the truth, thou canst not unite thy lips or join thy hands without a horror of thyself rising in thy heart."

She followed him meekly, over stony roads, under a burning sun. Her knees ached from fatigue, and her throat was parched with thirst. But, far from feeling any of the pity which softens the hearts of the profane, Paphnutius rejoiced at these propitiatory sufferings of the flesh which had so sinned. So infuriated was he with holy zeal that he would have liked to cut with rods the body that had preserved its beauty as a shining witness to its infamy. His meditations augmented his pious fury, and remembering that Thaïs had received Nicias in her bed, that idea seemed so horrible to him that his blood all flowed back to his heart, and his breast felt ready to burst. His curses were stifled in his throat, and he could only grind his teeth. He sprang forward and stood before her, pale, terrible, and filled with the Spirit of God—looked into her very soul, and then spat in her face.

She calmly wiped her face and continued to walk on. He followed, glaring at her in pious anger, as if she had been hell itself. He was thinking how he could avenge Christ in order that Christ should not avenge Himself, when he saw a drop of blood that had dripped from the foot of Thaïs on the sand. Then a hitherto unknown influence entered his opened heart, sobs rose to his lips, he wept, he ran and knelt before her, called her his sister, and kissed her bleeding feet. He murmured a hundred times, "My sister, my sister, my mother, O most holy!"

He prayed—

"Angels of heaven, receive carefully this drop of blood, and bear it before the throne of the Lord. And may a miraculous anemone blossom on the sand sprinkled with the blood of Thaïs, that those who see the flower may recover purity of heart and feeling. O holy, holy, most holy Thaïs!"

As he prayed and prophesied thus, a lad passed on an ass. Paphnutius ordered him to descend, seated Thaïs on the ass, and led it by the bridle. Towards evening they came to a canal shaded by fine trees; he tied the ass to the trunk of a date palm, and sitting on a mossy stone he shared with Thaïs a loaf, which they ate with salt and hyssop. They drank fresh water in their hands, and talked of things eternal. She said—

"I have never drunk water so pure, nor breathed an air so light, and I feel that God floats in the breezes that pass."

"Look! it is the evening, O my sister. The blue shadows of night cover the hills. But soon thou wilt see shining in the dawn the tabernacles of Light; soon thou wilt behold shine forth the roses of the eternal morning."

They journeyed all night, and, while the crescent moon gleamed on the silver crests of the waves, they sang psalms and hymns. When the sun rose, the Libyan desert stretched before them like a huge lion-skin. At the edge of the desert, and close to a few palm-trees, some white huts shimmered in the morning light.

"Are those the tabernacles of Light, father?" asked Thaïs.

"Even so, my daughter and my sister. Yonder is the House of Salvation, where I will confine you with my own hands."

Soon they saw a number of women busy around the buildings, like bees round their hives. There were some who baked bread, or prepared vegetables; many were spinning wool, and the light of heaven shone upon them like a smile of God. Others meditated in the shade of the tamarisk trees; their white hands hung by their sides, for, being filled with love, they had chosen the part of Magdalen, and performed no work but prayer, contemplation, and ecstasy. They were, therefore, called the Marys, and were clad in white. Those who worked with their hands were called the Marthas, and wore blue robes. All wore the hood, but the younger ones allowed a few curls to show on their foreheads—unintentionally, it is to be presumed, since it was forbidden by the rules. A very old lady, tall and white, walked from cell to cell, leaning on a staff of hard wood. Paphnutius approached her respectfully, kissed the hem of her veil, and said—

"The peace of the Lord be with thee, venerable Albina. I have brought to the hive, of which thou art queen, a bee I found lost on a flowerless road. I took it in the palm of my hand, and revived it with my breath. I give it to thee."

And he pointed to the actress, who knelt down before the daughter of the Cæsars.

Albina cast a piercing glance on Thaïs, ordered her to rise, kissed her on the forehead, and then, turning to the monk—

"We will place her," she said, "amongst the Marys."

Paphnutius then related how Thaïs had been brought to the House of Salvation, and asked that she should be at once confined in a cell. The abbess consented, and led the penitent to a hut, which had remained empty since the death of the virgin Læta, who had sanctified it. In this narrow chamber there was but a bed, a table, and a pitcher, and Thaïs when she crossed the threshold, felt filled with ineffable joy.

"I wish to close the door myself," said Paphnutius, "and put thereon a seal, which Jesus will come and break with His own hands."

He went to the side of the spring, and took a handful of wet clay, mixed with it a little spittle and a hair from his head, and plastered it across the chink of the door. Then, approaching the window, near which Thaïs stood peaceful and happy, he fell on his knees and praised the Lord three times.

"How beautiful are the feet of her who walketh in the paths of righteousness! How beautiful are her feet, and how resplendent her face!"

He rose, lowered his hood over his eyes, and walked away slowly.

Albina called one of her virgins.

"My daughter," she said, "take to Thaïs those things which are needful for her—bread, water, and a flute with three holes."

PART THE THIRD

THE EUPHORBIA

PART THE THIRD
THE EUPHORBIA

PAPHNUTIUS had returned to the holy desert. He took, near Athribis, the boat which went up the Nile to carry food to the monastery of Abbot Serapion. When he disembarked, his disciples advanced to meet him with great demonstrations of joy. Some raised their arms to heaven; others, prostrate on the ground, kissed the Abbot's sandals. For they knew already what the saint had accomplished in Alexandria. The monks generally received, by rapid and unknown means, information concerning the safety or glory of the Church. News spread through the desert with the rapidity of the simoon.

When Paphnutius strode across the sand, his disciples followed him, praising the Lord. Flavian, who was the oldest member of the brotherhood, was suddenly seized with a pious frenzy, and began to sing an inspired hymn—

"O blessed day! Now is our father restored to us.
He has returned laden with fresh merits, of which we reap the benefit.

For the virtues of the father are the wealth of the children, and the sanctity of the Abbot illuminates every cell.

Paphnutius, our father, has given a new spouse to Jesus Christ.

By his wondrous art, he has changed a black sheep into a white sheep.

And now, behold, he has returned to us, laden with fresh merits.

Like unto the bee of the Arsinœtid, heavy with the nectar of flowers.

Even as the ram of Nubia, which could hardly bear the weight of its abundant wool.

Let us celebrate this day by mingling oil with our food."

When they came to the door of the Abbot's cell, they fell on their knees, and said—

"Let our father bless us, and give each of us a measure of oil to celebrate his return."

Paul the Fool, who alone had remained standing, asked, "Who is this man?" and did not recognise Paphnutius. But no one paid any attention to what he said, as he was known to be devoid of intelligence, though filled with piety.

The Abbot of Antinoë, locked in his cell, thought—

"I have at last regained the haven of my repose and happiness. I have returned to my fortress of contentment. But how is it that this roof of rushes, so dear to me, does not receive me as a friend, and the walls say not to me, 'Thou art welcome.' Nothing has changed, since my departure, in this abode I have chosen. There is my table and my bed. There is the mummy's head which has so often inspired me with salutary thoughts; and there is the book in which I have so often sought conceptions of God. And yet nothing that I left is here. The things appear grievously despoiled of their customary charm, and it seems to me as though I saw them to-day for the first time. When I look at that table and couch, that in former days I made with my own hands, that black, dried head, these rolls of papyrus filled with the sayings of God, I seem to see the belongings of a dead man. After having known them all so well, I know them no longer. Alas! since nothing around me has really changed, it is I who am no longer what I was. I am another. I am the dead man! What has happened, my God? What has been taken from me? What is left unto me? And who am I?"

And it especially perplexed him to find, in spite of himself, that his cell was small, whereas, when viewed by the eye of faith, he ought to consider it immense, because the infinitude of God began there.

He began to pray, with his face against the ground, and felt a little happier. He had hardly been an hour in prayer, when a vision of Thaïs passed before his eyes. He returned thanks to God—

"Jesus! it is Thou who hast sent her. I acknowledge in that Thy wonderful goodness; Thou wouldst please me, reassure me and comfort me by the sight of her whom I have given to Thee. Thou presentest her to my eyes with her smile now disarmed; her grace, now become innocent; her beauty, from which I have extracted the sting. To please me, my God, thou showest her to me as I have prepared and purified her for Thy designs, as one friend pleasantly reminds another of the rich gift he has received from him. Therefore I see this woman with delight, being assured that the vision comes from Thee. Thou dost not forget that I have given her to Thee, Jesus. Keep her, since she pleases Thee, and suffer not her beauty to give joy to any but Thyself."

He could not sleep all night, and he saw Thaïs more distinctly than he had seen her in the Grotto of Nymphs. He commended himself, saying—

"What I have done, I have done to the glory of God."

Yet, to his great surprise, his heart was not at ease. He sighed.

"Why art thou sad, O my soul, and why dost thou trouble me?"

And his mind was still perturbed. Thirty days he remained in that condition of sadness which precedes the sore trials of a solitary monk. The image of Thaïs never left him day or night. He did not try to banish it, because he still thought it came from God, and was the image of a saint. But one morning she visited him in a dream, her hair crowned with violets, and her very gentleness seemed so formidable, that he uttered a cry of fright, and woke in an icy sweat. His eyes were still heavy with sleep, when he felt a moist warm breath on his face. A little jackal, its two paws placed on the side of the bed, was panting its stinking breath in his face, and grinning at him.

Paphnutius was greatly astonished, and it seemed to him as though a tower had given way under his feet. And, in fact, he had fallen, for his self-confidence had gone. For some time he was incapable of thought and when he did recover himself, his meditations only increased his perplexity.

"It is one of two things," he said to himself; "either this vision, like the preceding ones, came from God, and was a good vision, and it is my natural perversity which has misrepresented it, as wine turns sour in a dirty cup. I have, by my unworthiness, changed instruction into reproach, of which this diabolical jackal immediately took advantage. Or else this vision came, not from God, but, on the contrary, from the devil, and was evil. In that case I should doubt whether the former ones had, as I thought, a celestial origin. I am therefore incapable of that discernment which is necessary for the ascetic. In either case it is plain that God is no longer with me,—of which I feel the effects, though I cannot explain the cause."

He reasoned in this way, and anxiously asked—

"Just God, what trials dost Thou appoint for Thy servants if the apparitions of Thy saints are a danger for them? Give me to discern, by an intelligible sign, that which comes from Thee, and that which comes from the other."

And as God, whose designs are inscrutable, did not see fit to enlighten his servant, Paphnutius, lost in doubt, resolved not to think of Thaïs any more. But his resolutions were vain. Though absent, she was ever with him. She gazed at him whilst he read, or meditated, or prayed, or met his eyes wherever he looked. Her imaginary approach was heralded by a slight sound, such as is made by a woman's dress when she walks, and the visions had more verisimilitude than reality itself, which moves and is confused, whereas the phantoms which are caused by solitude are fixed and unchangeable. She came under various appearances—sometimes pensive, her head crowned with her last perishable wreath, clad as at the banquet at Alexandria, in a mauve robe spangled with silver flowers; sometimes voluptuously in a cloud of light veils, and bathed in the warm shadows of the Grotto of Nymphs; sometimes in a serge cassock, pious and radiant with celestial joy; sometimes tragic, her eyes swimming in the terrors of death, and showing her bare breast bedewed with the blood from her pierced heart. What disturbed him the most in these visions was that the wreaths, tunics, and veils, that he had burned with his own hands, should thus return; it became evident to him that these things had an imperishable soul, and he cried—

"Lo, all the countless souls of the sins of Thaïs come upon me!"

When he turned away his head, he felt that Thaïs was behind him, and that made him feel still more uneasy. His torture was cruel. But as his soul and body remained pure in the midst of all his temptations, he trusted in God, and gently complained to Him.

"My God, if I went so far to seek her amongst the Gentiles, it was for Thy sake, and not for mine. It would not be just that I should suffer for what I have done in Thy behalf. Protect me, sweet Jesus! My Saviour, save me! Suffer not the phantom to accomplish that which the body could not. As I have triumphed over the flesh, suffer not the shadow to overthrow me. I know that I am now exposed to greater dangers than I ever ran. I feel and know that the dream has more power than the reality. And how could it be otherwise, since it is itself but a higher reality? It is the soul of things. Plato, though he was but an idolater, has testified to the real existence of ideas. At that banquet of demons to which Thou accompaniedst me, Lord, I heard men—sullied with crimes truly, but certainly not devoid of intelligence—agree to acknowledge that we see real objects in solitude, meditation, and ecstasy; and Thy Scriptures, my God, many times affirm the virtue of dreams, and the power of visions formed either by Thee, great God, or by Thy adversary."

There was a new man in him and now he reasoned with God, but God did not choose to enlighten him. His nights were one long dream, and his days did not differ from his nights. One morning he awoke uttering sighs, such as issue, by moonlight, from the tombs of the victims of crimes. Thaïs had come, showing her bleeding feet, and whilst he wept, she had slipped into his couch. There was no longer any doubt; the image of Thaïs was an impure image.

His heart filled with disgust, he leaped out of his

profaned couch, and hid his face in his hands that he might not see the daylight. The hours passed, but they did not remove his shame. All was quiet in the cell. For the first time for many long days, Paphnutius was alone. The phantom had at last left him, and even its absence seemed dreadful. Nothing, nothing to distract his mind from the recollection of the dream. Full of horror, he thought—

"Why did I not drive her away? Why did I not tear myself from her cold arms and burning knees?"

He no longer dared to pronounce the name of God near that horrible couch, and he feared that his cell being profaned, the demons might freely enter at any hour. His fears did not deceive him. The seven little jackals, which had never crossed the threshold, entered in a file, and went and hid under the bed. At the vesper hour, there came an eighth, the stench of which was horrible. The next day, a ninth joined the others, and soon there were thirty, then sixty, then eighty. They became smaller as they multiplied, and being no bigger than rats, they covered the floor, the couch, and the stool. One of them jumped on the little table by the side of the bed, and standing with its four feet together on the death's head, looked at the monk with burning eyes. And every day fresh jackals came.

To expiate the abominable sin of his dream, and flee from impure thoughts, Paphnutius determined to leave his cell, which had now become polluted, go far into the desert, and practise unheard-of austerities, strange labours, and fresh works of grace. But before putting his design into action, he went to see old Palemon and ask his advice.

He found him in his garden watering his lettuces. It was the evening. The blue Nile flowed at the foot of violet hills. The good old man was walking slowly, in order not to frighten a pigeon that had perched on his shoulder.

"The Lord be with thee, brother Paphnutius," he said. "Admire his goodness; He sends me the animals that He has created that I may converse with them of His works, and praise Him in the birds of the air. Look at this pigeon; note the changing hues of its neck, and say, is it not a beautiful work of God? But have you not come to talk with me, brother, on some pious subject? If so, I will put down my watering-pot, and listen to you."

Paphnutius told the old man about his journey, his return, the visions of his days and the dreams of his nights,—without omitting the sinful one—and the pack of jackals.

"Do you not think, father," he added, "that I ought to bury myself in the desert, and perform some extraordinary austerities that would even astonish the devil?"

"I am but a poor sinner," replied Palemon, "and I know little about men, having passed all my life in this garden, with gazelles, little hares and pigeons. But it seems to me, brother, that your distemper comes from your having passed too suddenly from the noisy world to the calm of solitude. Such sudden transitions can but do harm to the health of the soul. You are, brother, like a man who exposes himself, almost at the same time, to great heat and great cold. A cough shakes him, and fever torments him. In your place, brother Paphnutius, instead of retiring at once into some awful desert, I should take such amusements as are fitting to a monk and a holy abbot. I should visit the monasteries in the neighbourhood. Some of them are wonderful, it is said. That of Abbot Serapion contains, I have been told, a thousand four hundred and thirty-two cells, and the monks are divided into as many legions as there are letters in the Greek alphabet. I am even informed that a certain analogy is observed between the character of the monks and the shape of the letter by which they are designated, and that, for example, those who are placed under Z have a tortuous character, whilst those under I have an upright mind. If I were you, brother, I should go and assure myself of this with my own eyes, and I should know no rest until I had seen such a wonderful thing. I should not fail to study the regulations of the various communities which are scattered along the banks of the Nile, so as to be able to compare one with another. Such study is befitting a religious man like yourself. You have heard say, no doubt, that Abbot Ephrem has drawn up for his monastery pious regulations of great beauty. With his permission, you might make a copy of them, as you are a skilful penman. I could not do so, for my hands, accustomed to wield the spade, are too awkward to direct the thin reed of the scribe over the papyrus. But you have the knowledge of letters, brother, and should thank God for it, for beautiful writing cannot be too much admired. The work of the copyist and the reader is a great safeguard against evil thoughts. Brother Paphnutius, why do you not write out the teachings of our fathers, Paul and Anthony? Little by little you would recover, in these pious works, peace of soul and mind; solitude would again become pleasant to your heart, and soon you would be in a condition to recommence those ascetic works which your journey has interrupted. But you must not expect much benefit from excessive penitence. When he was amongst us, our Father Anthony used to say, 'Excessive fasting produces weakness, and weakness begets idleness. There are some monks who ruin their body by fasts improperly prolonged. Of them it may be said that they plunge a dagger into their own breast, and deliver themselves up unresistingly into the power of the devil.' So said the holy man, Anthony. I am but a foolish old man, but, by the grace of God, I have remembered what our father told us."

Paphnutius thanked Palemon and promised to think over his advice. When he had passed the fence of reeds which enclosed the little garden, he turned round and saw the good old gardener engaged in watering his salads, whilst the pigeon walked about on his bent back, and at that sight Paphnutius felt ready to weep.

On returning to his cell, he found there a strange turmoil, as though it were filled with grains of sand blown about by a strong wind, and on looking closer, he saw these moving bodies were myriads of little jackals. That night he saw in a dream, a high stone column surmounted by a human face, and he heard a voice which said—

"Ascend this pillar!"

On awaking, he felt confident that this dream had been sent from heaven. He called his disciples, and addressed them in these words—

"My beloved sons, I must leave you, and go where God sends me. During my absence obey Flavian as you would me, and take care of our brother Paul. Bless you. Farewell."

As he strode away, they remained prostrate on the ground, and when they raised their heads, they saw his tall dark figure on the sandy horizon.

He walked day and night until he reached the ruins of the temple, formerly built by the idolaters, in which he had slept amongst the scorpions and sirens on his former strange journey. The walls, covered with magic signs, were still standing. Thirty immense columns, which terminated in human heads or lotus flowers, still supported a heavy stone entablature. But, at one end of the temple, a pillar had shaken off its old burden, and stood isolated. It had for its capital the head of a woman which smiled, with long eyes and rounded cheeks, and on her forehead cow's horns.

Paphnutius, on seeing it, recognised the column which had been shown him in his dream, and he calculated that it was thirty-two cubits high. He went to the neighbouring village, and ordered a ladder of that height to be made; and when the ladder was placed against the pillar, he ascended, knelt down on the top, and said to the Lord—

"Here, then, O God, is the abode Thou hast

chosen for me. May I remain here, in Thy Grace, until the hour of my death."

He had brought no provisions with him, trusting in divine providence, and expecting that charitable peasants would give him all that he needed. And, in fact, the next day, about the ninth hour, women came with their children, bringing bread, dates, and fresh water, which the boys carried to the top of the column.

The top of the pillar was not large enough to allow the monk to lie at full length, so that he slept with his legs crossed and his head on his breast, and sleep was a more cruel torture to him than his wakeful hours. At dawn the ospreys brushed him with their wings, and he awoke filled with pain and terror.

It happened that the carpenter who had made the ladder feared God. Disturbed at the thought that the saint was exposed to the sun and rain, and fearing that he might fall in his sleep, this pious man constructed a roof and a railing on the top of the column.

Soon the report of this extraordinary existence spread from village to village, and the labourers of the valley came on Sundays, with their wives and children, to look at the stylite. The disciples of Paphnutius, having learned with surprise the place of this wonderful retreat, came to him, and obtained from him permission to build their huts at the foot of the column. Every morning they came and stood in a circle round the master, and received from him the words of instruction.

"My sons," he said to them, "continue like those little children whom Jesus loved. That is the way of salvation. The sin of the flesh is the source and origin of all sins; they spring from it as from a parent. Pride, avarice, idleness, anger, and envy are its dearly beloved progeny. I have seen this in Alexandria; I have seen rich men carried away by the vice of lust, which, like a river with a turbid flood, swept them into the gulf of bitterness."

The abbots Ephrem and Serapion, being informed of his strange proceeding, wished to behold him with their own eyes. Seeing from afar, on the river, the triangular sail which was bringing them to him, Paphnutius could not prevent himself from thinking that God had made him an example to all solitary monks. The two abbots, when they saw him, did not conceal their surprise; and, having consulted together, they agreed in condemning such an extraordinary penance, and exhorted Paphnutius to come down.

"Such a mode of life is contrary to all usage," they said; "it is peculiar, and against all rules."

But Paphnutius replied—

"What is the monastic life if not peculiar? And ought not the deeds of a monk to be as eccentric as he is himself? It was a sign from God that caused me to ascend here; it is a sign from God that will make me descend."

Every day religious men came to join the disciples of Paphnutius, and they built for themselves shelters round the aerial hermitage. Several of them, to imitate the saint, mounted the ruins of the temple; but, being reproved by their brethren, and conquered by fatigue, they soon gave up these attempts.

Pilgrims flocked from all parts. There were some who had come long distances, and were hungry and thirsty. The idea occurred to a poor widow of selling fresh water and melons. Against the foot of the column, behind her bottles of red clay, her cups and her fruit under an awning of blue-and-white striped canvas, she cried, "Who wants to drink?" Following the example of this widow, a baker brought some bricks and made an oven close by, in the hope of selling loaves and cakes to visitors. As the crowd of visitors increased unceasingly, and the inhabitants of the large cities of Egypt began to come, some man, greedy of gain, built a caravanserai to lodge the guests and their servants, camels, and mules. Soon there was, in front of the column, a market to which the fishermen of the Nile brought their fish, and the gardeners their vegetables. A barber, who shaved people in the open air, amused the crowd with his jokes. The old temple, so long given over to silence and solitude was filled with countless sights and sounds of life. The innkeepers turned the subterranean vaults into cellars and nailed on the old pillars signs surmounted by the figure of the holy Paphnutius, and bearing this inscription in Greek and Egyptian—*"Pomegranate wine, fig wine, and genuine Cilician beer sold here."* On the walls, sculptured with pure and graceful carvings, the shop-keepers hung ropes of onions, and smoked fish, dead hares, and the carcases of sheep. In the evening, the old occupants of the ruins, the rats, scuttled in a long row to the river, whilst the ibises, suspiciously craning their necks, perched on the high cornices, to which rose the smoke of the kitchens, the shouts of the drinkers, and the cries of the tapsters. All around, builders laid out streets, and masons constructed convents, chapels, and churches. By the end of six months a city was established with a guardhouse, a tribunal, a prison, and a school, kept by an old blind scribe.

The pilgrims were innumerable. Bishops and other Church dignitaries, came, full of admiration. The Patriarch of Antioch, who chanced to be in

Egypt at that time, came with all his clergy. He highly approved of the extraordinary conduct of the stylite, and the heads of the Libyan Church followed, in the absence of Athanasius, the opinion of the Patriarch. Having learned which, Abbots Ephrem and Serapion came to the feet of Paphnutius to apologise for their former mistrust. Paphnutius replied—

"Know, my brothers, that the penance I endure is barely equal to the temptations which are sent me, the number and force of which astound me. A man, viewed externally, is but small, and, from the height of the pillar to which God has called me, I see human beings moving about like ants. But, considered internally, man is immense; he is as large as the world, for he contains it. All that is spread before me—these monasteries, these inns, the boats on the river, the villages, and what I see in the distance of fields, canals, sand, and mountains—is nothing in respect to what is in me. I carry in my heart countless cities and illimitable deserts. And evil—evil and death—spread over this immensity, cover them all, as night covers the earth. I am, in myself alone, a universe of evil thoughts."

He spoke thus because the desire for woman was in him.

The seventh month, there came from Alexandria,

Bubastis and Saïs, women who had long been barren, hoping to obtain children by the intercession of the holy man and the virtues of his pillar. They rubbed their sterile bodies against the stone. There followed a procession, as far as the eye could reach, of chariots, palanquins, and litters, which stopped and pushed and jostled below the man of God. From them came sick people terrible to see. Mothers brought to Paphnutius young boys whose limbs were twisted, their eyes starting, their mouth foaming, their voices hoarse. He laid his hands upon them. Blind men approached, groping with their hands, and raising towards him a face pierced with two bleeding holes. Paralytics displayed before him the heavy immobility, the deadly emaciation, and the hideous contractions of their limbs; lame men showed him their club feet; women with cancer, holding their bosoms with both hands, uncovered before him their breasts devoured by the invisible vulture. Dropsical women, swollen like wine skins were placed on the ground before him. He blessed them. Nubians, afflicted with elephantiasis, advanced with heavy steps and looked at him with streaming eyes and expressionless countenances. He made the sign of the cross over them. A young girl of Aphroditopolis was brought to him on a litter; after having vomited blood, she had slept for three days. She looked like a waxen image, and her parents, who thought she was dead, had placed a palm leaf on her breast. Paphnutius having prayed to God, the young girl raised her head and opened her eyes.

As the people reported everywhere the miracles which the saint had performed, unfortunate persons afflicted with that disease which the Greeks call "the divine malady," came from all parts of Egypt in incalculable legions. As soon as they saw the pillar, they were seized with convulsions, rolled on the ground, writhed, and twisted themselves into a ball. And—though it is hardly to be believed—the persons present were in their turn seized with a violent delirium, and imitated the contortions of the epileptics. Monks and pilgrims, men and women, wallowed and struggled pell-mell, their limbs twisted, foaming at the mouth, eating handfuls of earth and prophesying. And Paphnutius at the top of his pillar felt a thrill of horror pass through him, and cried to God—

"I am the scapegoat, and I take upon me all the impurities of these people, and that is why, Lord, my body is filled with evil spirits."

Every time that a sick person went away healed, the people applauded, carried him in triumph, and ceased not to repeat—

"We behold another well of Siloam!"

Hundreds of crutches already hung round the wonderful column; grateful women suspended wreaths and votive images there. Some of the Greeks inscribed distiches, and as every pilgrim carved his name, the stone was soon covered as high as a man could reach with an infinity of Latin, Greek, Coptic, Punic, Hebrew, Syrian, and magic characters.

When the feast of Easter came there was such an affluence of people to this city of miracles that old men thought that the days of the ancient mysteries had returned. All sorts of people, in all sorts of costumes, were to be seen there; the striped robes of the Egyptians, the burnoose of the Arabs, the white drawers of the Nubians, the short cloak of the Greeks, the long toga of the Romans, the scarlet breeches of the barbarians, the gold-spangled robes of the courtesans. A veiled woman would pass on an ass, preceded by black eunuchs, who cleared a passage for her by the free use of their sticks. Acrobats, having spread a carpet on the ground, juggled and performed skilful tricks before a circle of silent spectators. Snake-charmers unrolled their living girdles. A glittering, dusty, noisy, chattering crowd! The curses of the camel-drivers beating the animals; the cries of the hawkers who sold amulets against leprosy and the evil eye; the psalmody of the monks reciting verses of the Bible; the shrieking of the women who were prophesying; the shouting of the beggars singing old songs of the harem; the bleating of sheep; the braying of asses; the sailors calling tardy passengers; all these confused noises caused a deafening uproar, over which dominated the strident voices of the little naked negro boys, running about everywhere selling fresh dates.

And all these human beings stifled under the white sky, in a heavy atmosphere laden with the perfumes of women, the odour of negroes, the fumes of cooking and the smoke of gums, which the devotees bought of the shepherds to burn before the saint.

When night came, fires, torches, and lanterns were lighted everywhere, and nothing was to be seen but red shadows and black shapes. Standing amidst a circle of squatting listeners, an old man, his face lighted by a smoky lamp, related how, formerly, Bitiou had enchanted his heart, torn it from his breast, placed it in an acacia, and then transformed himself into a tree. He made gestures, which his shadow repeated with absurd exaggerations, and the audience uttered cries of admiration. In the taverns, the drinkers, lying on couches, called for beer and wine. Dancing girls, with painted eyes and bare stomachs, performed before them religious or lascivious scenes. In retired corners, young men played dice or other games, and old men followed prostitutes. Above all these rose the solitary, unchanging column; the head with the cow's horns gazed into the shadow, and above it Paphnutius watched between heaven and earth. All at once the moon rose over the Nile, like the bare shoulder of a goddess. The hills gleamed with blue light, and Paphnutius thought he saw the body of Thaïs shinning in the glimmer of the waters amidst the sapphire night.

The days passed, and the saint still lived on his pillar. When the rainy season came, the waters of heaven, filtering through the cracks in the roof, wetted his body; his stiff limbs were incapable of movement. Scorched by the sun, and reddened by the dew, his skin broke; large ulcers devoured his arms and legs. But the desire of Thaïs still consumed him inwardly, and he cried—

"It is not enough, great God! More temptations! More unclean thoughts! More horrible desires! Lord, lay upon me all the lusts of men, that I may expiate them all! Though it is false that the Greek bitch took upon herself all the sins of the world, as I heard an impostor once declare, yet there is a hidden meaning in the fable, the truth of which I now recognise. For it is true that the sins of the people enter the soul of the saints, and are lost there as in a well. Thus it is that the souls of the just are polluted with more filth than is ever found in the soul of the sinner. And, for that reason, I praise Thee, O my God, for having made me the cesspool of the world."

One day, a rumour ran through the holy city, and even reached the ears of the hermit: a very great personage, a man occupying a high position, the Prefect of the Alexandrian fleet, Lucius Aurelius Cotta, was about to visit the city—was, indeed, now on his way.

The news was true. Old Cotta, who was inspecting the canals and the navigation of the Nile, had many times expressed a desire to see the stylite and the new city, to which the name of Stylopolis had been given. The Stylopolitans saw the river covered with sails one morning. Cotta appeared on board a golden galley hung with purple, and followed by all his fleet. He landed, and advanced, accompanied by a secretary carrying his tablets, and Aristæus, his physician, with whom he liked to converse.

A numerous suite walked behind him, and the shore was covered with *laticlaves* * and military uniforms. He stopped, some paces from the column, and began to examine the stylite, wiping his face meanwhile with the skirt of his toga. Being of a naturally curious disposition, he had observed many things in the course of his long voyages. He liked to remember them, and intended to write, after he had finished his Punic history, a book on the remarkable things he had witnessed. He seemed much interested by the spectacle before him.

"This is very curious!" he said, puffing and blowing. "And—which is a circumstance worthy of being recorded—this man was my guest. Yes, this monk supped with me last year, after which he carried off an actress."

Turning to his secretary—

"Note that, my son, on my tablets; also the dimensions of the column, not omitting the shape of the top of it."

Then, wiping his face again—

"Persons deserving of belief have assured me that this monk has not left his column for a single moment since he mounted it a year ago. Is that possible, Aristæus?"

"That which is possible to a lunatic or a sick

---

* The *laticlave* was a toga, with a broad purple band, worn by Roman senators as the distinguishing mark of their high office.

man," replied Aristæus, "would be impossible to a man sound in body and mind. Do you know, Lucius, that sometimes diseases of the mind or body give to those afflicted by them a strength which healthy men do not possess? For, as a matter of fact, there is no such thing as good health or bad health. There are only different conditions of the organs. Having studied what are called maladies, I have come to consider them as necessary forms of life. I take pleasure in studying them in order to be able to conquer them. Some of them are worthy of admiration, and conceal, under apparent disorder, profound harmonies; for instance, a quartan fever is certainly a very pretty thing! Sometimes certain affections of the body cause a rapid augmentation of the faculties of the mind. You know Creon? When he was a child, he stuttered and was stupid. But, having cracked his skull by tumbling off a ladder, he became an able lawyer, as you are aware. This monk must be affected in some hidden organ. Moreover, this kind of existence is not so extraordinary as it appears to you, Lucius. I may remind you that the gymnosophists of India can remain motionless, not merely for a year, but during twenty, thirty, or forty years."

"By Jupiter!" cried Cotta, "that is a strange madness. For man was born to move and act, and idleness is an unpardonable crime, because it is an injury to the State. I do not know of any religion in which such an objectionable practice is permitted, though it possibly may be in some of the Asiatic creeds. When I was Governor of Syria, I found *phalli* erected in the porches at the city of Hera. A man ascended, twice a year, and remained there for a week. The people believed that this man talked with the gods, and interceded with them for the prosperity of Syria. The custom appeared senseless to me; nevertheless I did nothing to put it down. For I consider that a functionary ought not to interfere with the manners and customs of the people, but on the contrary, to see that they are preserved. It is not the business of the government to force a religion on a people, but to maintain that which exists, which, whether good or bad, has been regulated by the spirit of the time, the place, and the race. If it endeavours to put down a religion, it proclaims itself revolutionary in its spirit, and tyrannical in its acts, and is justly detested. Besides, how are you to raise yourself above the superstitions of the vulgar, except by understanding them and tolerating them? Aristæus, I am of opinion that I should leave this nephelo-coccygian * in the air, ex-

---

* Nephelo-coccygia, the cloud-city built by the cuckoos, in the *Birds* of Aristophanes.

posed only to the indignities the birds shower on him. I should not gain anything by having him pulled down, but I should by taking note of his thoughts and beliefs."

He puffed, coughed, and placed his hand on the secretary's shoulder.

"My child, note down that, amongst certain sects of Christians, it is considered praiseworthy to carry off courtesans and live upon columns. You may add that these customs are evidence of the worship of genetic divinities. But on this point we ought to question him himself."

Then, raising his head, and shading his eyes with his hand, to keep off the sun, he shouted—

"Hallo, Paphnutius! If you remember that you were once my guest, answer me. What are you doing up there? Why did you go up, and why do you stay there? Has this column any phallic signification in your mind?"

Paphnutius, considering Cotta as nothing but an idolater, did not deign to reply. But his disciple, Flavian, approached, and said—

"Illustrious Sir, this holy man takes the sins of the world upon him, and cures diseases."

"By Jupiter! Do you hear, Aristæus?" cried Cotta. "This nephelo-coccygian practises medicine, like you. What do you think of so high a rival?"

Aristæus shook his head.

"It is very possible that he may cure certain diseases better than I can; such, for instance, as epilepsy, vulgarly called the divine malady, although all maladies are equally divine, for they all come from the gods. But the cause of this disease lies, partly, in the imagination, and you must confess, Lucius, that this monk, perched up on the head of a goddess, strikes the minds of the sick people more forcibly than I, bending over my mortars and phials in my laboratory, could ever do. There are forces, Lucius, infinitely more powerful than reason and science."

"What are they?" asked Cotta.

"Ignorance and folly," replied Aristæus.

"I have rarely seen a more curious sight," continued Cotta, "and I hope that some day an able writer will relate the foundation of Stylopolis. But even the most extraordinary spectacles should not keep, longer than is befitting, a serious and busy man from his work. Let us go and inspect the canals. Farewell, good Paphnutius! or rather, till our next meeting! If ever you should come down to earth again, and revisit Alexandria, do not fail to come and sup with me."

These words, heard by all present, passed from mouth to mouth, and being repeated by the believers, added greatly to the reputation of Paphnutius. Pious minds amplified and transformed them, and it was stated that Paphnutius, from the top of his pillar, had converted the Prefect of the Fleet to the faith of the apostles and the Nicæan fathers. The believers found a figurative meaning in the last words uttered by Aurelius Cotta; to them, the supper to which this important personage had invited the ascetic, was a holy communion, a spiritual repast, a celestial banquet. The story of this meeting was embroidered with wonderful details, which those who invented were the first to believe. It was said that when Cotta, after a long argument, had embraced the truth, an angel had come from heaven to wipe the sweat from his brow. The physician and secretary of the Prefect of the Fleet had also, it was asserted, been converted at the same time. And, the miracle being public and notorious, the deacons of the principal churches of Libya recorded it amongst the authentic facts. After that, it could be said, without any exaggeration, that the whole world was seized with a desire to see Paphnutius, and that, in the West as well as the East, all Christians turned their astonished eyes towards him. The most celebrated cities of Italy sent deputations to him, and the Roman Cæsar, the divine Constantine, who favoured the

Christian religion, wrote him a letter which the legates brought to him with great ceremony. But one night, whilst the budding city at his feet slept in the dew, he heard a voice, which said—

"Paphnutius, thou art become celebrated by thy works and powerful by thy word. God has raised thee up for His glory. He has chosen thee to work miracles, heal the sick, convert the Pagans, enlighten sinners, confound the Arians, and establish peace in the Church."

Paphnutius replied—

"God's will be done!"

The voice continued—

"Arise, Paphnutius, and go seek in his palace the impious Constans, who, far from imitating the wisdom of his brother, Constantine, inclines to the errors of Arius and Marcus. Go! The bronze gates shall fly open before thee, and thy sandals shall resound on the golden floor of the basilica before the throne of the Cæsars, and thy awe-inspiring voice shall change the heart of the son of Constantinus. Thou shalt reign over a peaceful and powerful Church. And, even as the soul directs the body, so shall the Church govern the empire. Thou shalt be placed above senators, comites, and patricians. Thou shalt repress the greed of the people, and check the boldness of the barbarians.

Old Cotta, knowing that thou art the head of the government, will seek the honour of washing thy feet. At the death thy *cilicium* shall be taken to the patriarch of Alexandria, and the great Athanasius, white with glory, shall kiss it as the relic of a saint. Go!"

Paphnutius replied—

"Let the will of God be accomplished!"

And making an effort to stand up, he prepared to descend. But the voice, divining his intention, said—

"Above all, descend not by the ladder. That would be to act like an ordinary man, and to be unconscious of the gifts that are in thee. A great saint, like thee, ought to fly through the air. Leap! the angels are there to support thee. Leap, then!"

Paphnutius replied—

"The will of God be done, on earth as it is in heaven."

Extending his long arms like the ragged wings of a huge sick bird, he was about to throw himself down, when, suddenly, a hideous mocking laugh rang in his ears. Terrified, he asked—

"Who laughs thus?"

"Ah? ah!" screamed the voice, "we are yet but at the beginning of our friendship; thou wilt some day be better acquainted with me. My friend, it was I who caused thee to ascend here, and I ought to be satisfied at the docility with which thou hast accomplished my wishes. Paphnutius, I am pleased with thee."

Paphnutius murmured, in a voice stifled by fear—

"Avaunt, avaunt! I know thee now; thou art he who carried Jesus to a pinnacle of the temple, and showed him all the kingdoms of this world."

He fell, affrighted, on the stone.

"Why did I not know this sooner?" he thought. "More wretched than the blind, deaf, and paralysed who trust in me, I have lost all knowledge of things supernatural, and am more depraved than the maniacs who eat earth and approach dead bodies. I can no longer distinguish between the clamours of hell and the voices of heaven. I have lost even the intuition of the new-born child, who cries when its nurse's breast is taken from it, of the dog that scents out its master's footsteps, of the plant that turns towards the sun. I am the laughing-stock of the devils. So, then, it is Satan who led me here. When he elevated me on this pedestal, lust and pride mounted with me. It is not the magnitude of my temptations which terrifies me. Anthony, on his mountain, suffers the same. I wish that all their swords may pierce my flesh, before the eyes of the angels. I have even learned to like my sufferings.

But God does not speak to me, and His silence astonishes me. He has left me—and I had but Him to look to. He leaves me alone in the horror of His absence. He flies from me. I will follow after Him. This stone burns my feet. Let me leave quickly, and come up with God."

With that he seized the ladder which stood against the column, put his feet on it, and having descended a rung, found himself face to face with the monster's head; she smiled strangely. He was certain then that what he had taken for the site of his rest and glory, was but the diabolical instrument of his trouble and damnation. He hastily descended and touched the soil. His feet had forgotten their use, and he reeled. But, feeling on him the shadow of the cursed column, he forced himself to run. All slept. He traversed, without being seen, the great square surrounded by wine-shops, inns, and caravanserias, and threw himself into a by-street which led towards the Libyan Hills. A dog pursued him, barking, and stopped only at the edge of the desert. Paphnutius went through a country where there was no road but the trail of wild beasts. Leaving behind him the huts abandoned by the coiners, he continued all night and all day his solitary flight.

At last, almost ready to expire with hunger, thirst,

and fatigue, and not knowing if God was still far from him, he came to a silent city which extended from right to left, and stretched away till it was lost in the blue horizon. The buildings, which were widely separated and like each other, resembled, pyramids cut off at half their height. They were tombs. The doors were broken, and in the shadow of the chambers could be seen the gleaming eyes of hyænas and wolves who brought forth their young there, whilst the dead bodies lay on the threshold, despoiled by robbers, and gnawed by the wild beasts. Having passed through this funeral city, Paphnutius fell exhausted before a tomb which stood near a spring surrounded by palm trees. This tomb was much ornamented, and, as there was no door to it, he saw inside it a painted chamber, in which serpents bred.

"Here," he sighed, "is the abode I have chosen; the tabernacle of my repentance and penitence."

He dragged himself to it, drove out the reptiles with his feet, and remained prostrate on the stone floor for eighteen hours, at the end of which time he went to the spring, and drank out of his hand. Then he plucked some dates and some stalks of lotus, the seeds of which he ate. Thinking this kind of life was good, he made it the rule of his existence.

From morning to night he never lifted his forehead from the stone.

One day, whilst he was thus prostrated, he heard a voice which said—

"Look at these images, that thou mayest learn."

Then, raising his head, he saw, on the walls of the chamber, paintings which represented lively and domestic scenes. They were of very old work, and marvellously lifelike. There were cooks who blew the fire, with their cheeks all puffed out; others plucked geese, or cooked quarters of sheep in stewpans. A little farther, a hunter carried on his shoulders a gazelle pierced with arrows. In one place, peasants were sowing, reaping, or gathering. In another, women danced to the sounds of viols, flutes, and harp. A young girl played the theorbo. The lotus flower shone in her hair, which was neatly braided. Her transparent dress let the pure forms of her body be seen. Her bosom and mouth were perfect. The face was turned in profile, and the beautiful eye looked straight before her. The whole figure was exquisite. Paphnutius having examined it, lowered his eyes, and replied to the voice—

"Why dost thou command me to look at these images? No doubt they represent the terrestrial life of the idolater whose body rests here, under my feet, at the bottom of a well, in a coffin of black basalt. They recall the life of a dead man, and are, despite their bright colours, the shadows of a shadow. The life of a dead man! O vanity!"

"He is dead, but he lived," replied the voice; "and thou wilt die, and wilt not have lived."

From that day, Paphnutius had not a moment's rest. The voice spoke to him incessantly. The girl with the theorbo looked fixedly at him from underneath the long lashes of her eye. At last she also spoke—

"Look. I am mysterious and beautiful. Love me. Exhaust in my arms the love which torments you. What use is it to fear me? You cannot escape me; I am the beauty of woman. Whither do you think to fly from me, senseless fool? You will find my likeness in the radiancy of flowers, and in the grace of the palm trees, in the flight of pigeons, in the bounds of the gazelle, in the rippling of brooks, in the soft light of the moon, and if you close your eyes, you will find me within yourself. It is a thousand years since the man who sleeps here, swathed in linen, in a bed of black stone, pressed me to his heart. It is a thousand years since he received the last kiss from my mouth, and his sleep is yet redolent with it. You know me well, Paphnutius. How is it you have not recognised me? I am one of the innumerable incarnations of Thaïs. You are a learned monk, and well skilled in the knowledge of things. You have travelled, and it is by travel a man learns the most. Often a day passed abroad will show more novelties than ten years passed at home. You have heard that Thaïs lived formerly in Argos, under the name of Helen. She had another existence in Thebes Hecatompyle. And I was Thaïs of Thebes. How is it you have not guessed it? I took, when I was alive, a large share in the sins of this world, and now reduced here to the condition of a shadow, I am still quite capable of taking your sins upon me, beloved monk. Whence comes your surprise? It was certain that, wherever you went, you would find Thaïs again."

He struck his forehead against the pavement, and uttered a cry of terror. And every night the player of the theorbo left the wall, approached him, and spoke in a clear voice mingled with soft breathing. And as the holy man resisted the temptations she gave him, she said to him—

"Love me; yield, friend. As long as you resist me I shall torment you. You do not know what the patience of a dead woman is. I shall wait, if necessary, till you are dead. Being a sorceress, I shall put into your lifeless body a spirit who will reanimate it, and who will not refuse me what I have asked in vain of you. And think, Paphnutius, what a strange situation when your blessed soul sees, from the height of heaven, its own body given up to sin. God, who has promised to return you this body after the day of judgment and the end of time, will Himself be much puzzled. How can He place in celestial glory a human form inhabited by a devil, and guarded by a sorceress? You have not thought of that difficulty. Nor God either, perhaps. Between ourselves, He is not very knowing. Any ordinary magician can easily deceive Him, and if He had not His thunder, and the cataracts of heaven, the village urchins would pull His beard. He has certainly not as much sense as the old serpent, His adversary. *He,* indeed, is a wonderful artist. If I am so beautiful, it is because he adorned me with all my attractions. It was he who taught me how to braid my hair, and to make for myself rosy fingers with agate nails. You have misunderstood him. When you came to live in this tomb, you drove out with your feet the serpents which were here, without troubling yourself to know whether they were of his family, and you crushed their eggs. I am afraid, my poor friend, you will have a troublesome business on your hands. You were warned, however, that he was a musician and a lover. What have you done? You have quarrelled with science and beauty. You are altogether miserable, and Iaveh does not come to your help. It is not probable that he will come. Being as great as all things, he cannot move for want of space, and if, by an impossibility, he made the least movement, all creation would be pushed out of place. My handsome hermit, give me a kiss."

Paphnutius was aware that great prodigies are performed by magic arts. He thought—not without much uneasiness—

"Perhaps the dead man buried at my feet knows the words written in that mysterious book which exists hidden, not far from here, at the bottom of a royal tomb. By virtue of these words, the dead, taking the form which they had upon earth, see the light of the sun and the smiles of women."

His chief fear was that the girl with the theorbo and the dead man might come together, as they did in their lifetime, and that he should see them unite. Sometimes he thought he heard the sound of kissing.

He was troubled in his mind, and now, in the absence of God he feared to think as much as to feel. One evening, when he was kneeling prostrate according to his custom, an unknown voice said to him—

"Paphnutius, there are on earth more people than you imagine, and if I were to show you what I have seen, you would die of astonishment. There are men with a single eye in the middle of their forehead. There are men who have but one leg, and advance by jumps. There are men who change their sex, and the females become males. There are men-trees, who shoot out roots in the ground. And there are men with no head, with two eyes, a nose, and a mouth in their breast. Can you honestly believe that Jesus Christ died for the salvation of these men?"

Another time he had a vision. He saw, in a strong light, a broad road, rivulets, and gardens. On the road, Aristobulus and Chereas passed at a gallop on their Syrian horses, and the joyous ardour of the race reddened the cheeks of the two young men. Beneath a portico, Callicrates recited his verses; satisfied pride trembled in his voice and shone in his eyes. In the garden, Zenothemis picked apples of gold, and caressed a serpent with azure wings. Clad in white, and wearing a shining mitre, Hermodorus meditated beneath a sacred persea, which bore, instead of flowers, small heads of pure profile, wearing, like the Egyptian goddesses, vultures, hawks, or the shining disk of the moon; whilst in the background, by the side of a fountain, Nicias studied, on an armillary sphere, the harmonious movements of the stars.

Then a veiled woman approached the monk, holding in her hand a branch of myrtle. She said to him—

"Look! Some seek eternal beauty, and place their ephemeral life in the infinite. Others live without much thought. But by that alone they submit to fair Nature, and they are happy and beautiful in the joy of living only, and give glory to the supreme artist of all things; for man is a noble hymn to God. All think that happiness is innocent, and that pleasure is permitted to man. Paphnutius, if they are right, what a dupe you have been!"

And the vision vanished.

Thus was Paphnutius tempted unceasingly in body and mind. Satan never gave him a minute's repose. The solitude of the tomb was more peopled than the streets of a great city. The devils shouted with laughter, and millions of imps, evil genii, and phantoms imitated all the ordinary transactions of life. In the evening, when he went to the spring, satyrs and nymphs capered round him, and tried to drag him into their lascivious dances. The demons no longer feared him. They loaded him with insults, obscene jests, and blows. One day a devil, no longer than his arm, stole the cord he wore round his waist.

He said to himself—

"Thought, whither hast thou led me?"

And he resolved to work with his hands, in order to give his mind that rest of which it had need. Near the spring, some banana trees, with large leaves, grew under the shade of the palms. He cut the stalks, and carried them to the tomb. He crushed them with a stone, and reduced them to fibres, as he had seen ropemakers do. For he intended to make a cord, to replace that which the devil had stolen. The demons were somewhat displeased at this; they ceased their clamour, and the girl with the theorbo no longer continued her magic arts, but remained quietly on the wall. The courage and faith of Paphnutius increased whilst he pounded the banana stems.

"With Heaven's help," he said to himself, "I shall subdue the flesh. As to my soul, its confidence is still unshaken. In vain do the devils, and that accursed woman, try to instil into my mind doubts as to the nature of God. I will reply to them, by the mouth of the Apostle John, 'In the beginning was the Word, and the Word was God.' That I firmly believe, and that which I believe is absurd, I believe still more firmly. In fact it should be absurd. If it were not so, I should not *believe;* I should *know.* And it is not that which we know which gives eternal life; it is faith only that saves."

He exposed the separated fibres to the sun and the dew, and every morning he took care to turn them, to prevent them rotting; and he rejoiced to find that he had become as simple as a child. When he had twisted his cord, he cut reeds to make mats and baskets. The sepulchral chamber resembled a basket-maker's workshop, and Paphnutius could pass without difficulty from work to prayer. Yet still God was not merciful to him, for one night he was awakened by a voice which froze him with horror, for he guessed that it was the voice of the dead man.

The voice called quickly, in a light whisper—

"Helen! Helen! come and bathe with me! come quickly!"

A woman, whose mouth was close to the monk's ear, replied—

"Friend, I cannot rise; a man is lying on me."

Paphnutius suddenly perceived that his cheek rested on a woman's breast. He recognised the player of the theorbo, who, partly relieved of his weight, raised her breast. He clung tightly to the sweet, warm, perfumed body, and consumed with the desire of damnation, he cried—

"Stay, stay, my heavenly one!"

But she was already standing on the threshold. She laughed, and her smile gleamed in the silver rays of the moon.

"Why should I stay?" she said. "The shadow of a shadow is enough for a lover endowed with such a lively imagination. Besides, you have sinned. What more was needed?"

Paphnutius wept in the night, and when the dawn came, he murmured a prayer that was a meek complaint—

"Jesus, my Jesus, why hast Thou forsaken me? Thou seest the danger in which I am. Come, and help me, sweet Saviour. Since Thy Father no longer loves me, and does not hear me, remember that I have but Thee. From Him nothing is to be hoped; I cannot comprehend Him, and He cannot pity me. But thou was born of a woman, and that is why I trust in Thee. Remember that Thou wast a man. I pray to Thee, not because Thou art God of God, Light of light, very God of very God, but because Thou hast lived poor and humble on this earth where now I suffer, because Satan has tempted Thy flesh, because the sweat of agony has bedewed

THE EUPHORBIA

Thy face. It is to Thy humanity that I pray, Jesus, my brother Jesus!"

When he had thus prayed, wringing his hands, a terrible peal of laughter shook the walls of the tomb, and the voice which rang in his ears on the top of the column, said jeeringly—

"That is a prayer worthy of the breviary of Marcus, the heretic. Paphnutius is an Arian! Paphnutius is an Arian!"

As though thunderstruck, the monk fell senseless.

* * * * *

When he reopened his eyes, he saw around him monks wearing black hoods, who poured water on his temples, and recited exorcisms. Many others were standing outside, carrying palm leaves.

"As we passed through the desert," said one of them, "we heard cries issuing from this tomb, and, having entered, we found you lying unconscious on the floor. Doubtless the devils had thrown you down, and had fled at our approach."

Paphnutius, raising his head, asked in a feeble voice—

"Who are you, my brothers? And why do you carry palms in your hands? Is it for my burial?"

One of them replied—

"Brother, do you not know that our father, Anthony, now a hundred and five years old, having been warned of his approaching end, has come down from Mount Colzin, to which he had retired, to bless his numerous spiritual children? We are going with palm leaves to greet our holy father. But how is it, brother, that you are ignorant of such a great event? Can it be possible that no angel came to this tomb to inform you?"

"Alas!" replied Paphnutius, "I am not worthy of such a favour, and the only denizens of this abode are demons and vampires. Pray for me. I am Paphnutius, Abbot of Antinoë, the most wretched of the servants of God."

At the name of Paphnutius, all waved their palm leaves and murmured his praises. The monk who had previously spoken, cried in surprise—

"Can it be that thou art that holy Paphnutius, celebrated for so many works that it was supposed he would some day equal the great Anthony himself? Most venerable, it was thou who convertedst to God the courtesan, Thaïs, and who, raised upon a high column, was carried away by the seraphs. Those who watched by night, at the foot of the pillar, saw thy blessed assumption. The wings of the angels encircled thee in a white cloud, and with thy right hand extended thou didst bless the dwellings of man. The next day, when the people saw thou wert no longer there, a long groan rose to the

THE EUPHORBIA

summit of the discrowned pillar. But Flavian, thy disciple, reported the miracle, and took thy place as the head. But a foolish man, of the name of Paul, tried to contradict the general opinion. He asserted that he had seen thee, in a dream, carried away by the devils; the people wanted to stone him, and it was a miracle that he escaped death. I am Zozimus, abbot of these solitary monks whom thou seest prostrate at thy feet. Like them, I kneel before thee, that thou mayest bless the father with the children. Then thou shalt relate to us the marvels which God has deigned to accomplish by thy means."

"Far from having favoured me as thou believest," replied Paphnutius, "the Lord has tried me with terrible temptations. I was not carried away by angels. But a shadowy wall is raised in front of my eyes, and moves before me. I have lived in a dream. Without God all is a dream. When I made my journey to Alexandria, I heard, in a short space of time, many discourses, and I learned that the army of errors was innumerable. It pursues me, and I am compassed about with swords."

Zozimus replied—

"Venerable father, we must remember that the saints, and especially the solitary saints, undergo terrible trials. If thou wast not carried to heaven by the seraphs, it is certain that the Lord granted that favour of thy image, for Flavian, the monks, and the people were witnesses of thy assumption."

Paphnutius resolved to go and receive the blessing of Anthony.

"Brother Zozimus," he said, "give me one of these palm leaves, and let us go and meet our father."

"Let us go," replied Zozimus; "military order is most befitting for monks, who are God's soldiers. Thou and I, being abbots, will march in front, and the others shall follow us, singing psalms."

They set out on their march, and Paphnutius said—

"God is unity, for He is the truth, which is one. The world is many, because it is error. We should turn away from all the sights of nature, even those which appear the most innocent. Their diversity renders them pleasant, which is a sign that they are evil. For that reason, I cannot see a tuft of papyrus by the side of still waters without my soul being imbued with melancholy. All things that the senses perceive are detestable. The least grain of sand brings danger. Everything tempts us. Woman is but a combination of all the temptations scattered in the thin air, on the flowering earth, in the clear waters. Happy is he whose soul is a sealed vase!

Happy is he who knows how to be deaf, dumb, and blind, and who knows nothing of the world, in order that he may know God!"

Zozimus, having meditated upon these words, replied as follows—

"Venerable father, it is fitting that I should avow my sins to thee, since thou hast shown me thy soul. Thus we shall confess to each other, according to the apostolic custom. Before I was a monk, I led an abominable life. At Madaura, a city celebrated for its courtesans, I sought out all kinds of worldly love. Every night I supped in company with young debauchees and female flute players, and I took home with me the one who pleased me the best. A saint like thee could never imagine to what a pitch the fury of my desires carried me. Suffice it to say that it spared neither matrons nor nuns, and spread adultery and sacrilege everywhere. I excited my senses with wine, and was justly known as the heaviest drinker in Madaura. Yet I was a Christian, and, in all my follies, kept my faith in Jesus crucified. Having devoured my substance in riotous living, I was beginning to feel the first attacks of poverty, when I saw one of my companions in pleasure suddenly struck with a terrible disease. His knees could not sustain him; his twitching hands refused to obey him; his glazed eyes closed. Only horrible groans came from his breast. His mind, heavier than his body, slumbered. To punish him for having lived like a beast, God had changed him into a beast. The loss of my property had already inspired me with salutary reflections; but the example of my friend was of yet greater efficacy; it made such an impression on my heart that I quitted the world and retired into the desert. There I have enjoyed for twenty years a peace that nothing has troubled. I work with my monks as weaver, architect, carpenter, and even as scribe, though, to say the truth, I have little taste for writing, having always preferred action to thought. My days are full of joy, and my nights without dreams, and I believe that the grace of the Lord is in me, because, even in the midst of the most frightful sins, I have never lost hope."

On hearing these words, Paphnutius lifted his eyes to heaven and murmured—

"Lord, Thou lookest with kindness upon this man polluted by adultery, sacrilege, and so many crimes, and Thou turnest away from me, who have always kept Thy commandments! How inscrutable is Thy justice, O my God! and how impenetrable are Thy ways!"

Zozimus extended his arms.

"Look, venerable father! On both sides of the horizon are long, black files that look like emigrant ants. They are our brothers, who, like us, are going to meet Anthony."

When they came to the place of meeting, they saw a magnificent spectacle. The army of monks extended, in three ranks, in an immense semicircle. In the first rank stood the old hermits of the desert, cross in hand, and with long beards that almost touched the ground. The monks, governed by the abbots Ephrem and Serapion, and also all the cenobites of the Nile, formed the second line. Behind them appeared the ascetics, who had come from their distant rocks. Some wore, on their blackened and dried-up bodies, shapeless rags; others had for their only clothes, bundles of reeds held together by withies. Many of them were naked, but God had covered them with a fell of hair as thick as a sheep's fleece. All held branches of palm; they looked like an emerald rainbow, or they might have been also compared to the host of the elect—the living walls of the city of God.

Such perfect order reigned in the assembly, that Paphnutius found, without difficulty, the monks he governed. He placed himself near them, after having taken care to hide his face under his hood, that he might remain unknown, and not disturb them in their pious expectation. Suddenly, an immense shout arose—

"The saint!" they all cried. "The saint! Behold the great saint, against whom hell has not prevailed, the well-beloved of God! Our father, Anthony!"

Then a great silence followed, and every forehead was lowered to the sand.

From the summit of a dune, in the vast void space, Anthony advanced, supported by his beloved disciples, Macarius and Amathas. He walked slowly, but his figure was still upright, and showed the remains of a superhuman strength. His white beard spread over his broad chest, his polished skull reflected the rays of sunlight like the forehead of Moses. The keen gaze of the eagle was in his eyes; the smile of a child shone on his round cheek. To bless his people, he raised his arms, tired by a century of marvellous works, and his voice burst forth for the last time, with the words of love.

"How goodly are thy tents, O Jacob, and thy tabernacles, O Israel!"

Immediately, from one end to the other of the living wall, like a peal of harmonious thunder, the psalm, "Blessed is the man that feareth the Lord," broke forth.

Accompanied by Macarius and Amathas, Anthony passed along the ranks of the old hermits, anchorites, and cenobites. This seer, who had beheld heaven and hell; this hermit, who from a cave in the rock, governed the Christian Church; this saint, who had sustained the faith of the martyrs; this scholar, whose eloquence had paralysed the heretics, spoke tenderly to each of his sons, and bade them a kindly farewell, on the eve of the blessed death, which God, who loved him, had at last promised him.

He said to the abbots Ephrem and Serapion—

"You command large armies, and you are both great generals. Therefore, you shall put on in heaven an armour of gold, and the Archangel Michael shall give you the title of kiliarchs of his hosts."

Perceiving the old man Philemon, he embraced him, and said—

"Behold, the kindest and best of all my children. His soul exhales a perfume as sweet as the flower of the beans he sows every year."

To Abbot Zozimus he addressed these words—

"Thou hast never mistrusted divine goodness, and therefore the peace of the Lord is in thee. The lily of thy virtues has flowered upon the dunghill of thy corruption."

To all he spoke words of unerring wisdom.

To the old hermits he said—

"The apostle saw, round the throne of God, eighty old men seated, clad in white robes, and wearing crowns on their heads."

To the young men—

"Be joyful; leave sadness to the happy ones of this world."

Thus he passed along the front of his filial army, exhorting and comforting. Paphnutius, seeing him approach, fell on his knees, his heart torn by fear and hope.

"My father! my father!" he cried in his agony. "My father! come to my help, for I perish. I have given to God the soul of Thaïs; I have lived upon the top of a column, and in the chamber of a tomb. My forehead, unceasingly in the dust, has become horny as a camel's knee. And yet God has gone from me. Bless me, my father, and I shall be saved; shake the hyssop, and I shall be washed, and I shall shine as the snow."

Anthony did not reply. He turned to the monks of Antinoë those eyes whose looks no man could sustain. He gazed for a long time at Paul, called the Fool; then he made a sign to him to approach. And, as all were astonished that the saint should address himself to a man who was not in his senses, Anthony said—

"God has granted to him more grace than to any

of you. Lift thy eyes, my son Paul, and tell me what thou seest in heaven."

Paul the Fool raised his eyes; his face shone, and his tongue was unloosed.

"I see in heaven," he said, "a bed adorned with hangings of purple and gold. Around it three virgins keep constant watch that no soul may approach it, except the chosen one for whom the bed is prepared."

Believing that this bed was the symbol of his glorification, Paphnutius had already begun to return thanks to God. But Anthony made a sign to him to be silent, and to listen to the Fool, who murmured in his ecstasy—

"The three virgins speak to me; they say unto me: 'A saint is about to quit the earth; Thaïs of Alexandria is dying. And we have prepared the bed of her glory, for we are her virtues—Faith, Fear, and Love.'"

Anthony asked—

"Sweet child, what else seest thou?"

Paul gazed vacantly from the zenith to the nadir, and from west to east, when suddenly his eyes fell on the Abbot of Antinoë. His face grew pale with a holy terror, and his eyeballs reflected invisible flames.

"I see," he murmured, "three demons, who, full

of joy, prepare to seize that man. One of them is like unto a tower, one to a woman, and one to a mage. All three bear their name, marked with red-hot iron; the first on the forehead, the second on the belly, the third on the breast, and those names are—Pride, Lust, and Doubt. I have finished."

Having spoken thus, Paul, with haggard eyes and hanging jaw, returned to his old simple ways.

And, as the monks of Antinoë looked anxiously at Anthony, the saint pronounced these words—

"God has made known His just judgment. Let us bow to Him and hold our peace."

He passed. He bestowed blessings as he went. The sun, now descended to the horizon, enveloped him in its glory, and his shadow, immeasurably elongated by a miracle from heaven, unrolled itself behind him like an endless carpet, as a sign of the long remembrance this great saint would leave amongst men.

Upright, but thunderstruck, Paphnutius saw and heard nothing more. One word alone rang in his ears, "Thaïs is dying!" The thought had never occurred to him. Twenty years had he contemplated a mummy's head, and yet the idea that death would close the eyes of Thaïs astonished him hopelessly.

"Thaïs is dying!" An incomprehensible saying!

"Thaïs is dying!" In those three words what a new and terrible sense! "Thaïs is dying!" Then why the sun, the flowers, the brooks, and all creation? "Thaïs is dying!" What good was all the universe? Suddenly he sprang forward. "To see her again, to see her once more!" He began to run. He knew not where he was, or whither he went, but instinct conducted him with unerring certainty; he went straight to the Nile. A swarm of sails covered the upper waters of the river. He sprang on board a barque manned by Nubians, and lying in the forepart of the boat, his eyes devouring space, he cried, in grief and rage—

"Fool, fool, that I was, not to have possessed Thaïs whilst there was yet time! Fool to have believed that there was anything else in the world but her! Oh, madness! I dreamed of God, of the salvation of my soul, of life eternal—as if all that counted for anything when I had seen Thaïs! Why did I not feel that blessed eternity was in a single kiss of that woman, and that without her life was senseless, and no more than an evil dream? Oh, stupid fool! thou hast seen her, and thou hast desired the good things of the other world! Oh, coward! thou hast seen her, and thou hast feared God! God! heaven! what are they? And what have they to offer thee which are worth the least tittle of that which she would have given thee? Oh, miserable, senseless fool, who sought divine goodness elsewhere than on the lips of Thaïs! What hand was upon thy eyes? Cursed be he who blinded thee then! Thou couldst have bought, at the price of thy damnation, one moment of her love, and thou hast not done it! She opened to thee her arms—flesh mingled with the perfume of flowers— and thou wast not engulfed in the unspeakable enchantments of her unveiled breast. Thou hast listened to the jealous voice which said to thee, 'Refrain!' Dupe, dupe, miserable dupe! Oh, regrets! Oh, remorse! Oh, despair! Not to have the joy to carry to hell the memory of that never-to-be-forgotten hour, and to cry to God, 'Burn my flesh, dry up all the blood in my veins, break all my bones, thou canst not take from me the remembrance which sweetens and refreshes me for ever and ever!' . . . Thaïs is dying! Preposterous God, if thou knewest how I laugh at Thy hell! Thaïs is dying, and she will never be mine—never! never!"

And as the boat came down the river with the current, he remained whole days lying on his face, and repeating—

"Never! never! never!"

Then, at the idea that she had given herself to others, and not to him; that she had poured forth

THE EUPHORBIA 237

an ocean of love, and he had not wetted his lips therein, he stood up, savagely wild, and howled with grief. He tore his breast with his nails, and bit the flesh of his arms. He thought—

"If I could but kill all those she has loved!"

The idea of these murders filled him with delicious fury. He dreamed of killing Nicias slowly and leisurely, looking him full in the eyes whilst he murdered him. Then suddenly his fury melted away. He wept, he sobbed. He became feeble and meek. An unknown tenderness softened his soul. He longed to throw his arms round the neck of the companion of his childhood, and say to him, "Nicias, I love thee, because thou hast loved her. Talk to me about her. Tell me what she said to thee." And still, without ceasing, the iron of that phrase entered into his soul—"Thaïs is dying!"

"Light of day, silvery shadows of night stars, heavens, trees with trembling crests, savage beasts, domestic animals, all the anxious souls of men, do you not hear? 'Thaïs is dying!' Disappear, ye lights, breezes, and perfumes! Hide yourselves, ye shapes and thoughts of the universe! 'Thaïs is dying!' She was the beauty of the world, and all that drew near to her grew fairer in the reflection of her grace. The old man and the sages who sat near her, at the banquet at Alexandria, how pleasant they were, and how fascinating was their conversation! A host of brilliant thoughts sprang to their lips, and all their ideas were steeped in pleasure. And it was because the breath of Thaïs was on them that all they said was love, beauty, truth. A delightful impiety lent its grace to their discourse. They thoroughly expressed all human splendour. Alas! all that is but a dream. Thaïs is dying! Oh, how easy it will be to me to die of her death! But canst thou only die, withered embryo, fœtus steeped in gall and scalding tears? Miserable abortion, dost thou think thou canst taste death, thou who hast never known life? If only God exists, that he may damn me. I hope for it—I wish it. God, I hate Thee—dost Thou hear? Overwhelm me with Thy damnation. To compel Thee to, I spit in Thy face. I must find an eternal hell, to exhaust the eternity of rage which consumes me."

* * * * *

The next day, at dawn, Albina received the Abbot of Antinoë at the nunnery.

"Thou art welcome to our tabernacles of peace, venerable father, for no doubt, thou comest to bless the saint thou hast given us. Thou knowest that God, in his mercy, has called her to Him; how couldst thou fail to know tidings that the angels have carried from desert to desert? It is true that

THE EUPHORBIA 239

Thaïs is about to meet her blessed death. Her labours are accomplished, and I ought to inform thee, in a few words, as to her conduct whilst she was still amongst us. After thy departure, when she was confined in a cell sealed with thy seal, I sent her, with her food, a flute, similar to those which girls of her profession play at banquets. I did that to prevent her from falling into a melancholy mood, and that she should not show less skill and talent before God than she had shown before men. In this I showed prudence and foresight, for all day long Thaïs praised the Lord upon the flute, and the virgins, who were attracted by the sound of this invisible flute, said, 'We hear the nightingale of the heavenly groves, the dying swan of Jesus crucified.' Thus did Thaïs perform her penance, when, after sixty days, the door which thou hadst sealed opened of itself, and the clay seal was broken without being touched by any human hand. By that sign I knew that the trial thou hadst imposed upon her was at an end, and that God had pardoned the sins of the flute-player. From that time she has shared the ordinary life of my nuns, working and praying with them. She was an example to them by the modesty of her acts and words, and seemed like a statue of purity amongst them. Sometimes she was sad; but those clouds soon passed. When I saw that she was really drawn towards God by faith, hope, and love, I did not hesitate to employ her talent, and even her beauty, for the improvement of her sisters. I asked her to represent before us the actions of the famous women and wise virgins of the Scriptures. She acted Esther, Deborah, Judith, Mary, the sister of Lazarus, and Mary, the mother of Jesus. I know, venerable father, that thy austere mind is alarmed at the idea of these performances. But thou thyself wouldest have been touched if thou hadst seen her in these pious scenes, shedding real tears, and raising to heaven arms graceful as palm leaves. I have long governed a community of women, and I make it a rule never to oppose their nature. All seeds give not the same flowers. Not all souls are sanctified in the same way. It must also not be forgotten that Thaïs gave herself to God whilst she was still beautiful, and such a sacrifice is, if not unexampled, at least very rare. This beauty —her natural vesture—has not left her during the three months' fever of which she is dying. As, during her illness, she has incessantly asked to see the sky, I have her carried every morning into the courtyard, near the well, under the old fig tree, in the shade of which the abbesses of this convent are accustomed to hold their meetings. Thou wilt find her there, venerable father; but hasten, for God calls her, and this night a shroud will cover that face which God made both to shame and to edify this world."

Paphnutius followed her into a courtyard flooded with the morning light. On the edge of the brick roofs, the pigeons formed a string of pearls. On a bed, in the shade of the fig tree, Thaïs lay quite white, her arms crossed. By her side stood veiled women, reciting the prayers for the dying.

"Have mercy, upon me, O God, according to Thy loving kindness: according unto the multitude of Thy tender mercies blot out my transgressions."

He called her—

"Thaïs!"

She raised her eyelids, and turned the whites of her eyes in the direction of the voice.

Albina made a sign to the veiled women to retire a few paces.

"Thaïs!" repeated the monk.

She raised her head; a light breath came from her pale lips.

"Is it thou, my father? . . . Dost thou remember the water of the spring, and the dates that we picked? . . . That day, my father, love was born in my heart—the love of life eternal."

She was silent, and her head fell back.

Death was upon her, and the sweat of the last

agony bedewed her forehead. A pigeon broke the still silence with its plaintive cooing. Then the sobs of the monk mingled with the psalms of the virgins.

"Wash me thoroughly from mine iniquity, and cleanse me from my sin. For I acknowledge my transgressions: and my sin is ever before me."

Suddenly Thaïs sat up in the bed. Her violet eyes opened wide, and with a rapt gaze, her arms stretched towards the distant hills, she said in a clear, fresh voice—

"Behold them—the roses of the eternal dawn!"

Her eyes shone; a slight flush suffused her face. She had revived, more sweet and more beautiful than ever. Paphnutius knelt down, and threw his long black arms around her.

"Do not die!" he cried, in a strange voice, which he himself did not recognise. "I love thee! Do not die! Listen, my Thaïs. I have deceived thee? I was but a wretched fool. God, heaven—all that is nothing. There is nothing true but this wordly life, and the love of human beings. I love thee! Do not die! That would be impossible—thou art too precious! Come, come with me! Let us fly? I will carry thee far away in my arms. Come, let us love! Hear me, O my beloved, and say, 'I will live; I wish to live.' Thaïs, Thaïs, arise!"

She did not hear him. Her eyes gazed into infinity.

She murmured—

"Heaven opens. I see the angels, the prophets, and the saints. . . . The good Theodore is amongst them, his hands filled with flowers; he smiles on me and calls me. . . . Two angels come to me. They draw near. . . . How beautiful they are! I see God!"

She uttered a joyful sigh, and her head fell back motionless on the pillow. Thaïs was dead.

Paphnutius held her in a last despairing embrace; his eyes devoured her with desire, rage, and love.

Albina cried to him—

"Avaunt, accursed wretch!"

And she gently placed her fingers on the eyelids of the dead girl. Paphnutius staggered back, his eyes burning with flames and feeling the earth open beneath his feet.

The virgins chanted the song of Zacharias:

"*Blessed be the Lord God of Israel.*"

Suddenly their voices stayed in their throat. They had seen the monk's face, and they fled in affright, crying—

"A vampire! A vampire!"

He had become so repulsive, that passing his hand over his face, he felt his own hideousness.